Preface

Preface v

Previous booklets in the CCP6 Workshop series vii

Higher-order semiclassical initial value approximations for the
propagator
G. Hochman and K. G. Kay 1

First-principles implementation of semiclassical initial value
representation molecular dynamics
M. Ceotto, G. F. Tantardini, S. Atahan and A. Aspuru-Guzik 8

Non-Markovian thermalization in the Morse oscillator
W. Koch and F. Grossmann 17

Exploring the linearized approximation for condensed phase
non-adiabatic dynamics: multi-layered baths
D. F. Coker, L. Chen, P. Huo and S. Bonella 22

Accurate scaling laws for the matrix elements of strongly
anharmonic systems
M. S. Child 31

New theoretical methods for understanding chemical reactions in
the energy and time domains
J. N. L. Connor, X. Shan, A. J. Totenhofer and C. Xiahou 38

Two-dimensional nonadiabatic scattering: exact quantum solutions
V. I. Osherov and V. G. Ushakov 48

The semiclassical route to real time quantum dynamics
E. Pollak 53

Simulation of open quantum systems
F. Mintert and E. J. Heller 58

Dynamics with quantum trajectories: applications to reactive
scattering
R. E. Wyatt 62

Quantum hydrodynamics for mixed states
K. H. Hughes, S. M. Parry and I. Burghardt 74

Bohmian mechanics with complex action: an exact formulation of
quantum mechanics using complex trajectories
Y. Goldfarb, I. Degani, J. Schiff and D. J. Tannor 77

Quantum trajectories in phase space
C. C. Martens, A. Donoso and Y. Zheng   86

Capturing geometric phase effects near conical intersections
S. Yang and T. J. Martinez   103

Quantum dynamics using Gaussian wavepackets: the vMCG
method
G. A. Worth   113

Coupled Coherent States and other Gaussian-based techniques for
quantum propagation from the time-dependent variational principle
D. V. Shalashilin and I. Burghardt   119

The G-MCTDH method: correlated system-bath dynamics using
Gaussian wavepackets
I. Burghardt, R. Martinazzo, F. Martelli and G. A. Worth   124

Local coherent-state approximation to system-bath quantum
dynamics
R. Martinazzo, I. Burghardt, F. Martelli and M. Nest   133

Bipolar quantum trajectory simulations: trajectory surface
hopping and path integral Monte Carlo
J. B. Maddox and B. Poirier   145

The bipolar derivative propagation method for calculating
stationary states for high-dimensional reactive scattering systems
J. B. Maddox and B. Poirier   166

Theory and applications of the Ring Polymer Molecular Dynamics
model
S. Habershon   174

10060064 04

Preface

This booklet was produced in connection with the CCP6 Workshop on "Multidimensional Quantum Mechanics with Trajectories" held in the School of Chemistry of the University of Leeds, 1–3 September 2008. The meeting was sponsored by CCP6, the 6th Collaborative Computational Project funded by the UK Engineering and Physical Sciences Research Council (EPSRC). The focus of this meeting was on computational methods of quantum mechanics which in various ways rely on trajectories such as:

- semiclassical approximations in quantum mechanics;

- exact quantum techniques based on basis sets or grids guided by classical trajectories;

- exact and approximate quantum techniques which rely on various forms of "nonclassical" trajectories.

A common aspiration of all those approaches is to develop a quantum analog of classical molecular dynamics capable of simulating quantum effects in systems with many degrees of freedom. Many achievements in this direction have been reported in the last decade and the methods discussed at the workshop are now capable of simulating quantum dynamics in many dimensions. Also a number of new analytical semiclassical models have been presented. There were also two poster sessions. By bringing together people developing different methods we hoped for synergy between related approaches and groups. All speakers at the meeting contributed an article in this booklet and this represents an overview of the field.

We should warmly thank all contributors for their efforts, and more generally all those who attended the workshop, presented posters, and took part in the discussions.

Dmitrii V. Shalashilin
Marcelo P. de Miranda
Leeds, September 2008

Previous booklets in the CCP6 Workshop series

1. M. M. Law, J. M. Hutson and A. Ernesti (editors), *Fitting Molecular Potential Energy Surfaces*, 1993. ISBN 0-9522736-0-8.

2. G. G. Balint-Kurti and M. M. Law (editors), *Photodissociation Dynamics*, 1994. ISBN 0-9522736-1-6.

3. M. S. Child and M. M. Law (editors), *Intramolecular Dynamics in the Frequency and Time Domains*, 1995. ISBN 0-9522736-2-4.

4. A. Ernesti, J. M. Hutson and C. F. Roche (editors), *Molecular Collisions in the Atmosphere*, 1995. ISBN 0-9522736-3-2.

5. A. Ernesti, J. M. Hutson and N. J. Wright (editors), *Fashioning a Model: Optimization Methods in Chemical Physics*, 1998. ISBN 0-9522736-4-0.

6. R. Prosmiti, J. Tennyson and D. C. Clary (editors), *Molecular Quantum States at Dissociation*, 1998. ISBN 0-9522736-5-9.

7. M. M. Law, I. A. Atkinson and J. M. Hutson (editors), *Rovibrational Bound States in Polyatomic Molecules*, 1999. ISBN 0-9522736-6-7.

8. S. C. Althorpe, P. Soldán and G. G. Balint-Kurti (editors), *Time-Dependent Quantum Dynamics*, 2001. ISBN 0-9522736-7-5.

9. I. N. Kozin, M. M. Law and J. N. L. Connor (editors), *Wide-Amplitude Rovibrational Bound States in Polyatomic Molecules*, 2002. ISBN 0-9522736-8-3.

10. P. Soldán, M. T. Cvitaŝ, J. M. Hutson and C. S. Adams (editors), *Interactions of Cold Atoms and Molecules*, 2002. ISBN 0-9522736-9-1.

11. A. Miani, J. Tennyson, T. van Mourik (editors), *High Accuracy Potentials for Quantum Dynamics*, 2003. ISBN 0-9545289-0-5.

12. S. C. Althorpe and G. A. Worth (editors), *Quantum Dynamics at Conical Intersections*, 2004. ISBN 0-9545289-1-3.

13. S. Sen, D. Sokolovski and J. N. L. Connor (editors), *Semiclassical and Other Methods for Understanding Molecular Collisions and Chemical Reactions*, 2005. ISBN 0-9545289-3-X.

14. G. G. Balint-Kurti and M. P. de Miranda (editors), *Vector Correlation and Alignment in Chemistry*, 2006. ISBN 0-9545289-2-1.

15. B. Lasorne and G. A. Worth (editors), *Coherent Control of Molecules*, 2006. ISBN 0-9545289-5-6.

16. K. H. Hughes (editor), *Dynamics of Open Quantum Systems*, 2006. ISBN 978-09545289-6-6.

17. M. M. Law and A. Ernesti (editors), *Molecular Potential Energy Surfaces in Many Dimensions*, 2009. ISBN 978-0-9545289-7-3.

D. Shalashilin and M. P. de Miranda (eds.)
Multidimensional Quantum Mechanics with Trajectories
© 2009, CCP6, Daresbury

Higher-order semiclassical initial value approximations for the propagator

G. Hochman* and K. G. Kay†

Department of Chemistry, Bar-Ilan University, Ramat-Gan, Israel 52900

I. INTRODUCTION

The propagator $K_t(\mathbf{x}', \mathbf{x}) = \langle \mathbf{x}' | \exp(-i\hat{H}t/\hbar) | \mathbf{x} \rangle$ allows one to evolve any initial state from time zero to time t and is the key to quantum dynamics. Due to the well-known difficulties involved in the calculation of K_t by purely quantum methods, semiclassical approximations have been proposed. Currently, the most popular of these is the method of Herman and Kluk (HK)[1, 2], which is an example of an initial value treatment[3–5]. This approximation expresses the propagator for a system with f degrees of freedom as

$$K_t(\mathbf{x}', \mathbf{x}) = \left(\frac{1}{2\pi\hbar}\right)^f \int d\mathbf{p}d\mathbf{q} \, \langle \mathbf{x}' | \mathbf{p}_t \mathbf{q}_t \rangle R_t(\mathbf{p}, \mathbf{q}) e^{iS_t(\mathbf{p},\mathbf{q})/\hbar} \langle \mathbf{p}\mathbf{q} | \mathbf{x} \rangle. \quad (1)$$

Here $\mathbf{p}$ and $\mathbf{q}$ are f-dimensional vectors containing momentum and coordinate variables. $\mathbf{p}_t$ and $\mathbf{q}_t$ are vectors containing the values of these variables at t, obtained by solving the classical equations of motion with Hamiltonian function $H(\mathbf{p}, \mathbf{q})$ (corresponding to operator $\hat{H}$), and subject to the initial conditions $\mathbf{p}_0 = \mathbf{p}$ and $\mathbf{q}_0 = \mathbf{q}$ at time 0. The quantity

$$\langle \mathbf{x} | \mathbf{p}\mathbf{q} \rangle = \left(\frac{2\gamma}{\pi\hbar}\right)^{f/4} e^{-\gamma|\mathbf{x}-\mathbf{q}|^2/\hbar} e^{i\mathbf{p}\cdot(\mathbf{x}-\mathbf{q})/\hbar} \quad (2)$$

is a harmonic oscillator coherent state wave function. The positive width parameter γ is essentially arbitrary in the classical limit. Also, in Eq. (1),

$$S_t(\mathbf{p}, \mathbf{q}) = \int_0^t [\mathbf{p}_\tau \dot{\mathbf{q}}_\tau - H(\mathbf{p}_\tau, \mathbf{q}_\tau)] \, d\tau \quad (3)$$

---

*Electronic address: ch227@mail.biu.ac.il
†Electronic address: kay@mail.biu.ac.il

is the classical action integral for the trajectory initiated from $(\mathbf{p}, \mathbf{q})$ and R_t is the HK pre-exponential factor, defined by

$$R_t(\mathbf{p}, \mathbf{q}) = 2^{-f/2} \left[\det \left(\frac{\partial \mathbf{p}_t}{\partial \mathbf{p}} + \frac{\partial \mathbf{q}_t}{\partial \mathbf{q}} - 2i\gamma \frac{\partial \mathbf{q}_t}{\partial \mathbf{p}} + \frac{i}{2\gamma} \frac{\partial \mathbf{p}_t}{\partial \mathbf{q}} \right) \right]^{1/2}, \qquad (4)$$

where the partial derivatives are f-dimensional blocks of the monodromy matrix with elements such as $(\partial \mathbf{p}_t / \partial \mathbf{q})_{ij} = \partial p_{ti} / \partial q_j$.

Although this approximation is very successful for many purposes[3, 5], there are instances where it is unsatisfactory. The most important of these is perhaps the case of tunneling between disjoint classically-allowed regions[6]. It is therefore desirable to improve the accuracy of the HK approximation which possesses errors of $O(\hbar^2)$[7]. We discuss a technique that presents the HK approximation as the lowest-order term in a power series in Planck's constant, thus allowing the accuracy to be extended to higher orders in $\hbar$.[8]

We note that Pollak and coworkers[9–11] have developed another way of correcting the HK approximation that has a different set of properties. One distinguishing feature is that the present approach expands the propagator as a traditional semiclassical series in powers of $\hbar$ whereas the technique of Pollak involves terms with a more complicated $\hbar$ dependence.

II. THEORY

To improve (and derive) the HK approximation, we consider an Ansatz for the propagator having the form given in Eq. (1) except that the factor $R_t \exp(iS_t/\hbar)$ is replaced by an unknown function $k_t(\mathbf{p}, \mathbf{q})$. This function is determined by requiring that $K_t(\mathbf{x}', \mathbf{x})$ satisfy the Schrödinger equation. In this way, k_t is found to obey the condition

$$\left(\tilde{L}_t + i \frac{\partial}{\partial t} \right) k_t e^{-iS_t/\hbar} = 0. \qquad (5)$$

where $\tilde{L}_t$ is an operator containing partial derivatives (generally to all orders) with respect to the variables $z_j = p_j - 2i\gamma q_j$. To solve this equation, k_t is expressed as the semiclassical expansion

$$k_t \sim e^{iF_t/\hbar} C_t \sum_{n \geq 0} \hbar^n g_t^{(n)}, \qquad (6)$$

where $F_t(\mathbf{p}, \mathbf{q})$, $C_t(\mathbf{p}, \mathbf{q})$, and $g_t^{(n)}(\mathbf{p}, \mathbf{q})$ (with $n \geq 1$) are $\hbar$-independent functions and $g_t^{(0)} \equiv 1$. Substitution of Eq. (6) in Eq. (5) yields ordinary differential equations for F_t, C_t, and $g_t^{(n)}$. It is found that $F_t = S_t$ and $C_t = R_t$, so that truncating the sum in Eq. (6) at $n = 0$ yields the HK approximation. The ordinary time-dependent differential equations for the correction terms $g_t^{(n)}$ have the form

$$\dot{g}_t^{(n)} = i \sum_{j=1}^{n} \frac{1}{R_t} \tilde{L}_t^{(j)} R_t\, g_t^{(n-j)}, \qquad n = 1, 2, \ldots, \tag{7}$$

where the $\hbar$-independent operators $\tilde{L}_t^{(j)}$ contain partial derivatives with respect to the variables z_k. Explicit expressions in analytical form can be worked out. These equations form a closed hierarchy, determining the nth-order correction term $g_t^{(n)}$ in terms of the lower-order terms $g_t^{(k)}$, $k = 1, 2, \ldots, n - 1$.

To summarize, the corrected HK propagator has the same form as in the ordinary HK expression [Eq. (1)] except that the prefactor R_t is multiplied by the function $\sum_{n \geq 0} \hbar^n g_t^{(n)}$. Alternatively, the corrected propagator has the form

$$K_t \sim K_t^{(0)} + \hbar K_t^{(1)} + \hbar^2 K_t^{(2)} + \hbar^3 K_t^{(3)} + \ldots, \tag{8}$$

where $K_t^{(0)}$ is the HK propagator and each term $K_t^{(n)}$ has the same form as the HK propagator except for the presence of the additional factor $g_t^{(n)}$ in the integrand. Since $g_t^{(n)}$ is independent of $\hbar$, the factors $\hbar^n$ multiplying the terms $K_t^{(n)}$ in Eq. (8) provide the only new source of $\hbar$-dependence in the corrected propagator. The dimensionality of integration in the corrected propagator is the same as for the HK approximation so one anticipates that the number of trajectories required for convergence should not be much greater than for a conventional HK treatment.

III.   COMPUTATIONAL NOTES

To perform calculations, Eq. (7) must be expressed in an explicit algebraic form – a task that, in practice, usually requires computer algebra. For a one-dimensional system with Hamiltonian $H = p^2/2m + V(q)$, the differential equation for the lowest-order correction term can be expressed as[12]

$$i\dot{g}_t^{(1)} = \left(\frac{4\gamma^2}{m} - V_2 \right) \left(\frac{5}{8} \frac{b_t'^2}{b_t^4} - \frac{1}{4} \frac{b_t''}{b_t^3} \right) + V_3 \left(\frac{5}{12} \frac{b_t' c_t}{b_t^3} - \frac{1}{6} \frac{c_t'}{b_t^2} \right) - \frac{1}{8} V_4 \frac{c_t^2}{b_t^2}, \tag{9}$$

where $V_n = \partial^n V(q_t)/\partial q_t^n$,

$$b_t = \frac{1}{2} \left(\frac{\partial p_t}{\partial p} + \frac{\partial q_t}{\partial q} - 2i\gamma \frac{\partial q_t}{\partial p} + \frac{i}{2\gamma} \frac{\partial p_t}{\partial q} \right) = \frac{\partial p_t}{\partial z} - 2i\gamma \frac{\partial q_t}{\partial z}, \tag{10}$$

3

$$c_t \equiv \frac{1}{2}\frac{\partial q_t}{\partial p} - \frac{i}{4\gamma}\frac{\partial q_t}{\partial q} = \frac{\partial q_t}{\partial z}, \tag{11}$$

and primes denote differentiation with respect to z. This example reveals that the equations for the $g_t^{(n)}$ generally involve various derivatives of the monodromy elements. Differential equations for such quantities can be obtained by differentiating Hamilton's equations repeatedly with respect to z. Additionally, the equations for $g_t^{(n)}$ with $n > 1$ require derivatives, to various orders of z, of the functions $g_t^{(m)}$ with $m < n$. Differential equations for such functions can be obtained by differentiating Eq. (7) with respect to z. All these new equations can be numerically integrated together with those needed for standard HK calculations (Hamilton's equations and equations for the monodromy elements and for the action). As the order of the approximation increases from zero to one to two, the number of *real* differential equations that must be solved per trajectory for a one-dimensional system increases from 7 to 17 to 31.

Straightforward calculations for bound one-dimensional systems show that the first- and second-order corrections indeed provide successive corrections to the HK wave function, improving its accuracy for short times.[12] Beyond one or two periods of motion, however, the second-order contribution $K_t^{(2)}$ to the propagator becomes very large. After a short additional time, the first-order term $K_t^{(1)}$ also becomes large, dominating even the zeroth-order (ordinary HK) term, and destroying the accuracy of the semiclassical approximation.

An examination of the functions $g_t^{(n)}$ for individual trajectories helps one to understand these results and leads to strategies for overcoming the problems. At early times it is found that these quantities obey the expected condition $\ldots << g_t^{(2)} << g_t^{(1)} << 1$. However, the $g_t^{(n)}$ tend to grow with time. In particular, for the case of a double-well system, these correction terms are found to increase by orders of magnitude when trajectories approach the barrier with energies close to the barrier height. In such cases, $g_t^{(n+1)}$ increases faster than $g_t^{(n)}$ so that the condition $g_t^{(n+1)} >> g_t^{(n)}$ is soon obeyed for all n. This behavior can be traced to the existence of special complex-valued trajectories for which b_t vanishes at particular times, making the corrections g_t infinite [see Eq. (9)]. In such cases, one says that the trajectory has encountered a caustic. Although, strictly speaking, caustics cannot occur for the real-valued classical trajectories involved in these semiclassical calculations, the complex initial conditions leading to caustics can lie very close to the real axis with the result that the $g_t^{(n)}$ become extremely large in practice.

Clearly, this behavior indicates divergence of the asymptotic series given in Eq. (6). In accordance with the usual treatment of divergent asymptotic expansions, it was proposed in Ref. 12 that this series be truncated at order n for each trajectory whenever $|g_t^{(n+1)}|$ becomes larger than $|g_t^{(n)}|$. Since the corrections for trajectories with smaller values for $|g_t^{(n)}|$ continue to survive, this approach

4

allows one to extend calculations of the improved propagator to longer times. However, more recent results indicate that this approach is too conservative and does not fully exploit the power of semiclassical corrections. Numerical and analytical[13] evidence indicate that the convergence properties of the series in Eq. (8) are more relevant to the application of the corrected HK approximation than those of the series in Eq. (6). The series of integrals can have better convergence properties than the series of $g_t^{(n)}$ since the phases of the functions $g_t^{(n)}$ vary with initial conditions, allowing large contributions from different trajectories to cancel. While we cannot exclude the possibility that the series in Eq. (8) also diverges, the large values of the $K_t^{(n)}$ observed in the calculations of the corrected propagator appear to be of a numerical nature for most systems and times investigated.

Regardless of the source of the problem, there is little choice but to somehow remove the effect of a $g_t^{(n)}$ when it becomes too large. However, the present viewpoint suggests a different approach than that proposed in Ref. 12. In particular, the above discussion suggests that the contribution from a correction term should not be cut off sharply at a particular time since this can upset the phase cancellations associated with different trajectories and ruin the accuracy of the treatment. We have found it useful to reduce the effect of large correction terms smoothly by replacing $g_t^{(n)}$ with the function $g_t^{(n)}/[1 + \epsilon|g_t^{(n)}|]$ in Eq. (8), where ϵ is a real positive parameter. For $|g_t^{(n)}| \ll 1/\epsilon$, this substitution leaves the function $g_t^{(n)}$ effectively unchanged. However, for $|g_t^{(n)}| \gg 1/\epsilon$, it replaces $g_t^{(n)}$ by the function $g_t^{(n)}/\epsilon|g_t^{(n)}|$, which reduces the magnitude of $g_t^{(n)}$ to $1/\epsilon$ while maintaining its phase.

The parameter ϵ is chosen at each time as the smallest value which allows the Monte-Carlo calculation of $\sum_n \hbar^n K_t^{(n)}$ to converge using approximately the same number of trajectories as for an ordinary HK treatment. It is found that the resulting value of ϵ increases with time for bound systems: it typically has the value zero for times up to one or two periods and, for one-dimensional systems, takes on a value on the order of 0.1 for the next several periods of motion. For unbounded systems, ϵ can often be chosen as zero.

This approach to treating large $g_t^{(n)}$ allows one to apply the corrections successfully for longer times and to achieve greater accuracy than possible by the method of Ref. 12. One observation emerging from such calculations is that the importance of higher-order corrections grows with time. Similar behavior is also seen in calculations based on Pollak's approach[9–11].

IV. APPLICATIONS

We have applied the first-order corrected propagator to determine energy eigenvalues for a number of one- and two-dimensional systems by applying the harmonic inversion procedure to calculate the Fourier transform of the computed autocorrelation functions.[14] This treatment gives energies that are substantially more accurate than those obtained by the ordinary HK procedure. For a one-dimensional quartic oscillator, the accuracies of the HK and the first-order treatments are similar to those obtained with the first- and third-order phase integral methods, respectively. Similar, substantial, improvements in the low-lying energy eigenvalues are also obtained from the corrected HK approximation for the two-dimensional system with potential energy function $x^4/b + by^4 + 2\lambda x^2 y^2$, where $b = \pi/4$ and $\lambda = -0.15$. The partly chaotic nature of this system does not prevent successful first-order semiclassical calculations with a number of trajectories that is not much greater than needed for a standard HK treatment. It should be noted that semiclassical calculation of energies for multidimensional nonintegrable systems beyond the lowest order in $\hbar$ are far from routine in the literature.

Since one of the principal flaws of the HK technique is its failure to provide an accurate description of tunneling across barriers, it was important to test the present corrected propagator for such cases. We thus applied the first- and second-order corrected expressions to determine the energy-dependent transmission probability for scattering in the one-dimensional Eckart system.[13] For an important range of energies, the calculations were found to yield tunneling probabilities that were substantially more accurate than those obtained by the HK technique.

This result is surprising because one would not expect the applied corrections, which are apparently proportional to $\hbar$ and $\hbar^2$, to improve the ordinary HK results for tunneling. We recall that, with the use of complex trajectories, the usual WKB and Van Vleck semiclassical theories successfully treat tunneling using approximations that are lowest-order in $\hbar$ – no higher-order corrections are needed to provide very good accuracy. The HK approximation for "deep" tunneling, in contrast, remains inaccurate as $\hbar \to 0$[6]. It does not seem possible to overcome this problem by adding higher-order semiclassical terms that should become negligible for small $\hbar$.

The explanation for the observed improvements emerge from an analysis[13] that shows that, for the energy range of interest, the correction integrals of each order n in Eq. (8) actually contain terms of all orders in $\hbar^{1/3}$ due to the singular nature of the integrands. These terms include those that are $O(\hbar^0)$ and survive in the classical limit. Such lowest-order contributions from each each term in Eq. (8) can be summed and shown to give the accurate WKB tunneling amplitude.

The above analysis is strictly valid only for the case of the one-dimensional Eckart system. To determine the effectiveness of the correction series to tunneling in more general cases, we applied the first-order treatment to a two-dimensional system consisting of an Eckart barrier strongly coupled to a harmonic oscillator[14]. Calculations confirmed that the correction method improves the multidimensional tunneling probabilities in a manner very similar to that observed in the one-dimensional case.

V. CONCLUSIONS

With a proper treatment of the corrections $g_t^{(n)}$, the higher-order semiclassical method is effective for times that are sufficiently long to allow calculation of semiclassical energy eigenvalues from autocorrelation functions. These are found to be significantly more accurate than those obtained from the HK method. For unbound systems, this method is capable of substantially overcoming problems encountered in the ordinary HK treatment of tunneling through barriers. These improvements are accomplished using a number of classical trajectories that is not much greater than required for a conventional HK calculation. For systems with one or two degrees of freedom, the overall increase in computational effort per trajectory, required to apply the first- or second-order correction to a HK calculation, is not severe. The presence of a moderate degree of classical chaos has not been found to pose a serious obstacle to computation of the corrections for two-dimensional systems. Further tests and applications are in progress.

Acknowledgements. This work was funded by the Israel Science Foundation (grant no. 384/07).

[1] M. F. Herman and E. Kluk, Chem. Phys. **91**, 27 (1984).
[2] E. Kluk, M. F. Herman, and H. L. Davis, J. Chem. Phys. **84**, 326 (1986).
[3] K. G. Kay, Annu. Rev. Phys. Chem. **56**, 255 (2005).
[4] W. H. Miller, J. Chem. Phys. **95**, 9428 (1991).
[5] M. Thoss and H. Wang, Annu. Rev. Phys. Chem. **55**, 299 (2004).
[6] K. G. Kay, J. Chem. Phys. **107**, 2313 (1997).
[7] K. G. Kay, J. Chem. Phys. **100**, 4377 (1994).
[8] K. G. Kay, Chem. Phys. **322**, 3 (2006).
[9] E. Pollak and J. Shao, J. Phys. Chem. A **107**, 7112 (2003).
[10] D. H. Zhang and E. Pollak, Phys. Rev. Lett. **93**, 140401 (2004).
[11] J. Ankerhold, M. Saltzer, and E. Pollak, J. Chem. Phys. **116**, 5295 (2002).
[12] G. Hochman and K. G. Kay, Phys. Rev. A **73**, 064102 (2006).
[13] G. Hochman and K. G. Kay, J. Phys. A: Math. Theor. **41**, 385303 (2008).
[14] G. Hochman and K. G. Kay, unpublished.

D. Shalashilin and M. P. de Miranda (eds.)
Multidimensional Quantum Mechanics with Trajectories
© 2009, CCP6, Daresbury

First-principles implementation of semiclassical initial value representation molecular dynamics

M. Ceotto,[1, *] G. F. Tantardini,[1, 2] S. Atahan,[3] and A. Aspuru-Guzik[3, †]

[1]*Dipartimento di Chimica Fisica ed Elettrochimica,
Universitá degli Studi di Milano, via Golgi 19, 20133 Milano, Italy*
[2]*Istituto CNR di Scienze e Tecnologie Molecolari,
via Golgi 19, 20133 Milano, Italy*
[3]*Department of Chemistry and Chemical Biology,
Harvard University, 12 Oxford Street, 02138, Cambridge, MA (USA)*

I. INTRODUCTION

Quantum nuclear molecular dynamics simulations offer the ground of interplay between local electronic properties and non-local quantum nuclear effects. These opposite trends are conjugated in a first-principles approach to molecular dynamics, when the delocalization nature of the nuclear Schroedinger equation has been to some extent localized and its components are calculated by Quantum Chemistry methods [1]. The advantages of this kind of approaches are clear: the original interplay and close relashionship between electronic structure and nuclear chemistry are reinstated and one does not need to fit the ab initio data into mathematical spline anymore. The artificial procedure of fitting Potential Energy Surfaces (PES) is usually a trade-off between accuracy and human effort. Then, *on-the-fly* simulations are sometimes the only possible way of describing processes such as bond breaking and floppy molecules dynamics.

Up-to-date there have been several implementations of first-principles approaches to nuclear molecular dynamics with quantum effects [1]. In this report, a possible Semiclassical Initial Value Representation (SC-IVR) implementation for first-principles dynamics will be presented [2].

---

*Electronic address: michele.ceotto@unimi.it
†Electronic address: aspuru@chemistry.harvard.edu

II. THEORY

In the SC-IVR method, the propagator in F dimensions is approximated by the phase space integral,

$$e^{-i\hat{H}t/\hbar} = \frac{1}{(2\pi\hbar)^F} \int d\mathbf{p}(0) \int d\mathbf{q}(0)\, C_t(\mathbf{p}(0), \mathbf{q}(0))$$
$$\times\, e^{iS_t(\mathbf{p}(0),\mathbf{q}(0))/\hbar} |\mathbf{p}(t), \mathbf{q}(t)\rangle \langle \mathbf{p}(0), \mathbf{q}(0)|, \quad (1)$$

where $\{\mathbf{p}(t), \mathbf{q}(t)\}$ is the set of classically-evolved phase space coordinates, S_t is the classical action and C_t is a pre-exponential factor. In the Heller-Herman-Kluk-Kay (HHKK) [3] version of the SC-IVR, the prefactor involves mixed phase space derivatives as well as a set of coherent reference states $\langle \mathbf{q}|\mathbf{p}(t), \mathbf{q}(t)\rangle = \prod_i (\gamma_i/\pi)^{F/4} \exp[-\gamma_i(q_i - q_i(t))/2 + ip_i(t)(q_i - q_i(t))/\hbar]$ of fixed width γ_i. For bound systems, the widths are usually chosen to match the widths of the harmonic oscillator approximation to the wave function at the global minimum. The spectral density is usually obtained as Fourier transform of the surviving probability, however, if the simulation time is long enough, the phase space average can be replaced by a time averaging integral. This idea has been suggested and implemented by Kaledin and Miller [4] to obtain the TA (Time Averaging) SC-IVR approximation for the spectral density,

$$I(E) = \frac{\mathrm{Re}}{(2\pi\hbar)^F \pi\hbar T} \iint d\mathbf{p}(0)d\mathbf{q}(0) \int_0^T dt_1 \int_{t_1}^T dt_2\, C_{t_2}(\mathbf{p}(t_1), \mathbf{q}(t_1))$$
$$\times\, \langle \chi|\mathbf{p}(t_2), \mathbf{q}(t_2)\rangle e^{\frac{i}{\hbar}(S_{t_2}+Et_2)} \left[\langle \chi|\mathbf{p}(t_1), \mathbf{q}(t_1)\rangle e^{\frac{i}{\hbar}(S_{t_1}+Et_1)} \right]^* . \quad (2)$$

where $(\mathbf{p}(t_1), \mathbf{q}(t_1))$ and $(\mathbf{p}(t_2), \mathbf{q}(t_2))$ are variables that evolve from the same initial conditions but to different times, $|\chi\rangle$ is the reference state (usually a ground coherent state), and T is the total simulation time. The advantage of this approach is that the additional time integral can in principle replace the need for phase-space averaging in the large-time limit of a single trajectory. Calculations of the vibrational spectra of systems such as the water molecule have proved to be very accurate using the TA-SC-IVR approach and its inexpensive single-trajectory variant showed significant improvements over the simple harmonic approximation for excited vibrational levels [4]. In order to make Eq. (2) less computationally demanding, one can employ the separable approximation [4], where the pre-factor of Eq. (2) is approximated as a phase, and

9

State	Exact	1 Sep	1 Full	6 Sep	6 Full	Exact	1 Sep	1 Full	6 Sep	6 Full
ZPE	1213.19	1211	1208	1213	1207	0	0	0	0	0
(0,1)	1548.14	1554	1552	1553	1552	335	343	344	340	337
(0,2)	1865.07	1899	1897	1869	1868	317	345	345	316	316
(1,0)	3271.07	3282	3279	3278	3272	2058	2071	2071	2065	2061
(1,1)	3605.32	3626	3624	3615	3918	333	344	345	337	334
(1,2)	3920.81	3970	3969	3928	5314	315	344	345	313	312
(2,0)	5306.02	5353	5351	5316	5314	2034	2071	2072	2038	2042
(2,1)	5637.94	5697	5695	5653	5648	332	344	344	337	334
(2,2)	5952.05	6042	6041	5967	5960	314	345	346	314	312

TABLE I: Left, vibrational eigenvalues. Right, vibrational level spacings.

$\phi(t) = \text{phase}[C_t(\mathbf{p}(0), \mathbf{q}(0))]$. Using this approximation, Eq. (2) becomes

$$I(E) = \frac{1}{(2\pi\hbar)^F} \frac{1}{2\pi\hbar T} \int d\mathbf{p}(0) \int d\mathbf{q}(0)$$
$$\left| \int_0^T dt \langle \chi | \mathbf{p}(t), \mathbf{q}(t) \rangle e^{i(S_t(\mathbf{p}(0),\mathbf{q}(0))+Et+\phi_t(\mathbf{p}(0),\mathbf{q}(0))/\hbar)} \right|^2 \qquad (3)$$

leading to a simplification of the double-time integration to a single time integral. The resulting integral is positive definite.

Equations (2) and (3) become feasible for first-principles molecular dynamics if the number of trajectories is limited to few ones. One can push these expressions to the limit by reducing the phase-space integral to a single trajectory and stretch the simulation time. By choosing two coupled Morse oscillators with ground state frequencies of $2084\,\text{cm}^{-1}$ and $353\,\text{cm}^{-1}$, we have tested the one-trajectory TA-SC-IVR for a system where the significant time-scale difference represents a hard test for the time-averaging filter. The results are reported on Table I for Eq. (2) under the column "1 Sep" (Separable approximation) and for Eq. (3) under "1 Full" (no approximation is made).

On one side, one-trajectory simulations (both with and without invoking the separable approximation) correctly reproduce the Zero Point Energy value and add anharmonicity to the first vibrational excited state. On the other, higher vibrational states energies are equally spaced. This mayor limitation is overcome if one thinks that actually power spectra are collections of peaks located at the vibrational eigenvalues and its intensities are proportional to the overlap between the reference state $|\chi\rangle$ and the vibrational eigen-function at the corresponding eigenvalue. Then, one should keep in mind that each vibrational state classically corresponds to a trajectory with the same energy and turning points location. Thus, the reference state can more conveniently be written as a collection of coherent states

$$|\chi\rangle = \sum_{i=1}^{N} |\mathbf{p}_i^{eq}, \mathbf{q}_i^{eq}\rangle \tag{4}$$

which are located on the surroundings of the vibrational states. The resulting coherent states overlaps, $\langle\chi|\mathbf{p}(t),\mathbf{q}(t)\rangle\langle\mathbf{p}(0),\mathbf{q}(0)|\chi\rangle$, which are combinations of complex gaussian exponents, contribute mostly during the time averaging integration when the classical trajectory occurs to be in the surroundings of $(\mathbf{p}_i^{eq}, \mathbf{q}_i^{eq})$. Within this framework and in order to achieve a first-principles application of the method, we have reduced the IVR phase space integral to the collection of trajectories with initial conditions equal to each $(\mathbf{p}_i^{eq}, \mathbf{q}_i^{eq})$. In our applications, the $\mathbf{q}_i^{eq}$ are always given by the molecule equilibrium geometry, while the $\mathbf{p}_i^{eq}$ are chosen in a harmonic fashion. The results obtained by implementing six trajectories into the Multiple Reference States TA-SC-IVR approach above are shown in Table I. The method successfully reproduces not only ZPE effects but higher vibrational anharmonicity spacing within few wavemumbers of the exact one. The method was also tested on a strongly coupled system such as water molecule, and the results were equally satisfying.

III.   FIRST-PRINCIPLES APPLICATIONS

In first-principles dynamics applications of Multiple Reference States TA-SC-IVR, we have computed the potential energy surface at each nuclear configuration directly from the Kohn-Sham orbitals expanded on a non-orthogonal Gaussian basis. Gradients and Hessians at each nuclear configuration are obtained analytically. The evaluation of the potential represents half of the computational effort of our approach. The nuclear equations of motion are

$$M_I \ddot{\mathbf{R}}_I = -\nabla_I \, \min_{\mathbf{C}} \, E_{DFT}\,[\mathbf{C},\mathbf{R}_I] \tag{5}$$

where $\mathbf{C}$ is the rectangular matrix of the lowest occupied orbitals and the classical propagation is performed according to the velocity-Verlet algorithm, as implemented in the Q-Chem package [5]. At each time step, the potential, nuclear gradient and Hessian are used to calculate the action, pre-factor and coherent state overlaps necessary for the TA-SC-IVR power spectra calculations (Eqs. (2) and (3)). Each trajectory is monitored by calculating at each time step the deviation of the determinant of the monodromy matrix (stability matrix) from unity. The difference in the determinants was always smaller than 10^{-6} during the course of the calculations. A time step of 10 a.u. has been always found to satisfy the strict monodromy matrix restrictions even for the lightest atoms.

A challenging test for FP-SC-IVR method is the calculation of the full dimensional vibrational power spectrum of the CO_2 molecule. This linear molecule has

11

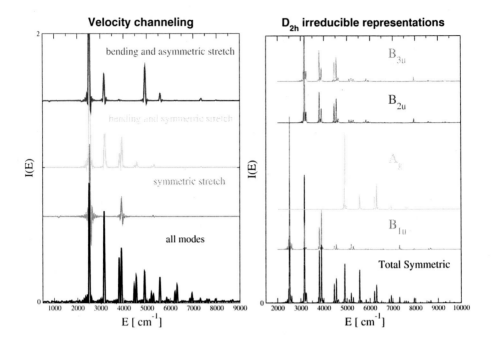

FIG. 1: Left: power spectra with selected initial momenta. Right panel: power spectra for each irreducible representation of the D_{2h} point group.

four vibrational normal modes: a symmetric stretching mode (ν_1), degenerate bending modes (ν_2 and $\bar{\nu}_2$) , and an antisymmetric stretching mode (ν_3). A successful method should reproduce spectral features such as degenerate bending modes, strong intermodal couplings and Fermi resonances. The dynamics was carried out using the B3LYP density functional [6] in the cc-pVDZ basis set [7]. The full power spectrum obtained using Eq. (2) after 3000 BOMD (Born-Oppenheimer molecular dynamics) steps of 10 a.u. each is shown on left-panels of Fig. 1. The calculated vibrational zero-point energy (ZPE) value was $\sim 2518\,\mathrm{cm}^{-1}$. In contrast, harmonic normal-mode analysis (whose frequencies are 656.62, 1363.46, 2423.47 wavenumbers) predicts a frequency of 2550.08cm^{-1}. The TA-SC-IVR method successfully reproduces the ZPE anharmonic effects and is in good agreement with the experimental value of 2508 cm^{-1}.

The Fermi resonance splittings are the result of anharmonic couplings, and they represent a stringent test for a semi-classical method that relies on a few short trajectories. The Fermi resonances occur when an accidental degeneracy between two excited vibrational levels of the same symmetry exists and it results in a repulsion between the corresponding energy levels. These resonances are

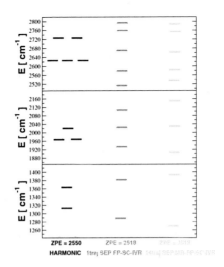

FIG. 2: CO_2 vibrational energies: Fermi Resonance induces level repulsion and the consequential energy splittings are bigger than the harmonic one. These effects are reproduced both by one-trajectories and by multiple trajectories simulations.

originated from purely anharmonic effects and are only present in polyatomic potentials. For the CO_2 molecule, the unperturbed frequencies for the symmetric stretching are roughly equal to the first bending overtone ($\nu_1 \cong 2\nu_2$). For these modes, the wavefunctions are transformed as the irreducible representation of $D_{\infty h}$, i.e. $\nu_1(10^00)$ as Σ_g^+, and $\nu_2^2(02^00)$ as $\Sigma_g^+ + \Delta_g$. Another Fermi doublet results from the addition of a quantum of bending mode to the previous Fermi doublet to yield the following states: $\nu_1\nu_2(11^10)$ and the $\nu_2^3(03^10)$ state.

Fermi resonances state are grouped in Fig. 2. From the first lower energy doublet, one can see how the original levels have been repelled by Fermi couplings, such that one excited mode is located at a higher frequency than the harmonic prediction, while the other is at a lower frequency. The latter effect could be explained also by ordinary anharmonicity effects, but the former is evidence of the ability of the FP-SC-IVR method even when a single trajectory in the separable approximation is used to capture Fermi resonance effects partially. The same reasoning can be used to explain other Fermi multiplets reported on Fig. 2.

A closer inspection at the vibrational eigenvalues shows the limits of the one-trajectory FP-SC-IVR in comparison to Multiple Reference States FP-SC-IVR, which reasonably mimics the quantum behavior of this molecule; while the bending levels are equally spaced for one-trajectory simulations, the Multiple Reference States FP-SC-IVR levels shows anharmonic spacings. A similar reasoning can be applied to the asymmetric and symmetric modes, where the Multiple

13

Reference States FP-SC-IVR approach reproduces part of the anharmonic contribution.

With the FP-SC-IVR method, one can also identify the couplings between vibrational modes and the appearance of Fermi resonance splittings by carrying out simulations with different initial conditions. This can be achieved by selectively setting the initial velocity of some vibrational modes to zero. The anharmonic coupling between levels leads to a consistent reproduction of the ZPE peak in the spectrum for all simulations. However the excited vibrational peaks related to the modes with zero initial kinetic energy show a very small signal in the power spectrum. Vibrational energy redistribution processes can be studied as well, by carrying out simulations at different timescales. In the left panel of Fig. 1, we show the resulting power spectra for different initial conditions. If the initial state contains only purely symmetric motion, the lowest Fermi resonance peaks are absent as well as for a bending (without symmetric stretching) motion. These results and the intensity of their peaks respect to that ones located at the same frequencies for the lower full power spectrum suggest that the Fermi resonance is indeed originated from the coupling between bending and the symmetric modes. Using the proposed approach, one can carefully detect the characteristics of each peak even for complicated power spectra.

An attractive method for obtaining the symmetry properties of the eigenstates involves arranging the initial basis vectors [4]. The basis for this method is the direct product of coherent states $|\chi\rangle = \prod_{k=1}^{4} |p_i^{(k)}, q_i^{(k)}\rangle^{\epsilon_k}$. These states can be chosen to have an initial symmetry by employing linear combinations of the form $|p_i^{(k)}, q_i^{(k)}\rangle^{\epsilon_k} = \left(|p_i^{(k)}, q_i^{(k)}\rangle + \epsilon_k|-p, -q_i^{(k)}\rangle\right)/\sqrt{2}$. The k-th mode can be made symmetric ($\epsilon_k = 1$), antisymmetric ($\epsilon_k = -1$) or have no symmetry restrictions ($\epsilon_k = 0$). In order to assign the proper symmetry to each peak on the bottom spectra of Fig. 1, the reduced D_{2h} symmetry group was adopted. All irreducible representations were reproduced and peaks were grouped by symmetry as reported in the right panel of Fig. 1. Note that the upper plots are identical since they only differ trivially by swapping coefficients between the degenerate bending modes in the original $D_{\infty h}$ symmetry group.

Finally one can use the above vibrational eigenvalues E_n to calculate the corresponding SC-IVR eigenfunctions [8],

$$\psi_n(\mathbf{x}) = \int_{-T}^{+T} dt \frac{\iint d\mathbf{p}(0)d\mathbf{q}(0)}{(2\pi\hbar)^F} C_t(\mathbf{p}(0), \mathbf{q}(0)) e^{\frac{i}{\hbar}(S_t + E_n t)} \langle \mathbf{x}|\mathbf{p}(0), \mathbf{q}(0)\rangle, \quad (6)$$

where the coherent wavefunction time evolution is approximated by the HHKK propagator [3] and the IVR integration was reduced to a single trajectory.

Some results are reported in Fig. 3. On the upper left panel is shown the eigenfunction for vibrational state 0, 3^1, 0, corresponding to a triple bending excitation. This figure clearly shows how vibrational eigenfunctions are on the top of the corresponding classical trajectory but with quantum delocalization

14

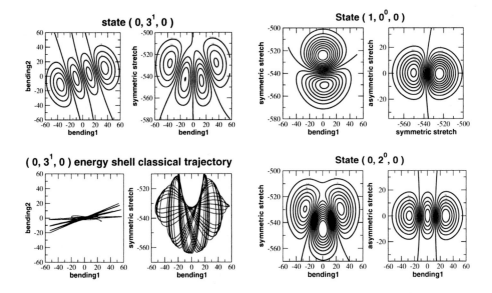

FIG. 3: Left panels: vibrational eigenfunctions (upper) and classical trajectory (lower) for the triple excited bending eigenstate. Right panels: two-dimensional cuts of CO_2 vibrational eigenfunction for the lower Fermi doublets coming from the mixing a single symmetric stretch excitation with a double bending one.

effects added. This is shown for example on the bending-asymmetric subspace plots by the range in the asymmetric stretch amplitude. On the right panels of Fig. 3, the eigenfunctions corresponding to the lower Fermi resonating states are reported. The resonant U-shape typical of 2:1 resonances is reproduced in one case by the node line (upper panel) and on the other by the eigenfunction peaks (lower panel). These findings are consistent with the eight-shapes showed by the classical trajectories in this subspace and by previous model calculations [9]. Finally the asymmetric cut subspaces clearly show once more how this mode is not significantly coupled to other ones.

IV.   CONCLUSION

A possible implementation of the TA-SC-IVR method for power spectra calculation has been introduced. The metod makes use of Multiple Reference States. The converged semiclassical integration involve a multiple Husimi distributions sampling. However, we have been focusing on its first-principles applications where the IVR phase space integration was reduced to single trajectories start-

15

ing from each reference state phase space location. The calculated vibrational eigenvalues were used for eigenfunction calculations by Fourier transforming the HHKK-SC-IVR single-trajectory wavepacket, evolved by first-principles dynamics as well.

Next we will calculate by grid methods the CO_2 eigenvalues to test the accuracy of the above calculations and compare the convergence properties of the Multiple Husimi sampling versus the standard one before tackling more complex systems.

Acknowledgements. This work was partially supported by the Research University Program (PUR) of "Universita' degli Studi di Milano" and by CILEA (Lombardy Interuniversity Consortium Supercomputing Center). A. A.-G. and S. A. thank the Faculty of Arts and Sciences of Harvard University for financial support.

---

[1] M. Ben-Nun, T. J. Martinez, Adv. Chem. Phys. **121**, 439 (2002); H. B. Schlegel, J. M. Millam, S. S. Iyengar, G. A. Voth, A. D. Daniels, G. E. Scuseria, and M. J. Frisch, J. Chem. Phys. **114**, 9758 (2001); M. Pavese, D. R. Berard, G. A. Voth, Chem. Phys. Lett. **300**, 93 (1999); G. A. Worth, M. A. Robb and I. Burghardt, Faraday Disc. **127**, 307 (2004).

[2] M. Ceotto, S. Atahan, A. Aspuru-Guzik, arXiv.org (cond-mat) 0712.0424 (2007).

[3] W. H. Miller, J. Chem. Phys. **53**, 3578 (1970); Adv. Chem. Phys. **25**, 69 (1974); J. Phys. Chem. A **105**, 2942 (2001); E. J. Heller, J. Chem. Phys. **67**, 3339 (1977); **75**, 2923 (1981); Acc. Chem. Res. **39**, 127 (2006); K. G. Kay, J. Chem. Phys. **100**, 4432 (1994); **100**, 4377 (1994); Annu. Rev. Phys. Chem. **56**, 255 (2005); M. F. Herman and E. Kluk, Chem. Phys. **91**, 27 (1984); F. Grossmann, Comments At. Mol. Phys. **34**, 243 (1999); R. Walton and D. E. Manolopoulos, Mol. Phys. **87**, 961 (1996); S. S. Zhang and E. Pollak, J. Chem. Phys. **121**, 3384 (2004); M. Thoss and H. Wang, Annu. Rev. Phys. Chem. **55**, 299 (2004).

[4] A. L. Kaledin and W. H. Miller, J. Chem. Phys. **118**, 7174 (2003); M. Ceotto, *PhD Dissertation*, University of California, Berkeley (2005); A. L. Kaledin and W. H. Miller, J. Chem. Phys. **119**, 3078 (2003); Y.. Elran and K. G. Kay, J. Chem. Phys. **110**, 3653 (1999); **110**, 8912 (1999); D. V. Shalashilin and M. S. Child, J. Chem. Phys. **115**, 5367 (2001).

[5] Y. Shao, *et al.* Phys. Chem. Chem. Phys. **8**, 3172 (2006).

[6] A. D. Becke, J. Chem. Phys. **98,** 5648 (1993); P. J. Stephens, F. J. Devlin, C. F. Chabalowski, and M. J. Frisch, J. Phys. Chem. **98,** 11623 (1994).

[7] T. Dunning, Jr. J. Chem. Phys. **90**, 1007 (1989).

[8] M. J. Davis and E. J. Heller, J. Chem. Phys. **71**, 3383 (1979); **75**, 3916 (1981); N. De Leon and E. J. Heller, J. Chem. Phys. **78**, 4005 (1982); J. H. Frederick and E. J. Heller, J. Chem. Phys. **87**, 6592 (1987).

[9] D. W. Noid, M. L. Koszykowski, R. A. Marcus, J. Chem. Phys. **71**, 2864 (1979).

D. Shalashilin and M. P. de Miranda (eds.)
Multidimensional Quantum Mechanics with Trajectories
© 2009, CCP6, Daresbury

Non-Markovian thermalization in the Morse oscillator

Werner Koch and Frank Grossmann*
*Institute of Theoretical Physics,
Technische Universität Dresden,
D-01062 Dresden, Germany*

I. INTRODUCTION

Based on a seminal paper by Feynman and Vernon [1], in the 1980s formally exact expressions for the dynamics of the reduced density matrix of the system have been derived within the path integral representation [2]. Central ingredient there is the influence functional which captures the correlations between system and reservoir via self-interactions *non-local* in time. Recently, it has been shown that the influence functional can be exactly recovered from a stochastic averaging procedure *without* non-local memory terms [3, 4] by reformulating the non-equilibrium quantum dynamics using stochastic Schrödinger equations with complex valued noise forces. Until recently, the convergence of the stochastic average for relatively long times was an unsolved problem, however. In Ref. 5 it has been shown that this issue can be tackled by combining the exact stochastic Schrödinger formulation with a proper semiclassical real-time technique based on a time-dependent initial value representation of the quantum mechanical propagator.

II. FEYNMAN-VERNON THEORY OF DISSIPATION

In order to model dissipation, we employ the standard decomposition of the total Hamiltonian

$$\hat{H} = \hat{H}_S + \hat{H}_B + \hat{H}_I \tag{1}$$

---

*Electronic address: frank@physik.tu-dresden.de

as a sum of a system part, that for reasons of simplicity shall here depend on one degree of freedom x, a bath part consisting of an infinity of harmonic oscillators together with a bi-linear interaction between the two systems. In case of a factorized initial density with the bath residing in thermal equilibrium at temperature T, a path integral expression for the time-evolved reduced density matrix of the form [2]

$$\rho(x_f, x'_f, t) = \int dx_i dx'_i \rho(x_i, x'_i, 0)$$

$$\times \int \mathcal{D}[q_1] \mathcal{D}[q_2] \exp\left\{\frac{i}{\hbar}(S_S[q_1] - S_S[q_2])\right\} F[q_1, q_2] \quad (2)$$

can be derived. Here the two real time paths q_1 and q_2 run in time t from x_i and x'_i to x_f and x'_f, respectively. They are coupled by the influence functional, which takes the form $F[y, r] = \exp(-\Phi[y, r]/\hbar)$ with

$$\Phi[y, r] = \int_0^t du \int_0^u dv\, y(u)[L'(u-v)y(v) + 2iL''(u-v)r(v)] + i\mu \int_0^t du\, y(u)r(u), \quad (3)$$

where $y = q_1 - q_2$, $r = (q_1 + q_2)/2$ denote difference and sum paths, respectively. The complex valued friction kernel $L(t) = L'(t) + iL''(t)$ is related to the force-force auto-correlation function of the bath and depends on the coupling strength η and the inverse temperature of the bath $\beta = 1/kT$. In particular, the static susceptibility is given by $\mu = \lim_{\hbar\beta\to0} \hbar\beta L(0)$.

In Ref. 4 it has been shown that a stochastic unraveling of the forward and the backward paths using noise forces z_i (i=1,2) leads to

$$\rho(x_f, x'_f, t) = \int dx_i \int dx'_i \rho(x_i, x'_i, 0) M[K_{z_1}(x_f, t; x_i, 0)(K_{z_2}(x'_f, t; x'_i, 0))^*]\,, \quad (4)$$

where M denotes the average over the noise distribution, with the augmented system actions

$$S_{z_i}[q_i] = S_S[q_i] + \mu \int_0^t du\, q_i(u)^2 + \int_0^t du\, q_i(u)z_i(u) \quad (5)$$

in the path integral expressions of the respective propagators K_{z_i}. Representing the initial density operator through $\hat{\rho}(t=0) = |\Psi_1\rangle\langle\Psi_2|$ leads to two uncoupled Schrödinger equations of the form

$$i\hbar|\dot{\Psi}_1\rangle = \left[H_S - \xi(t)q + \frac{\mu}{2}q^2 - \frac{\hbar}{2}\nu(t)q\right]|\Psi_1\rangle \quad (6a)$$

$$i\hbar|\dot{\Psi}_2\rangle = \left[H_S - \xi^*(t)q + \frac{\mu}{2}q^2 + \frac{\hbar}{2}\nu^*(t)q\right]|\Psi_2\rangle, \quad (6b)$$

18

where $\xi(t) = \frac{1}{2}[z_1(t) + z_2^*(t)]$ and $\nu(t) = \frac{1}{\hbar}[z_1(t) - z_2^*(t)]$. In order to mimic the influence functional in Eq. (3), these forces have to obey: $\langle\xi(t)\xi(t')\rangle = L'(t - t')$, $\langle\xi(t)\nu(t')\rangle = (2i/\hbar)L''(t - t')$, $(t > t')$, and $\langle\nu(t)\nu(t')\rangle = 0$.

The linear Eqs. (6) are formally exact, but they cannot be used for practical calculations since the norm of the density may diffuse and is conserved only on average. Hence, the transition from linear quantum state diffusion to a Girsanov transformed process [6] proved to be an important step towards robust numerical methods. This way, Eqs. (6) are mapped exactly onto a set of nonlinear Schrödinger equations by replacing $\xi \to \tilde{\xi} \equiv \xi - \int_0^t du\chi(t_u)\bar{r}_u$, where $\chi(u) = -L''(u)/2\hbar, u > 0$ is the response function and $\bar{r}_u = \langle q\rangle_u$ is the expectation value of the pointer variable of the system monitored by the bath. The benefit is that now the norm is conserved along a "guiding trajectory" $\bar{r}_u$ for each noise sample.

III.   THE SEMICLASSICAL PROPAGATOR

The semiclassical Herman-Kluk (HK) propagator is given in terms of a phase space integral as [7]

$$K(x_f, t, x_i, 0) = \int \frac{dp_i dq_i}{2\pi\hbar} \langle x_f|g_\gamma(p_t, q_t)\rangle R(p_i, q_i, t)e^{iS(p_i, q_i, t)/\hbar}\langle g_\gamma(p_i, q_i)|x_i\rangle. \quad (7)$$

Here complex valued Gaussian wave-packets $\langle x|g_\gamma\rangle \sim \exp\{-\frac{\gamma}{2}(x - q)^2 + \frac{i}{\hbar}p(x - q)\}$ of fixed width parameter γ have been introduced, centered around the initial phase space points p_i, q_i and the time-evolved phase space points p_t, q_t, respectively. The pre-exponential factor R contains a complex valued combination of stability matrix elements and the action reads as in Eq. (5) with the replacement of the noise force described above. The phase space integration is preferably performed via a Monte Carlo procedure, after a suitable initial state, typically a Gaussian with the width parameter σ, has been chosen.

Before this procedure can be applied though, one needs to know the guiding orbit, which in the exact formulation means to solve the full problem. In the spirit of a semiclassical approximation, however, we may determine it such that noise induced diffusion of the norm of the density matrix during the HK-propagation vanishes for each noise realization to lowest order in $\hbar$. This in turn provides

$$\bar{r}_u = \frac{q_1(u) + q_2(u)^*}{2} + \frac{i}{\hbar\gamma}\frac{p_1(u) + p_2(u)^*}{2}, \quad (8)$$

where we allowed for complex orbits according to the naive strategy to propagate classical trajectories driven by complex noise fields in a complex phase space.

Obtaining the final density matrix $\rho(x_f, x'_f, t)$ involves three Monte Carlo integrations, two over the forward and backward phase spaces of the semiclassical

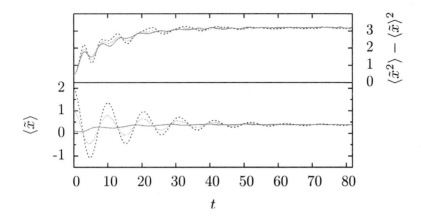

FIG. 1: Thermalization of the mean of position as well as of its variance for different initial mean position. Solid line: $\langle \tilde{x}(0) \rangle = 0.1$, dotted line: $\langle \tilde{x}(0) \rangle = 1$, dashed line: $\langle \tilde{x}(0) \rangle = 2$. Initial width parameter $\sigma = 1$ for all curves.

propagators and an additional one over the noise trajectory distribution. In Ref. 5 it has been shown that while in principle these are distinct integrations, they can be performed at once by sampling two phase space points and a noise trajectory and performing the semiclassical evaluation for this combination. The semiclassical propagators do not need to be converged for every noise sample separately, instead an increase in the number of trajectories improves the sampling of both, the noise distribution as well as the semiclassical phase space integrals.

IV. THERMALIZATION FOR DIFFERENT INITIAL CONDITIONS

The formalism lined out above has been shown to lead to converged results for thermal averages in the Morse oscillator [5]. Using the same dimensionless parameters for the Morse oscillator but *varying* initial conditions for the wavepacket, we will now show that the same thermal averages are reached for fixed heat bath parameters $\eta = 0.1$ and $\beta = 1$.

This is first done in Fig. 1 that shows the thermalization process for different initial centers in position of the wavepacket. In Fig. 2 thermalization to the same final expectation values is shown for different values of the initial width parameter σ of the wavepacket. Please note that due to the anharmonicity of the potential the mean values differ at intermediate times for a different choice of the initial variance.

20

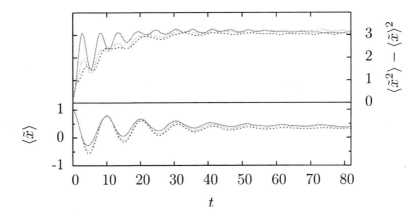

FIG. 2: Thermalization of the mean of position as well as of its variance for different initial width parameter. Solid line: $\sigma = 0.5$, dotted line: $\sigma = 1$, dashed line: $\sigma = 2$. The initial mean value of position was taken to be $\langle \tilde{x}(0) \rangle = 1$ for all the curves.

V. CONCLUSION

We have performed semiclassical calculations for an anharmonic system in contact with a harmonic heat bath. The thermalization of an initially excited wavepacket in a Morse oscillator has been shown to lead to the same expectation values for a range of initial wavepacket parameters.

Acknowledgements. The authors gratefully acknowledge fruitful discussions with Jürgen Stockburger and Joachim Ankerhold and financial support by the Deutsche Forschungsgemeinschaft (GR 1210/4-1).

[1] R. P. Feynman and F. L. Vernon, Ann. Phys. (N. Y.) **24**, 118 (1963).
[2] U. Weiss, *Quantum Dissipative Systems*, 2nd ed. (World Scientific, Singapore, 1999).
[3] J. T. Stockburger, H. Grabert, Chem. Phys. **268**, 249 (2001).
[4] J. T. Stockburger, H. Grabert, Phys. Rev. Lett. **88**, 170407 (2002).
[5] W. Koch, F. Grossmann, J. T. Stockburger and J. Ankerhold, Phys. Rev. Lett. **100**, 230402 (2008).
[6] D. Gatarek, N. Gisin, J. Math. Phys. **32**, 2152 (1991).
[7] M. F. Herman, E. Kluk, Chem. Phys. **91**, 27 (1984).

D. Shalashilin and M. P. de Miranda (eds.)
Multidimensional Quantum Mechanics with Trajectories
© 2009, CCP6, Daresbury

Exploring the linearized approximation for condensed phase non-adiabatic dynamics: multi-layered baths

David F. Coker,* Lina Chen, and Pengfei Huo
Department of Chemistry, Boston University,
590 Commonwealth Avenue, Boston, MA 02215, U.S.A.

Sara Bonella†
Dipartimento di Fisica, Università "La Sapienza",
Piazzale Aldo Moro, 2, 00185 Roma, Italy and
Centro Linceo Beniamino Segre, Via della Lungara 10, 00165 Roma, Italy

I. INTRODUCTION

Recent work in the field of mixed quantum-classical dynamics has employed linearized approximations to the evolution of the full system. The linearized approximation is applied in particular when calculating the time dependent density matrix of a non-equilibrium system or equilibrium time correlation functions. The general idea is to first separate the interacting degrees of freedom of the condensed phase system of interest into a quantum subset and a classical bath based on relative thermal wavelength or energy considerations. The forward and backward time propagators in the evolution of the density matrix, or of the correlation function, are represented as path integrals. The phase in the integrands is then expanded to linear order in the difference between the forward and backward paths of the bath. The resulting approximate form still contains the full evolution of the quantum subsystem. If an appropriate representation for this dynamics is available (e.g. the mapping hamiltonian or some semiclassical formulation) the linearized approximation can be computed using classical trajectories. While the benefits of the truncation to linear order in the difference paths for the bath variables are well known and have been exploited in a number of applications [1–23], a general understanding of the conditions under

---
*Electronic address: coker@bu.edu
†Electronic address: sara.bonella@roma1.infn.it

which the approximation is reliable is as yet unavailable. When the linearized approximation is reliable only for short times, correction schemes can be applied. Recently, an iterative scheme employing the linearized approximation for the mixed quantum-classical propagator in the mapping hamiltonian formulation as a short time approximation in a path integral expression for long time propagation has been suggested [24]. The approach provides a systematic way to extend the linearized approximation to longer times but this comes at a numerical cost that can be substantially reduced in conditions where linearization is reliable for longer periods.

In this work we explore how linearization becomes accurate for a class of problems important in condensed phase chemical physics. A model in which the quantum system is coupled to a local bath, which in turn interacts with an environment represented as a set of harmonic oscillators with bi-linear coupling is introduced [25], and conditions under which linearization is accurate for this hierarchical bath, condensed phase model are investigated . The critical parameters in this analysis are the temperature, and relative strengths of coupling between the various subsystems. Depending on the interplay between the parameters in the hamiltonian, the linearized expression can provide a good approximation for evolving the density matrix over different periods of time. Benchmark calculations exploring the relevant range of parameters in the special case of a spin coupled to a local harmonic bath (spin-boson), that is bilinearly coupled to a global harmonic environment are presented in the results section. These calculations compare the performance of the linearized propagation with that of calculations based on the iterative scheme mentioned above. While the results that we present here provide only numerical evidence on the range of validity of linearization, they can be corroborated by a theoretical analysis inspired by the well-known work of Caldeira and Leggett [26]. This analysis also leads to an interesting variation on the theme of linearization in which the evolution of the system becomes brownian. Both the theoretical analysis and model calculations based on the brownian propagation will be presented in an upcoming publication.

II. THEORY

A. Hierarchical System-Bath: The reduced density matrix

Condensed phase systems can often be represented in terms of a quantum system (*e.g.* electrons, protons, or high frequency vibrations, *etc.*) that may be influenced by its local environment, the "local bath". This local bath mediates the interaction of the quantum subsystem with the rest of the environment or "global bath". We will thus assume that there is no direct interaction between the quantum subsystem and the global bath, but the local environment and the quantum sub-system are coupled. The local and global baths also can interact in our model.

For convenience we will define the system-local bath interaction hamiltonian

$$\hat{h}(\hat{s}, \hat{r}) = \hat{H}_s + V_b(\hat{r}) + \Phi_{s-b}(\hat{s}, \hat{r}) \tag{1}$$

where $\hat{s}$ and $\hat{r}$ are the system and local bath coordinate operators respectively, and the full hamiltonian for the condensed phase models we will consider is thus

$$\hat{H} = \hat{h}(\hat{s}, \hat{r}) + \hat{h}_{bB}(\hat{p}, \hat{r}, \hat{P}, \hat{R}) \tag{2}$$

The second term on the right hand side represents the kinetic energy of the local and global bath and all potential energy terms relative to the global bath, including interactions with the local bath.

We represent the quantum subsystem in terms of a basis set of diabatic states, $|n\rangle$. The local and global baths are described in the coordinate basis, and the composite system states are tensor products $|r, \{R_k\}, n\rangle$. Time dependent properties of the system can be obtained from the density operator $\hat{\rho}(t)$. Suppose the initial density operator has the product form: $\hat{\rho}(0) = \hat{\rho}_s \hat{\rho}_{b0} \hat{\rho}_{B0}$. In the following we shall focus on non-equilibrium experiments for which the quantum subsystem is initially prepared in some non-thermal mixture of states $|\psi^0\rangle$ by, for example, interaction with a fast laser pulse. We will thus be interested in the evolution of the initial quantum subsystem density matrix $\hat{\rho}_s(0) = |\psi^0\rangle\langle\psi^0| = \sum_{n^0} \sum_{m^0} c^*_{m^0} c_{n^0} |n^0\rangle\langle m^0|$, where the c_{n^0} are the amplitudes of the different basis states comprising the initial quantum subsystem state $|\psi^0\rangle$. We shall consider experiments that probe the quantum subsystem states. The quantity of interest is thus the reduced density matrix, whose elements are obtained from the full density by tracing over all the bath degrees of freedom

$$
\begin{aligned}
\rho^{red}_{nm}(t) &= \int dr \int dR \langle r, R, n|\hat{\rho}(t)|r, R, m\rangle \\
&= \int dr^N \int dR^N \int dr^0 \int dR^0 \int d\tilde{r}^0 \int d\tilde{R}^0 \sum_{n^0} \sum_{m^0} c^*_{m^0} c_{n^0} \\
&\quad \times \langle r^N, R^N, n|e^{-i\hat{H}t/\hbar}|r^0, R^0, n^0\rangle \langle r^0, R^0|\hat{\rho}_{b0}\hat{\rho}_{B0}|\tilde{r}^0, \tilde{R}^0\rangle \\
&\quad \times \langle \tilde{r}^0, \tilde{R}^0, m^0|e^{i\hat{H}t/\hbar}|r^N, R^N, m\rangle \\
&= \sum_{n^0} \sum_{m^0} c^*_{m^0} c_{n^0} (\rho^{red}_{nm})^{n^0 m^0}(t)
\end{aligned} \tag{3}
$$

B. Linearized form of the reduced density matrix

A computable expression for the reduced density matrix can be obtained by approximating the full quantum evolution of the system using linearization. The steps that lead to this expression are described in detail in [22, 27], and can be summarized as follows. A hybrid coordinate-momentum path integral representation of the forward and backward propagators for the local and global bath is introduced together with the mapping hamiltonian [28–30] representation of the evolution of the quantum subsystem. The latter can be evaluated explicitly and exactly as a parametric function of the local bath's paths by averaging the contributions of a set of auxiliary classical trajectories for the mapping variables. The functions to be averaged contain a phase that combines with that of the bath's path integrals. A change of variables is introduced that transforms the integration over forward, r_t, and backward, r'_t, bath paths into integration over the mean $\bar{r}_t = (r_t + r'_t)/2$ and difference paths, with similar definitions for the global bath variables, e.g. $\bar{R}_t$. The total phase of the new path integral expression is then expanded to linear order in the difference path. This approximation makes it possible to evaluate all difference integrals analytically to arrive at the following result for the reduced density matrix elements

$$(\rho^{red}_{nm})^{n^0 m^0}_{lin}(t) =$$

$$= \int d\bar{r}_0 \int \prod_{k=1}^{N} d\bar{r}_k \frac{d\bar{p}_k}{2\pi\hbar} \int d\bar{R}_0 \int \prod_{k=1}^{N} d\bar{R}_k \frac{d\bar{P}_k}{2\pi\hbar} \int dp_q^0 dq^0 \int d\bar{p}_q^0 d\bar{q}^0$$

$$\times (\hat{\rho}_{b0}\rho_{B0})_W(\bar{R}_0, \bar{P}_1, \bar{r}_0, \bar{p}_1) a_{n^0,0}\tilde{a}_{m^0,0} e^{-i(\Theta_{n^0,0} - \tilde{\Theta}_{m^0,0})} G_0 \tilde{G}_0$$

$$\times a_{n,t}(\{\bar{r}_k\})\tilde{a}_{m,t}(\{\bar{r}_k\}) e^{i\epsilon \sum_{k=1}^{N} \left[\theta_n(\{\bar{r}_k\}) - \tilde{\theta}_m(\{\bar{r}_k\})\right]}$$

$$\times \prod_{k=1}^{N} \delta(\frac{\bar{p}_k}{M_b} - \frac{(\bar{r}_k - \bar{r}_{k-1})}{\epsilon})$$

$$\times \prod_{k=1}^{N} \delta\left[\frac{(\bar{p}_{k+1} - \bar{p}_k)}{\epsilon} + \frac{\nabla_{\bar{r}_k}\theta_n(\bar{r}_k) + \nabla_{\bar{r}_k}\theta_m(\bar{r}_k)}{2} + \nabla_{\bar{r}_k} h_{bB}(\bar{R}_k, \bar{r}_k)\right]$$

$$\times \prod_{k=1}^{N} \delta(\frac{\bar{P}_k}{M_B} - \frac{(\bar{R}_k - \bar{R}_{k-1})}{\epsilon})$$

$$\times \prod_{k=1}^{N} \delta\left[\frac{(\bar{P}_{k+1} - \bar{P}_k)}{\epsilon} + \nabla_{\bar{R}_k} h_{bB}(\bar{R}_k, \bar{r}_k)\right] \tag{4}$$

In the expression above, the amplitude and phase of the time evolved mapping variables (p^t, q^t) are indicated as $a_{n,t}(\{r_k\}) = \sqrt{(p_n^t)^2(\{r_k\}) + (q_n^t)^2(\{r_k\})}$, and

$$
\begin{aligned}
\Theta_{n,t}(\{r_k\}) &= \tan^{-1}\left(\frac{q_n^0}{p_n^0}\right) + \int_0^t d\tau\, h_{n,n}(r_\tau) \\
&\quad + \int_0^t d\tau \sum_{\lambda \neq n} \left[h_{n,\lambda}(r_\tau) \frac{(q_n^\tau q_\lambda^\tau + p_n^\tau p_\lambda^\tau)}{[(q_n^\tau)^2 + (p_n^\tau)]} \right] \\
&= \tan^{-1}\left(\frac{q_n^0}{p_n^0}\right) + \int_0^t \theta_n(r_\tau)d\tau
\end{aligned}
\tag{5}
$$

(similar notation is used to indicate the evolution in time of the set of mapping variables that represent the quantum transition amplitude evolved backward in time in the reduced density matrix element). These quantities are obtained by propagating a set of initial conditions sampled according to the probability density $G_0 = e^{-\frac{1}{2}\sum_\lambda [(p_\lambda^0)^2 + (q_\lambda^0)^2]}$. The classical dynamics of these initial conditions is governed by the hamiltonian

$$
h_m(\{r_k\}) = \frac{1}{2}\sum_\lambda h_{\lambda,\lambda}(\{r_k\})[p_\lambda^2 + q_\lambda^2 - \hbar] + \frac{1}{2}\sum_{\lambda,\lambda'} h_{\lambda,\lambda'}(\{r_k\})[p_{\lambda'}p_\lambda + q_{\lambda'}q_\lambda] \tag{6}
$$

where the sum runs over all relevant states of the quantum subsystem and $h_{\lambda,\lambda'}(\{r_k\})$ are the matrix elements of the quantum hamiltonian ($\hat{h}$ in equation (1)). The products of δ-functions in equation (4) amount to a time-stepping prescription for the evolution of the local and global bath degrees of freedom. This evolution too, is essentially classical (in the absence of the quantum subsystem the δ-functions enforce the Newtonian dynamics of the coupled baths), but the force in the propagation of the local bath contains a non-classical term, $\frac{\nabla_{\bar{r}_k}\theta_n(\bar{r}_k)+\nabla_{\bar{r}_k}\theta_m(\bar{r}_k)}{2}$, that describes the response to non-adiabatic transitions of the quantum degrees of freedom. The dynamics of the bath is integrated starting from initial conditions determined by the Wigner transform[31] of the bath density matrix $(\hat{\rho}_{b0}\rho_{B0})_W(\bar{R}_0, \bar{P}_1, \bar{r}_0, \bar{p}_1)$. Given these prescriptions for the coupled dynamics of the quantum subsystem and of the local and global bath, the reduced density matrix is computed as a time dependent average value. The function to be averaged is the product of the mapping amplitudes and phases which depends parametrically on the time evolution of the full system.

The linearized approximation for the density is always reliable at sufficiently short times. We have recently developed [24] an iterative approach for applying the linearized result in successive short time slices enabling accurate mixed quantum-classical nonadiabatic propagation to longer times. While this new scheme is quite efficient, it still introduces a non negligible computational overhead that can be substantially reduced when the time slices based on linearization can be stretched. In the following we present a preliminary exploration of

26

the range of parameters in which this can be done for the hierarchical system-bath model. The results of a fully linearized approximation will be compared to those of the iterative scheme mentioned above that we shall take as an exact reference calculation. As tested by comparison with full MCTDH calculations in reference [24] the iterative scheme does indeed converge to the exact result as the number of iterations is increased. Since this is the only use of the iterative scheme in this work, we shall not describe it any further and refer the reader to [24] for a detailed derivation and exploration of the method.

III. RESULTS

The hamiltonian we consider here provides a simple flexible model with which to explore the reliability of the linearized approximate density matrix propagation scheme developed in the previous section. The form of our model hamiltonian is:

$$\hat{H} = \hat{h} + \hat{h}_{bB} \tag{7}$$

where the quantum system - local bath hamiltonian, $\hat{h}$ is the standard spin-boson form

$$\hat{h} = \sum_{j=1}^{m} \frac{1}{2}(p_j^2 + \omega_j^2 r_j^2)\hat{\mathbf{1}} + \sum_{j=1}^{m} c_j r_j \hat{\sigma}_z + \Omega \hat{\sigma}_x \tag{8}$$

(for consistency with the usual writing we have included in this definition the kinetic energy of the local bath), and the local bath oscillators are bi-linearly coupled to a dissipative global bath of other harmonic oscillators

$$\hat{h}_{bB} = [\sum_{J=1}^{M} \frac{1}{2}(P_J^2 + \Omega_J^2 R_J^2) + \sum_{J=1}^{M}\sum_{j=1}^{m} C_J R_J r_j]\hat{\mathbf{1}} \tag{9}$$

In the calculations reported here we employ the smooth, exponential cutoff Ohmic spectral density $J(\omega) = \eta\omega \exp[-\omega/\omega_c]$ for a global bath medium with damping constant η [10, 32–38]. The quantum system-local bath coupling constants, c_j, and local bath frequencies, ω_j, are determined by a similar exponential cutoff Ohmic spectral density with damping constant η^{loc} and cutoff frequency ω_c^{loc}. The observable of interest is the average state population difference $\langle \sigma_z(t) \rangle$, defined as

$$\langle \sigma_z(t) \rangle = Tr\{\rho^{red}(t)\sigma_z\} \tag{10}$$

where σ_z is the Pauli matrix. The calculation described below explores the effect of the coupling between the local and global baths, as controlled by η, on the

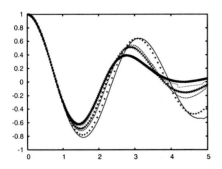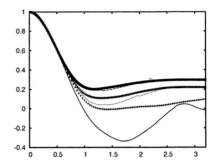

FIG. 1: State population difference $\langle \sigma_z \rangle$ as a function of scaled time, Ωt at $\beta = 12.5$. Left panel shows results for weak coupling between the quantum subsystem and the local bath ($\eta^{loc} = 0.09$), and right panel shows results for strong coupling between the quantum subsystem and the local bath ($\eta^{loc} = 0.5$). Solid curves are results from converged iterative scheme density matrix dynamics calculations, and symbols assume that the linearized approximation can be applied for evolution for the full time interval. (See text for details of values of local bath - global bath couplings, η scanned in these figures.)

reliability of linearization. As this quantity increases, decoherence effects due to coupling to the global environment should make the linearization approximation more accurate for longer times. In Figure 1 we present calculations of the average state population difference as a function of time for two different strengths of coupling between the quantum system and the local environment, controlled by η^{loc}, for increasing values of the global bath friction parameter η. In all calculations the local and global bath were each represented by 5 oscillators. The value of the cut-off frequency was $\omega_c = 1$. for both baths, while the coupling between the states of the two level system is $\Omega = 0.333$. The low temperature used in these calculations corresponds to $\beta = 12.5$.

Results presented in the left panel are for weak coupling between the quantum and local bath subsystems corresponding to $\eta^{loc} = 0.09$ where we see long lived coherent dynamics. The lines are converged results of the iterative scheme mentioned in the theory section that we use as an exact benchmark for the performance of the linearized calculations (symbols). We shall use as reference point to identify the different runs the value of the population difference at $t = 5$. The lowest curves at this final time of are obtained with no coupling between the local and global bath oscillators ($\eta = 0.0$), the middle curves were calculated with $\eta = 0.05$, while the top result corresponds to $\eta = 0.08$. While the agreement of the linearized and iterative methods is reasonable for all values of the friction coefficient, the improvement with increasing η is detectable, in particular, in the increasing agreement among the curves at the first peak and at longer times.

The good performance of the linearized approximation for weak quantum system - local bath coupling, $\eta^{loc} = 0.09$ which results in the long lived coherent oscillations occurs because under these conditions the spin-boson model is well approximated - at least for short times - by two independent systems: the two level problem that linearization treats exactly via the mapping representation of the propagator, and a set of harmonic oscillators for which the linearized approximation of the dynamics is also exact. This approximation breaks down as we increase the coupling as can be seen in the right panel of the figure. Here we set $\eta^{loc} = 0.5$. The solid line and the cross symbols (the two lower curves in the figure) were obtained in the absence of coupling between the local and global bath. In this case, linearization (crosses) fails to capture qualitatively important features of the exact result (solid line): it completely misses the negative values of the observable for $t \in [1, 2.5]$. As we increase the coupling between the local and global bath, however, linearization becomes more and more accurate. For $\eta = 0.1$ the final time value is correct, although the depth of the minimum is underestimated by linearization. For $\eta = 0.2$ this discrepancy disappears and linearization provides a very good approximation for all times.

IV. CONCLUSIONS

The linearized expression for the reduced density matrix describing the properties of quantum degrees of freedom coupled with a local bath that interacts with a global environment was presented. The reliability of the approximation has been explored numerically for a spin-boson quantum-local bath subsystem, immersed in a global bath of harmonic oscillators as a function of the coupling between the local and global bath. Our results show that when the coupling between the local and global baths increases linearization becomes accurate even for relatively long times. The preliminary exploration presented here can be refined and complemented by a theoretical analysis based on the influence functional that permits exploration of the effect of the different parameters in the model on the linearization. Work in this direction is in progress and will be the subject of a future publication [39].

Acknowledgements. We gratefully acknowledge support for this research from the National Science Foundation under grant CHE-0616952.

[1] R. Hernandez and G. Voth, Chem. Phys. **223**, 243 (1998).
[2] J. Poulsen, G. Nyman, and P. Rossky, J. Chem. Phys. **119**, 12179 (2003).
[3] J. Poulsen and G. Nyman, J. Phys. Chem. A **108**, 8743 (2004).
[4] J. Poulsen, G. Nyman, and P. Rossky, Proc. Nat. Acad. Sci. **102**, 6709 (2005).
[5] Q. Shi and E. Geva, J. Phys. Chem. A **107**, 9059 (2003).

[6] Q. Shi and E. Geva, J. Chem. Phys. **118**, 8173 (2003).
[7] Q. Shi and E. Geva, J. Chem. Phys. **119**, 9030 (2003).
[8] Q. Shi and E. Geva, J. Chem. Phys. **118**, 7562 (2003).
[9] K. Thompson and N. Makri, Phys. Rev. E **59**, 4729 (1999).
[10] K. Thompson and N. Makri, J. Chem. Phys. **110**, 1343 (1999).
[11] J. Shao and N. Makri, J. Phys. Chem. A **103**, 9479 (1999).
[12] J. Shao and N. Makri, J. Chem. Phys. **113**, 3681 (2000).
[13] O. Khun and N. Makri, J. Phys. Chem. A **103**, 9487 (1999).
[14] X. Sun and W. Miller, J. Chem. Phys. **110**, 6635 (1999).
[15] H. Wang, M. Thoss, and W. Miller, J. Chem. Phys. **112**, 47 (2000).
[16] M. Thoss, H. Wang, and W. Miller, J. Chem. Phys. **114**, 9220 (2001).
[17] X. Sun and W. Miller, J. Chem. Phys. **106**, 6346 (1997).
[18] W. Miller, J. Phys. Chem. A **105**, 2942 (2001).
[19] M. Herman and D. Coker, J. Chem. Phys. **111**, 1801 (1999).
[20] Q. Shi and E. Geva, J. Phys. Chem. A **108**, 6109 (2004).
[21] Q. Shi and E. Geva, J. Chem. Phys. **121**, 3393 (2004).
[22] S. Bonella and D. F. Coker, J. Chem. Phys. **122**, 194102 ((2005)).
[23] S. Bonella, D. Montemayor, and D. Coker, Proc. Natl. Acad. Sci. **102**, 6715 ((2005)).
[24] E. Dunkel, S. Bonella, and D. Coker, J. Chem. Phys. **129**, 114106 (2008).
[25] K. Shiokawa and R. Kapral, J. Chem. Phys. **117**, 7852 (2002).
[26] A. Caldeira and A. Leggett, Physica **121A**, 587 (1983).
[27] D. Coker and S. Bonella, in *Computer simulations in condensed matter: From materials to chemical biology*, edited by M. Ferrario, G. Ciccotti, and K. Binder (Springer-Verlag, Lecture Notes in Physics 703, Berlin, 2006), p. 553.
[28] G. Stock and M. Thoss, Phys. Rev. Lett. **78**, 578 (1997).
[29] M. Thoss and G. Stock, Phys. Rev. A. **59**, 64 (1999).
[30] X. Sun, H. Wang, and W. Miller, J. Chem. Phys. **109**, 7064 (1998).
[31] Z. Ma and D. Coker, J. Chem. Phys. **128**, 244108 (2008).
[32] C. Mak and D. Chandler, Phys. Rev. A **44**, 2352 (1991).
[33] R. Egger and C. Mak, Phys. Rev. B **50**, 15210 (1994).
[34] M. Topaler and N. Makri, J. Chem. Phys. **101**, 7500 (1994).
[35] K. Thompson and N. Makri, Chem. Phys. Lett. **291**, 101 (1998).
[36] D. Mackernan, G. Ciccotti, and R. Kapral, J. Chem. Phys. **116**, 2346 (2002).
[37] A. Golosov and D. Reichman, J. Chem. Phys. **114**, 1065 (2001).
[38] D. Evans, A. Nitzan, and M. Ratner, J. Chem. Phys. **108**, 6387 (1998).
[39] P. Huo, L. Chen, D. Coker, and S. Bonella, *Analysis of linearized approximations for mixed quantum-classical dynamics in condensed phase*, in preparation (2009).

D. Shalashilin and M. P. de Miranda (eds.)
Multidimensional Quantum Mechanics with Trajectories
© 2009, CCP6, Daresbury

Accurate scaling laws for the matrix elements of strongly anharmonic systems

Mark S. Child

Physical and Theoretical Chemistry Laboratory,
Oxford University, South Parks Rd, Oxford, OX1 3QZ

I. INTRODUCTION

The modelling of quantum level structures and resonant energy flow in polyatomic systems is heavily dependent on effective Hamiltonian methods, which are written in terms of harmonic oscillator creation and annihilation operators[1]. No such harmonic oscillator theory can however cope with the extreme anharmonicity encountered when a Morse oscillator approaches dissociation or, even more severely when a system approaches a saddle point

The purpose of this note is to report a new approach to the modelling of strongly anharmonic systems[2]. The relevant matrix elements are accurately approximated by combining novel scaling laws with the Heisenberg correspondence principle[3]. The result is a set of generic expressions for the matrix elements $\langle n' | \hat{A} | n \rangle$ with arbitrary n and n', which naturally differ according to the choice of the system and the operator $\hat{A}$. However variations within a given system type, arising from the relevant reduced mass and binding energy, for example, are taken into account by the scaling laws. Examples are given for the Morse oscillator; for the 'champagne bottle' model for vibrational-rotational states at the barrier to linearity in H_2O[4]; and for the 'spherical pendulum', which is used to model isomerization in HCP[5].

II. HEISENBERG CORRESPONDENCE AND SCALING LAWS

The Heisenberg correspondence principle is best seen in the light of classical angle-action theory[6]. The actions are related to quantum numbers by the Bohr-Sommerfeld rule

$$I = \frac{1}{2\pi} \int p \, dx = (n + \delta)\hbar, \tag{1}$$

where the Maslov index δ depends on the number of turning points for the motion, with the value $\delta = 1/2$ for vibration and libration. The conjugate classical angle variable, α, which increases linearly with time, appears in the semi-classical wavefunction in the deceptively simple form

$$\psi_n(\alpha) = \frac{1}{\sqrt{2\pi}} e^{in\alpha}. \tag{2}$$

The serious complication is that the specification of α in terms of the Cartesian variables $(p.x)$ varies with the energy of the system. Thus the Heisenberg form for the matrix element

$$\langle n' | \hat{A} | n \rangle = \frac{1}{2\pi} \int_{-\pi}^{\pi} A(\bar{I}, \alpha) e^{i(n-n')\alpha} d\alpha, \tag{3}$$

requires a rule for evaluating the average action $\bar{I}$ or energy $\bar{E}$, at which the classical function in the integrand is evaluated.

The situation is particularly interesting for systems with three parameter Hamiltonians of the form

$$H = \frac{1}{2\mu} p^2 + B v(ax), \tag{4}$$

because the quantization condition of Eq. (1) can be expressed in the scaled form

$$(n+\delta)b = F(\varepsilon) = \frac{1}{\pi} \int_{z_-}^{z_+} \sqrt{\varepsilon - v(z)} dz, \tag{5}$$

where $z = ax$ and

$$\varepsilon = \frac{E}{B}, \qquad b = \sqrt{\frac{a^2 \hbar^2}{2\mu B}}. \tag{6}$$

The implication of Eq. (5) is that $F(\varepsilon)$ is the generic quantization function for the scaled potential $v(z)$, with the reduced energies, $\varepsilon_n = E_n/B$, for different physical systems being determined by different values of the single capacity parameter, b.

The extension of Eq. (5) to Hamiltonians with additional angular momenta,

$$H = \frac{1}{2\mu}\left(p_r^2 + \frac{p_\phi^2}{r^2}\right) + B v(ar), \qquad p\phi = m\hbar \tag{7}$$

is readily verified to be

$$(n+\delta)b = F(\varepsilon, mb) = \frac{1}{\pi} \int_{r_-}^{r_+} \sqrt{\varepsilon - v(z) - \frac{m^2 b^2}{r^2}} dr. \tag{8}$$

A corresponding scaling law for the matrix element in Eq. (3) is obtained by evaluating the integrand at the mean energy, $\bar{E} = (E_n + E_{n'})/2$, and plotting the result on a reduced energy scale $\varepsilon = \bar{E}/B$.

There was some discussion at the workshop about alternative choices for the mean energy, or action at which the integrand in Eq. (3) is evaluated. Other choices can acheive higher accuracy for a given matrix element, but it is hard to think of an alternative choice that is equally applicable to whole families of elements. The matrix elements of powers of the scaled harmonic oscillator creation operator, $\left(\hat{a}^{\dagger}\right)^{k}$ say, provides a simple illustration. The exact result is,

$$\langle n + k | \left(\hat{a}^{\dagger}\right)^{k} | n \rangle = \sqrt{(n+1)(n+2)\cdots(n+k)} \tag{9}$$

and the Heisenberg approximation is derived from the angle-action identity $a^{\dagger} = \sqrt{\bar{n} + 1/2}e^{i\alpha}$, with Fourier components

$$\frac{1}{2\pi}\int_{-\pi}^{\pi} \left(a^{\dagger}\right)^{k} e^{-ik\alpha} d\alpha = [\bar{n} + 1/2]^{k/2} \tag{10}$$

Thus the choice

$$\bar{n} + 1/2 = [(n+1)(n+2)\cdots(n+k)]^{1/k} \tag{11}$$

leads to the exact result for any individual $\Delta n = k$ matrix element, but it is difficult to assess the error in applying this prescription for to other Δn elements. The stuation is somewhat simplified by a systematic choice of the the arithmetic average, $n_{av} + 1/2 = n + (k+1)/2$, which correponds to the average scaled energy of the harmonic system. One sees from the table that $[\bar{n} + 1/2]^{k/2}$ overestimates the exact matrix element $\langle n + k | \left(\hat{a}^{\dagger}\right)^{k} | n \rangle$ by terms which become negligible for $(n_{av} + 1/2)^2 \gg (k-1)^2/4$. The accuracy of the of $\bar{n} = n_{av}$ approximation therefore increases rapidly with increasing n_{av} at fixed k; but decreases with increasing k at fixed n. For example the error in applying the formula $[n_{av} + 1/2]^{k/2}$ at $n = 2$ is zero for $k = 1$ and within 1%, 3% and 7% for $k = 2$, 3 and 4 respectively.

k	$\langle n + k | \left(\hat{a}^{\dagger}\right)^{k} | n \rangle$
1	$\sqrt{(n_{av} + 1/2)}$
2	$\sqrt{\left[(n_{av} + 1/2)^2 - 1/4\right]}$
3	$\sqrt{(n_{av} + 1/2)\left[(n_{av} + 1/2)^2 - 1\right]}$
4	$\sqrt{\left[(n_{av} + 1/2)^2 - 9/4\right]\left[(n_{av} + 1/2)^2 - 1/4\right]}$

33

The situation is much more difficult for anharmonic systems, because there is usually no simple transformation between energy and quantum number. The only feasible general way to exploit the scaling property is to take the mean in Eq. (3) as the average reduced energy $\varepsilon = (E_n + E_{n'})/2B$. Examples are given in the following sections.

III. MORSE OSCILLATOR

Computations of coupled Morse oscillator systems commonly employ expansions in the Morse variable $y = 1 - \exp(-ax)$, which has the following action-angle form[6]

$$y = 1 - \frac{1 - \varepsilon}{1 + \sqrt{\varepsilon} \cos \alpha} \tag{12}$$

Consequently

$$
\begin{aligned}
\langle n + j | y | n \rangle &= \delta_{0j} - \frac{1}{2\pi} \int_{-\pi}^{\pi} \frac{(1 - \varepsilon)e^{-ij\alpha}}{1 + \sqrt{\varepsilon} \cos \alpha} d\alpha \\
&= \delta_{0j} - \sqrt{1 - \varepsilon} \left[\frac{\sqrt{1 - \varepsilon} - 1}{\sqrt{\varepsilon}} \right]^j
\end{aligned}
\tag{13}
$$

The resulting functions, for $j = 0 - 3$, are plotted as continuous curves in Fig. 1. The points are the exact Morse oscillator matrix elements for OH local bond vibrations in H_2O with $\omega_e = 3874.62 \text{cm}^{-1}$ and $\omega_e x_e = 81.20 \text{ cm}^{-1}$. The diagram displays both the relative magnitudes of the various matrix elements, and the remarkable accuracy of the new scaling law. The published paper[2] shows that other types of matrix element are equally well approximated.

IV. CHAMPAGNE BOTTLE

Bending vibrations of H_2O at energies close to the barrier to linearity have been modelled by the champagne bottle Hamiltonian[4]

$$H_{Champ} = \frac{1}{2\mu} \left(p_r^2 + \frac{p_\phi^2}{r^2} \right) + B(1 - a^2 r^2)^2. \tag{14}$$

The relevant angle-action transformations are expressed as elliptic integrals[8] in terms of the roots, $zz_1 > z_2 > z_3$, of the polynomial equation

$$z^3 - 2z^2 + (1 - \varepsilon)z + m^2 b^2 = 0, \tag{15}$$

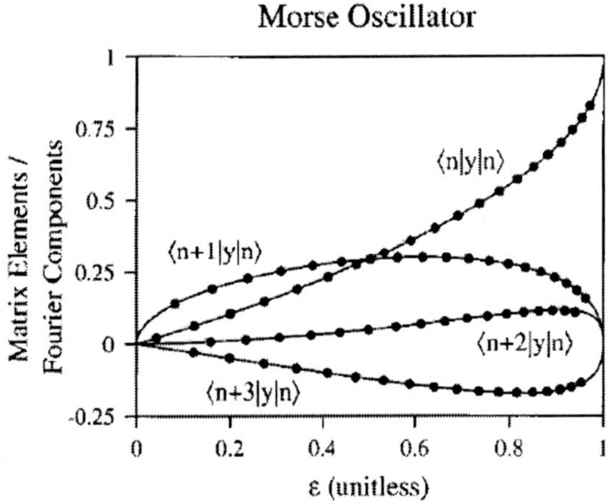

Morse Oscillator

FIG. 1: Morse matrix elements of $y = 1 - e^{-ax}$. The points correspond to the reduced mean eigenvalues for an OH stretching mode of H_2O.

and the combination

$$k^2 = \frac{z_1 - z_2}{z_1 - z_3}. \tag{16}$$

Leading perturbations between stretching and bending modes require matrix elements of r^2 which are given by[2]

$$\langle v + \mu, m | r^2 | v, m \rangle = a^{-2} \left[z_1 - (z_1 - z_2) A_0^{(2)}(k) \right], \qquad \mu = 0$$

$$= -\frac{1}{2a^2} (z_1 - z_2) A_{2\mu}^{(2)}(k), \qquad \mu \neq 0, \tag{17}$$

where $A_{2\mu}^{(2)}(k)$ is a combination of complete elliptic integrals[8].

The resulting curves, plotted for $\mu = 0 - 3$ and zero angular momentum in Fig. 2, show sharp cusps the the reduced energy of the barrier maximum, $\varepsilon = 1$. Similar curves for $m = 2$ in Ref. 2 show more rounded behavior. The points were obtained by diagonalization of the quantum equivalent of Eq. (14), with parameters appropriate to the bending mode of H_2O. Again the remarkable accuracy of the new scaling law is amply demonstrated.

V. SPHERICAL PENDULUM

The large amplitude bending motions of HCP are known to go over to relative rotation of the H atom and CP fragments, with no evidence for a stable HPC

Champagne Bottle

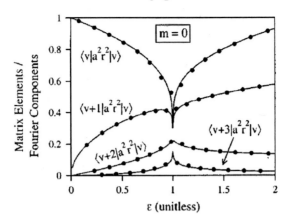

FIG. 2: Matrix elements of $a^2 r^2$ for the champagne bottle Hamiltonian with $m = 0$. Points correspond to bending levels of H_2O above and below the barrier to linearity at $\varepsilon = 1$.

isomer [1]. The qualitative aspects of such motion may be modelled by the spherical pendulum Hamiltonian

$$H_{Pend} = \frac{1}{2I} \left(p_\theta^2 + \frac{p_\phi^2}{\sin^2 \theta} \right) + B \sin^2 \theta / 2. \tag{18}$$

The exact angle-action transformation again involves elliptic integrals[2, 5], now involving of roots of the cubic polynomial

$$\left(2\varepsilon - 1 + z \right) \left(1 - z^2 \right) - m^2 b^2 = 0. \tag{19}$$

A perturbation model [9] involves leading matrix elements of the form $\langle v + \mu, m | \sin^2 \theta | v - \mu, m \rangle$, for which the equivalent Heisenberg Fourier components can again be expressed in terms of elliptic integrals[2, 5]. The resulting curves for $m = 0$ in Fig. 3 again show cusps at the barrier maximum, which are rounded off[2] for $m = 2$. The points are obtained by exact diagonalization of the quantum equivalent of Eq. (18). Again one sees the remarkable accuracy of the scaling theory.

VI. SUMMARY AND CONCLUSIONS

The Heisenberg correspondence principle has been combined with scaling laws for three parameter Hamiltonian models to obtain new scaling laws for the ma-

Pendulum

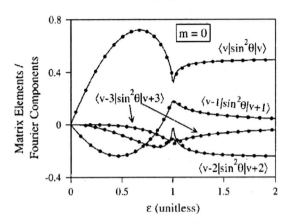

FIG. 3: Matrix elements of $\sin^2 \theta$ between $m = 0$ eigenfunctions of the spherical pendulum. Points correspond to eigenvalues of an HCP model at energies above and below the potential maximum at $\varepsilon = 1$.

trix elements of strongly anharmonic systems. The diagrams demonstrate the excellent quality of the new approximations, even in the vicinity of potential maxima.

Acknowledgements. The financial assistance of the UK EPSRC is gratefully acknowledged.

[1] H. Ishikawa, R. W. Field, S.C. Farantos, M. Joyeux, J. Koput, C. Beck and R. Schinke, Ann. Rev. Phys. Chem. **50**, 443 (1999).
[2] M. S. Child, M. P. Jacobson and C. D. Carter, J. Phys. Chem. A, **105**, 10791 (2001).
[3] W. Heisenberg, Z. Phys. **33**, 879 (1925).
[4] M. S. Child, J. Phys. A **31**, 657 (1998).
[5] M. P. Jacobson and M. S. Child, J. Phys. Chem. A **105**, 2834 (2001).
[6] M. S. Child, *Semiclassical Mechanics with Molecular Applications* (Oxford University Press, Oxford, 2001).
[7] L. Halonen, Adv. Chem. Phys. **104**, 41 (1998).
[8] I. S. Gradsteyn and I. M. Ryzik, *Tables of Integrals, Series and Products, 5th Ed.* (Academic Press, New York, 1994).
[9] M.P. Jacobson and M.S. Child, J. Chem. Phys. **114**, 262 (2001).

D. Shalashilin and M. P. de Miranda (eds.)
Multidimensional Quantum Mechanics with Trajectories
© 2009, CCP6, Daresbury

New theoretical methods for understanding chemical reactions in the energy and time domains

J. N. L. Connor,* X. Shan, A. J. Totenhofer, and C. Xiahou

School of Chemistry, The University of Manchester, Manchester, M13 9PL, UK

I. INTRODUCTION

The angular scattering of reactive molecular collisions provides important information on their dynamics and intermolecular potentials. Theoretical research is necessary to understand angular distributions measured by the most advanced experimental techniques. In this paper, we outline six tools being developed at the University of Manchester to understand the physical content of structure in the differential cross sections (DCSs) of state-to-state reactions.

The scattering theory we present is for the following generic state-to-state chemical reaction:

$$A + BC(v_i, j_i, m_i = 0) \rightarrow AB(v_f, j_f, m_f = 0) + C$$

Here v_i, j_i, m_i and v_f, j_f, m_f are the initial and final vibrational, rotational and helicity quantum numbers respectively. It is also assumed that the reaction occurs at a fixed total energy, or equivalently a fixed initial translational wavenumber. We use the notation θ_R for the reactive scattering angle, which is the angle between the outgoing molecule AB and the incoming A atom (all in the centre-of-mass collision frame).

The scattering amplitude, $f(\theta_R)$, can be written as a partial wave series (PWS):

$$f(\theta_R) = \frac{1}{2ik} \sum_{J=0}^{\infty} (2J+1) S_J P_J(\cos(\pi - \theta_R)) \tag{1}$$

---

*Electronic address: j.n.l.connor@manchester.ac.uk

or

$$f(\theta_R) = \frac{1}{2ik} \sum_{J=0}^{\infty} (2J+1)\tilde{S}_J P_J(\cos\theta_R) \tag{2}$$

where $\tilde{S}_J = \exp(i\pi J)S_J$. In equations (1) and (2), $k = \sqrt{2\mu E}/\hbar$ is the initial translational wavenumber, μ is the reduced mass, E is the collision energy, J is the total angular momentum quantum number, $\tilde{S}_J$ is the Jth modified scattering (S-) matrix element and $P_J(\bullet)$ is a Legendre polynomial of degree J. The subscript, v_i, j_i, $m_i \rightarrow v_f$, j_f, m_f, has been omitted from $f(\theta_R)$, S_J, and $\tilde{S}_J$ in equations (1) and (2) in order to keep the notation simple, as has the label, v_i, j_i, from k. The corresponding differential cross section is given by

$$\sigma(\theta_R) = |f(\theta_R)|^2 \tag{3}$$

Under semiclassical conditions, the PWS, defined by equation (2), will contain many numerically significant terms, typically of order kR, where R is the radius of the interaction region.

The theories and results we describe are taken from Refs. 1–14, as well as from unpublished research.

II.   FORWARD ANGLE GLORY SCATTERING

The state-to-state reaction, F + H$_2$ → FH + H, is an example of a benchmark chemical reaction where the forward angle scattering into the $v_f = 3$ state has been extensively studied by both experiment and theory. However it has only recently been shown that this forward angle scattering is an example of a *glory* [7]. Figure 1 compares $\sigma(\theta_R)$ computed from the PWS (2) with a *uniform semiclassical approximation* (USA) for the glory scattering. Both theories use the same quantum (numerical) S-matrix elements. There is good agreement between the PWS and USA angular distribution, especially for $\theta_R \lesssim 10°$.

The USA approximation is given by [7]

$$\sigma(\theta_R) = \frac{\pi}{2}\zeta(\theta_R)\left[\sigma_-(\theta_R)^{1/2} + \sigma_+(\theta_R)^{1/2}\right]^2 J_0(\zeta(\theta_R))^2$$
$$+ \frac{\pi}{2}\zeta(\theta_R)\left[\sigma_-(\theta_R)^{1/2} - \sigma_+(\theta_R)^{1/2}\right]^2 J_1(\zeta(\theta_R))^2 \tag{4}$$

where $J_0(\bullet)$ and $J_1(\bullet)$ are Bessel functions of order zero and unity respectively, and

$$\zeta(\theta_R) = \frac{1}{2}\left[\beta_+(\theta_R) - \beta_-(\theta_R)\right] \tag{5}$$

39

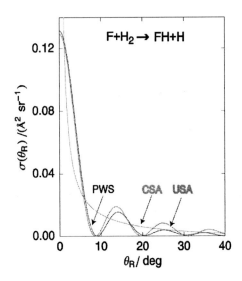

FIG. 1: Forward angle scattering for the F + H$_2$ → FH + H reaction. The transition is v_i=0, j_i=0 → v_f=3, j_f=3 and the total energy is E = 0.3872 eV. Black curve: PWS DCS; red curve: USA DCS; green curve: CSA DCS.

The $\sigma_\pm(\theta_R)$ are "classical-like" farside (F) and nearside (N) cross sections and the $\beta_\pm(\theta_R)$ are F and N phases respectively. Their explicit definitions in terms of $\tilde{S}_J$, and its continuation, $\tilde{S}(J)$ to real values of J, can be found in Ref. 7.

Figure 1 also shows the *classical semiclassical approximation* (CSA)

$$\sigma_{CSA}(\theta_R) = \sigma_+(\theta_R) + \sigma_-(\theta_R) \tag{6}$$

in which the NF oscillations are neglected. Further information on the semiclassical theory of forward glory scattering can be found in Refs. 7, 10, 11.

III. PARAMETERIZED SCATTERING MATRIX ELEMENTS

The analysis of glory scattering in section II followed the standard procedure:

Potential energy function → S-matrix → Differential cross section

An alternative procedure for understanding scattering dynamics is to omit the potential energy function and use an S-matrix to compute the angular distribution, *i.e.*,

S-matrix → Differential cross section

40

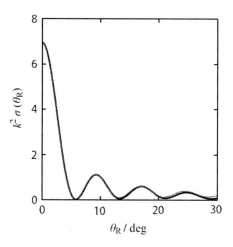

FIG. 2: Forward angle scattering for the H + D_2 → HD + D reaction. The transition is v_i=0, j_i=0 → v_f=3, j_f=0 and the total energy is E = 2.00 eV. Black curve: PWS DCS using accurate numerical S-matrix elements; red curve: PWS DCS using the parameterization (7).

We have found that simple S-matrix parametrizations can reproduce the forward angle scattering of chemical reactions. An example is shown in Fig. 2 for the H + D_2 → HD + D reaction. The black line uses accurate quantum (numerical) S-matrix elements, whereas the red line displays the DCS from a simple parameterization of the form

$$\tilde{S}(J) = \left\{ \begin{array}{l} \text{constant} \\ \text{linear in } J \\ 0 \end{array} \right\} \times \exp[\mathrm{i}(aJ^2 + bJ)] \quad \left\{ \begin{array}{l} 0 \le J \le J_c \\ J_c \le J \le J_z \\ J_z \le J \end{array} \right. \quad (7)$$

where J_c = 19.2 and J_z = 28.6 for the present example.

IV. COMPLEX ANGULAR MOMENTUM THEORY

In the complex angular momentum (CAM) approach to reactive scattering, the total angular momentum quantum number J is analytically continued from integer values, J = 0, 1, 2, ..., into the complex J plane. The Watson transformation is then used to convert the PWS into a contour integral around the Re J axis. This is followed by a deformation of the contour of integration in the CAM plane, which yields a background integral together with a sum over the (Regge) poles of $\tilde{S}(J)$. In the semiclassical limit, the scattering amplitude can

41

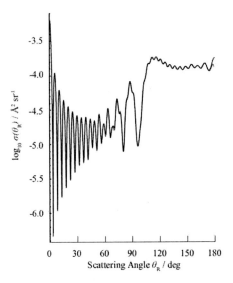

FIG. 3: Angular distribution for the I + HI → IH + I reaction. The transition is v_i=0, j_i=0 → v_f=0, j_f=2 and the translational energy is 21.3 meV. Black curve: PWS DCS; red curve: uniform semiclassical CAM DCS.

be written as the sum of four subamplitudes:

$$f(\theta_R) = f^{\text{direct}}(\theta_R) + f^{\text{residue}}(\theta_R) + f^{\text{erfc}}(\theta_R) + f^{\text{pole}}(\theta_R) \qquad (8)$$

The semiclassical result (8) is uniform in that the (real) saddle point associated with the background integral can come close to the positions of the Regge poles, as θ_R is varied.

Figure 3 shows DCSs for the I + HI → IH + I reaction, calculated from the PWS and the semiclassical CAM theory. There is excellent agreement between the two curves even for small features in the angular scattering. The subamplitudes in Eq. (8) can be used to provide a physical interpretation of structure in the DCS. For example, the high frequency oscillations at forward angles in Fig. 3 are an example of interference between the N and F scattering.

The results in Fig. 3 use a parameterized S-matrix of the form [1]

$$\tilde{S}(J) = \left[A \exp(-\alpha J^2) + \frac{a_0}{J - J_0} \right] \theta_{\text{cut}}(J) \exp[i(a J^2 + b J)] \qquad (9)$$

where

$$\theta_{\text{cut}}(J) = \frac{1}{2} \left[1 - \tanh \left(\frac{J - J_{\text{cut}}}{C_{\text{cut}}} \right) \right] \qquad (10)$$

is a "cutoff" function and J_0 is the position of the Regge pole in the CAM plane.

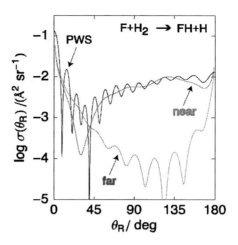

FIG. 4: NF analysis of the F + H$_2$ → FH + H reaction. The transition is v_i=0, j_i=0 → v_f=3, j_f=3 and the total energy is E = 0.3872 eV. Black curve: PWS DCS; red curve: N PWS DCS; blue curve: F PWS DCS.

V. NEARSIDE-FARSIDE THEORY

Nearside-Farside (NF) theory is a simple, yet powerful tool, for understanding complicated structure in a PWS DCS. It can be used when it is difficult (or impossible) to deduce the semiclassical limit of the PWS. In NF theory, $f(\theta_R)$ is decomposed into the sum of two subamplitudes

$$f(\theta_R) = f_N(\theta_R) + f_F(\theta_R) \tag{11}$$

where (for $\theta_R \neq 0, \pi$)

$$f_N(\theta_R) = \frac{1}{2ik}\sum_{J=0}^{\infty}(2J+1)\tilde{S}_J\frac{1}{2}\left[P_J(\cos\theta_R) + \frac{2i}{\pi}Q_J(\cos\theta_R)\right] \tag{12}$$

$$f_F(\theta_R) = \frac{1}{2ik}\sum_{J=0}^{\infty}(2J+1)\tilde{S}_J\frac{1}{2}\left[P_J(\cos\theta_R) - \frac{2i}{\pi}Q_J(\cos\theta_R)\right] \tag{13}$$

and $Q_J(\bullet)$ is a Legendre function of the second kind. The interference structure in the DCS may then arise from $f_N(\theta_R)$, or from $f_F(\theta_R)$, or from interference between the two. It is usual to plot $\sigma(\theta_R)$, $\sigma_N(\theta_R)$ and $\sigma_F(\theta_R)$ where

$$\sigma_{N,F}(\theta_R) = |f_{N,F}(\theta_R)|^2 \tag{14}$$

Figure 4 shows a NF analysis of the PWS DCS for F + H$_2$ → FH + H shown (partially) in Fig. 1. It can be seen that the reaction is N-dominated at sideward

43

and backward angles, but F-dominated at forward angles. Also the oscillations in the forward direction are a NF interference effect, which agrees with the semiclassical glory analysis of section II. Sometimes additional structure in the F DCS can be removed or diminished by resumming the PWS (2) before making the NF decomposition (11) - this procedure is called "cleaning". Additional information on NF theory can be found in Refs. 2–14.

VI. LOCAL ANGULAR MOMENTUM THEORY

Local angular momentum (LAM) analysis is a new technique [8] that extracts physical information from a PWS. A NF decomposition and resummations can also be incorporated into LAM theory. A LAM analysis identifies the full and N,F total angular momenta that contribute to the scattering at a particular angle, under semiclassical conditions. The definitions of the full and N,F LAMs are

$$\text{LAM}(\theta_R) = \frac{\text{d arg } f(\theta_R)}{\text{d}\theta_R}, \qquad \text{LAM}_{N,F}(\theta_R) = \frac{\text{d arg } f_{N,F}(\theta_R)}{\text{d}\theta_R}. \qquad (15)$$

Figure 5(a) shows a LAM analysis of the F + H$_2$ → FH + H reaction including one and two resummation of the PWS. It can be seen that the F LAM is approximately constant for $2° \lesssim \theta_R \lesssim 120°$ corresponding to rotation of the FHH complex into the forward direction. In contrast, the N LAM decreases in magnitude approximately monotonically towards large angles. This is the behaviour expected for a reaction dominated by repulsive interactions, i.e., hard-sphere like dynamics. Comparing Figs. 5(a) and 5(b) shows that the NF LAM analysis is complementary (and consistent) with the NF DCS analysis. Further information on LAM theory can be found in Refs. 6, 8, 9, 11–14.

VII. REACTIONS IN THE TIME DOMAIN

The theory and examples described in sections II-VI have all been in the *energy domain*. Important new insights into reaction dynamics are obtained by working in the *time domain* (see Ref. 12).

The two domains are related by half-Fourier transforms:

$$f(\theta_R, t) = \int_0^\infty F(E)f(\theta_R, E)\exp(-iEt/\hbar)dE, \qquad (16)$$

$$f(\theta_R, E) = \frac{1}{2\pi\hbar F(E)} \int_0^\infty f(\theta_R, t)\exp(iEt/\hbar)dt \qquad (17)$$

where $F(E)$ is an energy filter function, which is choosen to extract interesting information from $f(\theta_R, E)$. Also a time-dependent angular distribution can be

44

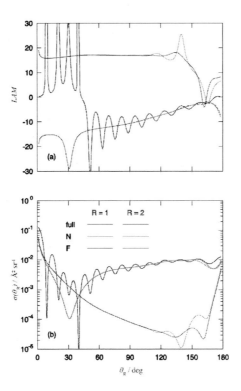

FIG. 5: NF analysis for one (R=1) and two (R=2) resummations of the PWS. (a) black curve: LAM(θ_R); blue curves: LAM$_F$(θ_R) for R=1 amd R=2; red curves: LAM$_N$(θ_R) for R=1 and R=2. (b) Same as (a) except for $\sigma(\theta_R)$ amd $\sigma_N(\theta_N)$, $\sigma_F(\theta_R)$ for R=1 and R=2.

defined,

$$\sigma(\theta_R, t) = |f(\theta_R, t)|^2. \tag{18}$$

If $f(\theta_R, E)$ is written as the PWS (2), then we obtain an analogous PWS for $f(\theta_R, t)$ from Eq. (16). This allows us to make a NF decomposition of $f(\theta_R, t)$ similar to equations (11)-(13). In addition, NF LAM theory can be applied to $f(\theta_R, t)$. Ref. [12] describes NF analyses in the time domain for the H + D$_2 \rightarrow$ HD + D reaction. A useful concept introduced in [12] is that of a *cumulative time-evolving* DCS, in which the upper infinite limit in Eq. (17) is replaced by a

45

finite time. We have

$$f_t(\theta_R, E) = \frac{1}{2\pi\hbar F(E)} \int_0^t f(\theta_R, t') \exp(iEt'/\hbar) dt', \tag{19}$$

$$\sigma_t(\theta_R, E) = |f_t(\theta_R, E)|^2 \tag{20}$$

Figure 6 plots $\sigma_t(\theta_R, E) \sin\theta_R$ versus E and θ_R at the times $t = 29.8$, 50.3, 70.1, 102.2 fs for the H + D_2 reaction. At $t = 29.8$ fs and 50.3 fs, the scattering is mainly in the backward direction, followed by forward angle scattering at $t = 70.1$ fs and 102.2 fs. Note that the reaction is almost over at $t = 102.2$ fs.

Acknowledgements This research has been supported by the U.K. Engineering and Physical Sciences Research Council.

---

[1] D. Vrinceanu, A. Z. Msezane, D. Bessis, J. N. L. Connor and D. Sokolovski, Chem. Phys. Lett. **324**, 311 (2000).

[2] P. McCabe, J. N. L. Connor and D. Sokolovski, J. Chem. Phys. **114**, 5194 (2001).

[3] T. W. J. Whiteley, C. Noli and J. N. L. Connor, J. Phys. Chem. A, **105**, 2792 (2001).

[4] C. Noli, J. N. L. Connor, N. Rougeau and C. Kubach, Phys. Chem. Chem. Phys. **3**, 3946 (2001).

[5] C. Noli and J. N. L. Connor,, Russ. J. Phys. Chem. **76** (Suppl. 1), S77 (2002). Also available at: http://arXiv.org/abs/physics/0301054

[6] R. Anni, J. N. L. Connor and C. Noli, Phys. Rev. C **66**, 044610 (2002).

[7] J. N. L. Connor, Phys. Chem. Chem. Phys. **6**, 377 (2004).

[8] J. N. L. Connor and R. Anni, Phys. Chem. Chem. Phys. **6**, 3364 (2004).

[9] R. Anni, J. N. L. Connor and C. Noli, Khim. Fiz. **23**(2), 6 (2004). Also available at: http://arXiv.org/abs/physics/0410266

[10] J. N. L. Connor, Mol. Phys. **103**, 1715 (2005).

[11] C. Xiahou and J. N. L. Connor, Mol. Phys. **104**, 159 (2006).

[12] P. D. D. Monks, J. N. L. Connor and S. C. Althorpe, J. Phys. Chem. A, **110**, 741 (2006).

[13] P. D. D. Monks, C. Xiahou and J. N. L. Connor, J. Chem. Phys. **125**, 133504, pp. 1−13 (2006).

[14] P. D. D. Monks, J. N. L. Connor and S. C. Althorpe, J. Phys. Chem. A, **111**, 10302 (2007).

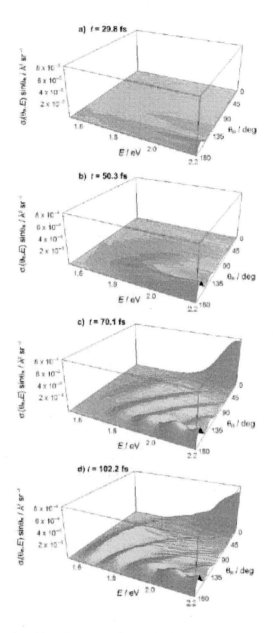

FIG. 6: Plots of $\sigma_t(\theta_R, E)\sin\theta_R$ versus E and θ_R for the $H + D_2 \rightarrow HD + D$ reaction. The transition is $v_i=0$, $j_i=0 \rightarrow v_f=3$, $j_f=0$. (a) $t = 29.8$ fs, (b) $t = 50.3$ fs, (c) $t = 70.1$ fs, (d) $t = 102.2$ fs.

47

D. Shalashilin and M. P. de Miranda (eds.)
Multidimensional Quantum Mechanics with Trajectories
© 2009, CCP6, Daresbury

Two-dimensional nonadiabatic scattering: exact quantum solutions

V. I. Osherov* and V. G. Ushakov[†]

*Institute of Problems of Chemical Physics,
Russian Academy of Sciences, 142432 Chernogolovka, Russia*

I. INTRODUCTION

An accurate calculation of the dynamics in the vicinity of the intersection of potential energy surfaces implies precise consideration of the topological properties both of the wave functions and of the potential. As a result the calculation of partial-wave phases turns out to be a very subtle problem. To clarify the problem we tried to find an accurate analytical results for, at least, some special models and restricted physical conditions. In this paper we consider a neutron scattering in the magnetic field of a linear current, that represent the only example of the exactly solvable nonadiabatic transitions problem in the physical system. The Jahn-Teller and Renner-Teller models and the triple intersection of a double cone with a plane are considered at an energy equal to the potential energy in the intersection point.

II. NEUTRON SCATTERING IN THE MAGNETIC FIELD OF A LINEAR CURRENT

The Schroedinger equation for the neutron in the magnetic field of the linear current oriented along the z axis of the space-fixed coordinate system after the separation of the variable z has the form

$$\left(T - \frac{F}{\rho}\begin{pmatrix} 0, & e^{i\varphi} \\ e^{-i\varphi}, & 0 \end{pmatrix} - E\right)\Psi = 0. \tag{1}$$

---

*Electronic address: osherov@icp.ac.ru
[†]Electronic address: uvg@icp.ac.ru

The accurate analytical solutions for diabatic amplitudes can be found using the contour Bessel transformation of Eq. (1). These solutions are expressed in the form of integrals containing Kummer functions.

The asymptotic behavior of the adiabatic solutions is found in the form

$$\varphi_{1,m}^{(1)} = e^{\pi\nu/2}\rho^{-1/2}\left(e^{i(S_1-\xi)} + e^{-i(S_1-\xi)}\right)$$

$$\varphi_{2,m}^{(1)} = ie^{-\pi\nu/2}\rho^{-1/2}\left(e^{i(S_2+\xi)} - e^{-i(S_2+\xi)}\right)$$

$$\varphi_{1,m}^{(2)} = e^{-\pi\nu/2}\rho^{-1/2}\left(e^{i(S_1-\xi)} - e^{-i(S_1-\xi)}\right)$$

$$\varphi_{2,m}^{(2)} = -ie^{\pi\nu/2}\rho^{-1/2}\left(e^{i(S_2+\xi)} + e^{-i(S_2+\xi)}\right).$$

S_{12} are the radial Coulomb phases, ξ is the nonadiabatic phase,

$$\xi = \arg\Gamma(2i\nu) - 2\arg\Gamma(i\nu) - 2\nu\ln 2 - \pi/4 - \arg\Gamma(m+1/2+i\nu),, \quad (2)$$

ν is the Massey parameter,

$$\nu = F\hbar^{-1}(M/2E)^{1/2}. \quad (3)$$

The incoming and outgoing waves of the partial adiabatic amplitudes are connected by the relation

$$\mathbf{A}_m = -\hat{S}\mathbf{B}_m \quad (4)$$

which is the equation for the $S-$matrix calculation.

Finally, the $S-$matrix is obtained in the form

$$\hat{S} = -\begin{pmatrix} e^{-2i\xi}\tanh(\pi\nu), & \dfrac{i}{\cosh(\pi\nu)} \\[2ex] \dfrac{i}{\cosh(\pi\nu)}, & e^{2i\xi}\tanh(\pi\nu) \end{pmatrix}. \quad (5)$$

To set up the scattering problem, we take the diabatic plane wave as the eigenvector of operator σ_y. In the adiabatic representation this wave looks as follows:

$$\mathbf{\Phi}_0 = e^{ikx}\begin{pmatrix} -\sin\frac{\varphi}{2} \\ i\cos\frac{\phi}{2} \end{pmatrix}. \quad (6)$$

The final expression for the differential cross section of the scattering in the adiabatic channel has the form

$$\frac{d\sigma}{d\varphi} = \frac{\tanh^2(\pi\nu)}{2\pi k}\left|\sum_{m=\frac{2l-1}{2}} \frac{\Gamma(m+1/2+i\nu)}{\Gamma(m+1/2-i\nu)}e^{im\varphi}\right|^2 \equiv \frac{\nu}{2k}\frac{\tanh(\pi\nu)}{\sin^2(\varphi/2)}. \quad (7)$$

49

This equality is the two-dimension analog of the quantum Rutherford's formula however unlike it contains the Planck's constant and coincides with the corresponding classical expression only at $\hbar \to 0$.

III. THE SCATTERING MODEL FOR THE SYSTEM WITH TWO INTERACTING ELECTRONIC STATES

The simplest model of scattering process influenced by the interaction between electronic states is described by the following Shroedinger equation in diabatic representation

$$
\left(T + \begin{pmatrix} 0, & -\rho^n e^{2i\kappa\varphi} \\ -\rho^n e^{-2i\kappa\varphi}, & 0 \end{pmatrix} - E \right) \Psi = 0, \qquad E = 0. \tag{8}
$$

In the case of $\kappa = 1/2$, $n = 1$, the system represents the well known Jan-Teller model of the conical intersection of adiabatic potential energy surfaces. The case $\kappa = 1$, $n = 2$ corresponds to a Renner-Teller glancing intersection of potential energy surfaces for the linear molecules.

The scattering problem is formulated using the accurate representations of plane wave, which are given by

$$
\exp(-ip_0 x) = \sum_{-\infty}^{+\infty} \exp\left(im\varphi - i\frac{\pi |m|}{2} \right) J_{|m|}(p_0\rho) \tag{9}
$$

for integer m and

$$
\exp(-ip_0 x)\,\mathrm{erf}\left(e^{-i\pi/4}\sqrt{2p_0\rho}\cos\frac{\varphi}{2} \right) = \sum_{-\infty}^{+\infty} \exp\left(im\varphi - i\frac{\pi |m|}{2} \right) J_{|m|}(p_0\rho) \tag{10}
$$

for half-integer m. As the result, both for the integer and for the half-integer parameter κ the scattering amplitude is expressed as

$$
f(\varphi) = \frac{\exp(i\pi/4)}{\sqrt{2\pi p_0}} \sum_{-\infty}^{+\infty} \exp\left(im\varphi - i\pi |m| \right) \left(\exp(2i\delta_m) - 1 \right), \tag{11}
$$

where δ_m are the phase shifts defined by the asymptotic behavior of partial adiabatic radial amplitudes

$$
\varphi_1^{(m)}(\rho) = \sqrt{\frac{2}{\pi p_0 \rho}} \cos\left(p_0\rho - \frac{\pi |m|}{2} - \frac{\pi}{4} + \delta_m \right), \qquad p_0\rho \gg 1, |m|. \tag{12}
$$

The equations for radial amplitudes have accurate analytical solutions in the form of Meijer functions and the scattering phases can be found in the form

$$\delta_m = \delta_{ad,m}, \quad |m| \geq \kappa,$$
$$\delta_m = \delta_{ad,m} + \frac{\pi}{k}(|m| - \kappa), \quad |m| < \kappa. \tag{13}$$

Thus, the scattering amplitude $f(\varphi)$ can be presented as a sum of two contributions

$$f(\varphi) = \frac{\exp(i\pi/4)}{\sqrt{2\pi p_0}} \left[\sum_{-\infty}^{+\infty} \exp\left(im\varphi - i\pi |m|\right) \left(\exp(2i\delta_{ad,m}) - 1\right) \right.$$
$$\left. + \sum_{|m|<\kappa} \exp\left(im\varphi - i\pi |m|\right) \left(\exp(2i\delta_m) - \exp(2i\delta_{ad,m})\right) \right]. \tag{14}$$

The first term in this equation describes unperturbed scattering in the field of the lower adiabatic state potential. The scattering pattern coincides with that of classical mechanics: any trajectory deviates from the initial direction of motion by the angle $\Delta\varphi = \pi - 2\pi/k$. This deviation angle is equal to $\pi/3$ for the Jan-Teller conic intersection and it is equal to $\pi/2$ for the Renner-Teller glancing intersection.

The second term in Eq. (14) represents the superposition of spherical outgoing waves corresponding to relatively small values of quantum number m ($|m| < \kappa$). This quantum scattering is a consequence of nuclear angular momentum uncertainty caused by the coupling between electronic and nuclear motion. Note, that for the Jan-Teller model there are no states with $|m| < \kappa$ and the quantum scattering can not arise.

The peculiar feature of the result is the abrupt change of the behavior of the phase shift δ_m at $m = \kappa$. The coupling between electronic and nuclear motion does not modify the scattering process when the total angular momentum m exceeds the electronic momentum κ. Possibly, this effect is a consequence of simplifications adopted in the model under consideration.

IV. THE SCATTERING MODEL FOR THE SYSTEM WITH THREE INTERACTING ELECTRONIC STATES

We specify three state Hamiltonian in the form

$$\left(T + \begin{pmatrix} 0, & -\rho^n e^{i\kappa\varphi}, & 0 \\ -\rho^n e^{-i\kappa\varphi}, & 0, & -\rho^n e^{i\kappa\varphi} \\ 0, & -\rho^n e^{-i\kappa\varphi}, & 0 \end{pmatrix} \right) \Psi = 0. \tag{15}$$

At $n = 1$, $\kappa = 1$, this system represents the basic model for electronic nonadiabatic transitions between the states with triple intersection of the double-cone and plane adiabatic potentials. Independent partial solutions to this equation are found in terms of the Meijer functions and result in the phase shifts δ_m for the adiabatic radial amplitudes $\varphi_1^{(m)}$

$$\delta_m = \delta_{ad,m} + \frac{\pi}{k}\left(|m| - \tilde{m}\right) + \pi\frac{\sqrt{m^2 + \kappa^2} - |m|}{2k}, \tag{16}$$

where

$$\tilde{m} = \begin{cases} |m|, & |m| \geq \kappa, \\ \kappa, & |m| < \kappa. \end{cases} \tag{17}$$

Similar to the two states systems, the quantitative pattern of the scattering is the sum of the adiabatic scattering in the field of the lower potential peak and the quantum scattering induced by the nonadiabatic coupling.

V. CONCLUSION

The exact cross section of neutron scattering coincide with cross section for the artificial adiabatic system . The adiabatic limit $\nu \to \infty$ removes the nonadiabatic transitions and the topological effects simultaneously and the scattering becomes classical. The accurate semiclassical limit can be used to check trajectories results.

For the standard Jan-Teller intersection, at zero energy, the geometric phase effect results in half-integer angular momentum for the adiabatic phase of partial scattering amplitudes. The dynamical nonadiabatic phase is absent. For the Renner-Teller intersection, the geometric phase effect is absent. The phase of the partial wave with momentum $m = 0$ is modified by the nonadiabatic phase, which brings the additional isotropic contribution to the angular distribution of adiabatic scattering. For the system with the double-cone-plane intersection, the dynamical nonadiabatic phase modifies the phases of all partial waves.

The scattering amplitudes calculated with and without the geometric phase effect differs undoubtedly. The difference depends on the phase shifts decrease at large values of angular momentum and is determined by the quenching interference of partial waves at large m.

[1] V. I. Osherov and V. G. Ushakov, Phys. Rev. A **69**, 052710 (2004).
[2] V. I. Osherov and V. G. Ushakov, Phys. Rev. A **75**, 032716 (2007)
[3] A. Kuppermann, in *Dynamics of molecules and chemical reactions*, ed. by R. E. Wyatt and J. Z. H. Zhang (Marcel Dekker Inc., 1996).

D. Shalashilin and M. P. de Miranda (eds.)
Multidimensional Quantum Mechanics with Trajectories
© 2009, CCP6, Daresbury

The semiclassical route to real time quantum dynamics

Eli Pollak*

Chemical Physics Department, Weizmann Institute of Science, 76100 Rehovoth, Israel

I. INTRODUCTION

Two central challenges face theoretical chemistry at the turn of the 21st century. One is the ability to compute the real time quantum dynamics of systems with many degrees of freedom. The other, is to provide a reliable and accurate representation of the force field. Much progress has been achieved during the last ten years with regards to the first challenge. Notably the Multi-Configuration Time Dependent Hartree (MCTDH) method [1–5] has allowed the computation of the quantum dynamics of strongly coupled systems with a few tens of degrees of freedom.

Although the success of the method is already impressive it suffers from two drawbacks. The numerical effort increases exponentially with the number of degrees of freedom of the system. But perhaps more seriously, implementation of the methodology demands the knowledge of the global potential energy surface. This makes it virtually impossible to use ab-initio potential energy surfaces. One must first find a way of representing the force field, and this is a notoriously difficult task. Although here too progress has been achieved [6], provided that the system is not too large, it does present a formidable challenge.

Many approximate methodologies have been developed, most of them dependent on a mixed quantum classical representation. The great advantage of classical mechanics is that the theory is local and therefore classical trajectories can be computed on the fly [7–9]. However the scope of validity of classical approximations is limited, they do not account satisfactorily for interference phenomena and hence for the quantization of energy levels, tunneling and resonance phenomena. It is thus tantalizing to develop semiclassical based methods which by construction can deal reasonably well with quantum phenomena, while the fundamental object underlying the semiclassical approach is a classical trajectory

---

*Electronic address: eli.pollak@weizmann.ac.il

which can be computed on the fly.

Much progress has been achieved in using the SemiClassical approach, based on Initial Value Representations (SCIVR) [10]. The quantum propagator (quantum operators are denoted by a "hat") is represented in terms of a Gaussian based propagation scheme. The initial state $|\psi\rangle$ is projected onto a coherent state $|g(p,q)\rangle$ (where p,q are the momenta and coordinate variables, and for simplicity we use a one dimensional notation), which is then evolved in time according to classical mechanics, weighted by an action $S(p_t, q_t)$ and a prefactor $R(p_t, q_t)$:

$$\hat{K}_0(t) = \int \frac{dpdq}{2\pi\hbar} R(p_t, q_t) e^{iS(p_t, q_t)/\hbar} |g(p_t, q_t)\rangle\langle g(p,q)|\psi\rangle. \qquad (1)$$

This approximate form of the propagator makes it possible to use it within a Monte Carlo scheme. The coherent states provide a natural Gaussian weighting so that all that is needed is to propagate classical trajectories which at least in principle can be computed on the fly.

The SCIVR prescription has though some serious deficiencies. It would seem to be an ad-hoc theory. For example, the coherent states are functions of an arbitrary width parameter, usage of different width parameters would give differing results, so what is the best way to proceed? Moreover, the prefactor [11] depends on the elements of the monodromy matrix. For a system with N degrees of freedom this implies the computation of an additional $4N^2$ equations of motion, which demand knowledge of second derivatives of the force field. Finally, the convergence of the SCIVR methodology, even within a Monte Carlo approach is much slower than ordinary classical trajectory computations, due to the oscillatory phase factor.

In the next section we briefly review the SCIVR series methodology which we have developed during the past five years [12–15]. This methodology shows that the SCIVR approximation as given in Eq. 1 is just a leading order term in a series representation of the exact quantum propagator. Each term in the series may be computed using only classical trajectories, thus providing at least in principle a local route to the exact quantum dynamics, which is amenable to on the fly computations.

II. THE SCIVR SERIES METHOD

In standard time dependent perturbation theory the Hamiltonian is divided into two parts, $\hat{H}_0$ and $\hat{V}$. The perturbation $\hat{V}$ is assumed to be small. We have developed a more general time dependent perturbation theory, in which the central object is the propagator, not the Hamiltonian. We assume that the Hamiltonian $\hat{H}$ of the system is known and that we have constructed an approximate propagator $\hat{K}_0(t)$ whose time evolution law is known and who has

54

the (almost trivial) property that $\hat{K}_0(0) = \hat{I}$ where $\hat{I}$ is the identity operator. The approximate propagator might take the form as given in Eq. 1. We then construct a "correction operator" defined to be:

$$\hat{C}(t) = i\hbar \frac{d\hat{K}_0(t)}{dt} - \hat{H}\hat{K}_0(t). \tag{2}$$

The Schrödinger equation

$$i\hbar \frac{d\hat{K}(t)}{dt} = \hat{H}\hat{K}(t) \tag{3}$$

for the exact propagator $\hat{K}(t)$ is just the homogeneous part of Eq. 2. One thus readily finds that the formal solution of the equation for the approximate propagator, may be given in terms of the exact propagator as:

$$\hat{K}_0(t) = \hat{K}(t) + \frac{1}{i\hbar} \int_0^t dt' \hat{K}(t - t')\hat{C}(t'). \tag{4}$$

We now assume that our approximate propagator is a "good" one, in the sense that the correction operator is "small". We may thus write the exact propagator as a series

$$\hat{K}(t) = \sum_{j=0}^{\infty} \hat{K}_j(t) \tag{5}$$

where the j-th term in the series is of the order of $\hat{C}^j$. The zero-th order term in the series is by definition $\hat{K}_0(t)$ while the higher order terms in the series are given through the recursion relation:

$$\hat{K}_{j+1}(t) = \frac{i}{\hbar} \int_0^t dt' \hat{K}_j(t - t')\hat{C}(t'). \tag{6}$$

Provided that the series converges, this leads to the representation of the exact propagator in terms of the zero-th order SCIVR propagator and its associated correction operator.

The structure of the correction operator associated with the SCIVR propagator as given in Eq. 1 is very similar:

$$\hat{C}(t) = \int \frac{dpdq}{2\pi\hbar} R(p_t, q_t) e^{iS(p_t,q_t)/\hbar} \Delta V(\hat{x}, q_t, p_t)|g(p_t, q_t)\rangle\langle g(p, q)|\psi\rangle. \tag{7}$$

where the energy operator $\Delta V(\hat{x}, q_t, p_t)$ depends on the coordinate operator $\hat{x}$ and on the time evolving phase space variables q_t, p_t.

The fact that one can create an exact series representation of the propagator based on the choice of a zero'th order form allows one much freedom. Especially, one may choose the SCIVR propagator to be the frozen Gaussian propagator [16], where the prefactor $R(p_t, q_t)$ is set to unity. One then readily finds that the correction operator also does not have a prefactor in it. The resulting computational expense is reduced as there is no need to compute the monodromy matrix. Alternatively, especially when dealing with system-bath Hamiltonians one may use a hybrid approach [14] in which one only computes the Herman-Kluk prefactor [11] with respect to the system variables. Setting the prefactor to unity does entail a price. It is well known that the frozen Gaussian approximation does not keep the normalization, in fact, it is precisely this loss of normalization which was corrected by introduction of the Herman-Kluk prefactor. Here too, the fact that that one may use the series representation provides an easy way to correct for this loss. One may multiply the SCIVR propagator by any arbitrary function of time $g(t)$ provided that initially $g(0) = 1$ to define the SCIVR propagator $\hat{K}_0(t; g) = g(t)\hat{K}_0(t)$. This then causes the correction operator to change, such that:

$$\hat{C}(t; g) = g(t)\hat{C}(t) + i\hbar\frac{\partial \ln g(t)}{\partial t}\hat{K}_0(t; g). \tag{8}$$

One may then compute the normalization function

$$N(t) = \langle\psi|\hat{K}_0^\dagger(t)\hat{K}_0(t)|\psi\rangle \tag{9}$$

and choose $g(t) = N^{-1/2}(t)$ to assure that the frozen Gaussian propagator obeys unitarity exactly with respect to the wavefunction ψ.

This renormalization procedure [13] opens the way for computing the SCIVR propagator for systems with many degrees of freedom. Past experience has shown that such a renormalization does not lead to a severe deterioration of the results [14, 15] and typically only the first or second order terms in the perturbation series are needed to obtain a numerical answer that is within a few percent of the numerically exact answer.

III. CONCLUSION

The SCIVR series method for computing real time quantum dynamics has been applied in recent years to numerous examples. The most recent ones include an on the fly computation of the absorption spectrum of Formaldehyde [17]. This pioneering example demonstrates that indeed one can use the local property of the classical trajectories underlying the SCIVR approach to obtain accurate results for systems of real interest. The SCIVR generated spectrum is much more accurate than an analogous spectrum created using only a harmonic theory approximation.

56

In the standard SCIVR approach, the central trajectory is derived from Hamiltonian mechanics. It has been a long standing challenge to construct an SCIVR theory when the underlying classical dynamics is derived from a generalized Langevin equation. We have recently shown that this is indeed possible [18, 19]. The resulting expressions for thermal correlation functions are somewhat involved, but their central object are Langevin trajectories. Applications [19] to a dissipative harmonic and Morse oscillator are encouraging as only the zero-th and first order terms were needed to obtain numerically exact quantum results. Preliminary results for the scattering of a He atom on a Cu surface are also promising [20], as the computed SCIVR angular distribution exhibits the correct diffraction pattern which is not obtained when using a classical Wigner theory.

This brief description of the SCIVR series method should convey the message that the SCIVR methodology may be considered as a practical way of obtaining real time quantum dynamical information from ab-initio theory.

Acknowledgements. This work has been supported by grants from the Israel Science Foundation, the Minerva Foundation, Munich and The German Israeli Foundation for Scientific Research and Development.

[1] H.-D. Meyer, U. Manthe, and L. S. Cederbaum, Chem. Phys. Lett. **165**, 73 (1990).
[2] M. H. Beck, A. Jäckle, G. A. Worth, and H.-D. Meyer, Phys. Rep. **324**, 1 (2000).
[3] H. Wang, J. Chem. Phys. **113**, 9948 (2000).
[4] H. Wang and M. Thoss, J. Chem. Phys. **119**, 1289 (2003).
[5] M. Nest, P. Ramanathan and P. Saalfrank, J. Chem. Phys. **126**, 214106 (2007).
[6] M.A. Collins, Adv. Chem. Phys. **93**, 389 (1996); Theor. Chem. Acc. **108**, 313 (2002).
[7] R. Car and M.Parrinello, Phys. Rev. Lett. **55**, 2471 (1985).
[8] N.L. Doltsinis and D. Marx, J. Theor. Comp. Chem. 1, **319** (2002).
[9] H.B. Schlegel, Bull. Kor. Chem. Soc. **24**, 1 (2003) and references therein.
[10] W.H. Miller, J. Phys. Chem. A **105**, 2942 (2001).
[11] M.F. Herman and E. Kluk, Chem. Phys. **91**, 27 (1984).
[12] S. Zhang and E. Pollak, Phys. Rev. Lett. **91**, 190201 (2003).
[13] S. Zhang and E. Pollak, J. Chem. Phys. **121**, 3384 (2004).
[14] S. Zhang and E. Pollak, J. Chem. Theor. Comp. 1, 345 (2005).
[15] E. Martin-Fierro and E. Pollak, J. Chem. Phys. **126**, 164108 (2007).
[16] E.J. Heller, J. Chem. Phys. **75**, 2923 (1981).
[17] J. Tatchen and E. Pollak, to be published.
[18] E. Pollak, J. Chem. Phys. **127**, 074505 (2007).
[19] J. Moix and E. Pollak, J. Chem. Phys., in press.
[20] J. Moix and E. Pollak, to be published.

D. Shalashilin and M. P. de Miranda (eds.)
Multidimensional Quantum Mechanics with Trajectories
© 2009, CCP6, Daresbury

Simulation of open quantum systems

Florian Mintert[1,*] and Eric J. Heller[2,†]

[1] *Physikalisches Institut, Albert-Ludwigs Universität Freiburg,*
Hermann-Herder-Str. 3, Freiburg, Germany
[2] *Department of Physics, Harvard University,*
17 Oxford Street, Cambridge Massachusetts, USA

We describe an approach to open system dynamics based on the propagation of Gaussian states in the thawed Gaussian state approximation [1–3]. This allows an expansion into *localized* states which permits effectively reducing the size of the environment, taking into account only environment particles in close proximity of the system particle.

Any Gaussian state is completely characterized in terms of the expectation values of all coordinates and momenta $\mathbf{x} = [r_1, p_1, r_2, p_2, \ldots, r_n, p_n] = \mathrm{Tr}\ \hat{\mathbf{x}}\varrho$, and the corresponding covariances $\Sigma_{ij} = \mathrm{Tr}\ ((\hat{\mathbf{x}}_\mathbf{i}\hat{\mathbf{x}}_\mathbf{j} + \hat{\mathbf{x}}_\mathbf{j}\hat{\mathbf{x}}_\mathbf{i})/2)\varrho - \mathbf{x}_i\mathbf{x}_j$. The Weyl symbol of the density matrix, *i.e.* the Wigner function

$$W(x) = \int d^n q \langle \vec{r} - \frac{\vec{q}}{2}|\varrho|\vec{r} + \frac{\vec{q}}{2}\rangle e^{\frac{i}{\hbar}\vec{p}\vec{q}} = \frac{1}{\sqrt{\pi^n \det \Sigma}} e^{-\frac{1}{2}(x-\mathbf{x})\Sigma^{-1}(x-\mathbf{x})} \tag{1}$$

is easily parametrized in terms of these quantities.

The evolution of a Gaussian quantum state due to a quadratic Hamiltonian gives rise to Newton's equations of motion $\dot{x} = \mathcal{S}\nabla H$ with the symplectic matrix S, and

$$\frac{\partial \Sigma}{\partial t} = 2(\Sigma \mathcal{H} \mathcal{S} - \mathcal{S}\mathcal{H}\Sigma) , \tag{2}$$

where $\mathcal{H}$ contains the second derivatives of the Hamiltonian H with respect to the coordinates and momenta, *i.e.* $\mathcal{H}_{ij} = \frac{1}{2}\frac{\partial^2 H}{\partial \mathbf{x}_i \partial \mathbf{x}_j}$

Eq. (2) describes the *unitary* evolution of the system and its surrounding environment. Any dissipative nature of the the dynamics is due to tracing over

---

*Electronic address: florian.mintert@physik.uni-freiburg.de
†Electronic address: heller@physics.harvard.edu

environmental degrees of freedom. Obviously, the expectation value of any observable A on particles that are not being traced over are unaffected by the partial tracing

$$\text{Tr}A\rho = \text{Tr}A(\text{Tr}_p\rho) \ . \tag{3}$$

Therefore, tracing over some degrees of freedom is equivalent to simply dropping all components of $\mathbf{x}$ and Σ corresponding to the degrees of freedom being traced over. In turn, adding a particle corresponds to extending $\mathbf{x}$ and Σ by the respective quantities, with vanishing correlations between the added particle, and the residual system.

Any quantum state ϱ (pure or mixed) can be decomposed into an incoherent mixture of coherent states $\varrho = \int d\mu(\alpha) \, P_\alpha(\varrho) \, |\alpha\rangle\langle\alpha|$, with the P-function $P_\alpha(\varrho)$. The central merit of this representation is that different initial states $|\alpha\rangle$ can be propagated individually, and the overall final state is then the incoherent sum over the individually propagated states. In the present framework of an open system, this implies that partial traces can be taken at any instant. The big disadvantage of such a representation is the often wild behavior of P_α. In particular for non-classical states P_α is rapidly oscillating, and close to singular, which severely limits its usefulness for practical purposes.

Often it is significantly easier to expand the state $|\Psi\rangle$ into a coherent sum of Gaussian states $|\Psi\rangle \simeq \sum_\alpha \Psi_\alpha|\alpha\rangle$. Due to the linearity of the Schrödinger equation, one can of course propagate each initial term $|\alpha_i\rangle$ individually, In order to take partial traces, however, one needs to consider the corresponding density matrix $\varrho = \sum_{\alpha\beta} \Psi_\alpha \Psi_\beta^* \, \mathcal{U}(t)|\alpha\rangle\langle\beta|\mathcal{U}^\dagger(t)$. Therefore, we will consider the evolution of the individual operators $\rho_{\alpha\beta}$ resulting from $|\alpha\rangle\langle\beta|$. Since those operators are not necessarily normalized, all expectation values will be defined including normalization $\langle A\rangle_\rho = \text{Tr}A\rho/\text{Tr}\rho$. Doing so, one obtains the equations of motion

$$\frac{\partial\Sigma}{\partial t} = 2(\Sigma\mathcal{H}_+\mathcal{S} - \mathcal{S}\mathcal{H}_+\Sigma) - \frac{i\hbar}{2}\mathcal{S}\mathcal{H}_-\mathcal{S} - \frac{2i}{\hbar}\Sigma\mathcal{H}_-\Sigma \ , \tag{4}$$

with $\mathcal{H}_+ = 1/2(\mathcal{H}_\alpha + \mathcal{H}_\beta)$, and $\mathcal{H}_- = \mathcal{H}_\alpha - \mathcal{H}_\beta$; and with $\mathcal{H}_\alpha$, $\mathcal{H}_\beta$ being the second order expansion coefficients of H taken along the phase space positions $\langle\alpha|\hat{\mathbf{x}}|\alpha\rangle$, $\langle\beta|\hat{\mathbf{x}}|\beta\rangle$. The equations of motion for the positions and momenta $\mathbf{x}$ are a bit more lengthy, and they are most conveniently characterized by the relation

$$\vec{\mathbf{x}} = \frac{1}{2}(\vec{\mathbf{x}}_\alpha + \vec{\mathbf{x}}_\beta) - \frac{i}{\hbar}\Sigma\mathcal{S}(\vec{\mathbf{x}}_\alpha - \vec{\mathbf{x}}_\beta) \ , \tag{5}$$

and $\mathbf{x}_\alpha$ and $\mathbf{x}_\beta$ evolving according to Newton's equation of motion.

The Weyl symbol corresponding to those complex phase space coordinates and uncertainties is given by Eq. (1) up to the additional factor $\exp(\eta)$ with

$$\eta = \frac{1}{2\hbar^2}(\vec{\mathbf{x}}_\alpha - \vec{\mathbf{x}}_\beta)\mathcal{S}\Sigma\mathcal{S}(\vec{\mathbf{x}}_\alpha - \vec{\mathbf{x}}_\beta) - \frac{i}{2\hbar}(\vec{p}_\alpha + \vec{p}_\beta)(\vec{r}_\alpha - \vec{r}_\beta) \ , \tag{6}$$

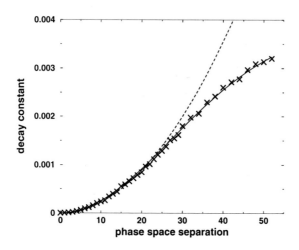

FIG. 1: Decay constants for the coherence between two wave-packets $|\alpha\rangle$ and $|\beta\rangle$ as function of the initial relative phase space separation $\delta \mathbf{x}$ between $|\alpha\rangle$ and $|\beta\rangle$. For small δx he decay constants grow quadratically with the phase space separation. Starting with δz exceeding the interaction range (25 oscillator length), a deviation from the quadratic growth (dashed line) sets in, and the behavior is described better by a Gaussian (solid line).

and a phase φ whose evolution is given by $\dot{\varphi} = \mathcal{L}_\alpha - \mathcal{L}_\beta - \frac{1}{2}\mathrm{Tr}\Sigma\mathcal{H}_-$, where $\mathcal{L}_i$, $(i = 1, 2)$ is the Lagrange function with variables $\vec{r}_i$, and $\vec{p}_i$.

So far we were concerned mainly with the unitary dynamics of the system. However, some care has to be taken while tracing over an environmental particle. As mentioned before, the dynamical variables $\mathbf{x}$, and Σ remain unchanged under partial tracing. However, $\mathbf{x}_\alpha$, and $\mathbf{x}_\beta$ are propagated rather than $\mathbf{x}$, and for a general state any entry of $\mathbf{x}$ depends on all the entries of $\mathbf{x}_\alpha$, and $\mathbf{x}_\beta$ as shown in Eq. (5). Therefore, one has to explicitly keep track of the contribution of the dropped particles to $\mathbf{x}$ (and similarly also for η), so that Eq. (5) reads

$$\vec{\mathbf{x}} = \frac{1}{2}(\vec{\mathbf{x}}_\alpha + \vec{\mathbf{x}}_\beta) - \frac{i}{\hbar}\Sigma\mathcal{S}(\vec{\mathbf{x}}_\alpha - \vec{\mathbf{x}}_\beta) + \sum_i \delta\mathbf{x}_i \ , \qquad (7)$$

where each partial trace results in an additional summand $\delta\mathbf{x}_i$.

In order to illustrate the present method we will apply it to the investigation of decoherence rates of superpositions of harmonic oscillator coherent states $|\alpha\rangle + |\beta\rangle$. The decoherence rate is predicted [4, 5] and experimentally verified [6, 7] to grow quadratically with increasing phase-space separation $\delta\mathbf{x}$ between $|\alpha\rangle$ and $|\beta\rangle$. However, this quadratic dependence holds only for small phase space separations, and once the separation is much larger then the range of the interaction potential a saturation is expected [8]. We consider the full 3-dimensional problem with a thermal environment of mutually noniteracting particles that, however, interact with the oscillator via a short range Gaussian interaction. The environment is dilute so that only two-body interactions are taken into account. A thermal environment is realized via an average over 2000 realizations of an environment consisting of 1500 particles. Due to the possibility of adding and removing particles this requires the integration of 182 coupled differential equations, whereas the simulation of the entire system with all particles present during the entire integration would yield 8×10^7 differential equations.

Fig.1 displays the decay constant of the Hilbert Schmidt norm $\mathrm{Tr}\varrho_{\alpha\beta}\varrho_{\alpha\beta}^{\dagger}$ as function of the initial phase space separation. Even for $\delta\mathbf{x}$ vanishing, there is some decoherence with a decay constant of about 10^{-5} since a coherent state is not an eigenstate to the interaction potential, but the decay time for this case is significantly longer than that for a coherent superposition of two coherent states. For small values of $\delta\mathbf{x}$, we recover the predicted quadratic increase of the decay constant, and once the phase space separation exceeds the range of the interaction potential (25 oscillator lengths in this case), the increase with $\delta\mathbf{x}$ gets slower and, as expected, saturation sets in.

Acknowledgements. Financial support by the Alexander von Humboldt fundation is gratefully acknowledged.

---

[1] E. J. Heller, J. Chem. Phys. **62**, 1544 (1975).

[2] E. J. Heller, J. Chem. Phys. **65**, 4979 (1976).

[3] E. J. Heller, J. Chem. Phys. **67**, 3339 (1977).

[4] D. F. Walls and G. J. Milburn, Phys. Rev. A **31**, 2403 (1985).

[5] A. O. Caldeira and A. J. Leggett, Phys. Rev. A **31**, 1059 (1985).

[6] M. Brune, E. Hagley, J. Dreyer, X. Maître, A. Maali, C. Wunderlich, J. M. Raimond and S. Haroche, Phys. Rev. Lett. **77**, 4887 (1996).

[7] C. J. Myatt. B. E. King, Q. A. Turchette, C. A. Sackett, D. Kielpinski, W. M. Itano, C. Monroe and D. J. Wineland, Nature **403**, 269 (2000)

[8] K. Hornberger and J. E. Sipe, Phys. Rev. A **68**, 012105 (2003)

D. Shalashilin and M. P. de Miranda (eds.)
Multidimensional Quantum Mechanics with Trajectories
© 2009, CCP6, Daresbury

Dynamics with quantum trajectories: applications to reactive scattering

Robert E. Wyatt
Department of Chemistry and Biochemistry,
University of Texas at Austin, Austin, Texas 78712

I. INTRODUCTION

The development and application of trajectory methods continues to be a very active area of research in quantum dynamics. Semiclassical techniques, including the time-dependent WKB approximation, continue to improve in efficiency and accuracy [1]. In addition, over the past decade there has also been a significant growth in the development and application of methods involving the use of quantum trajectories to solve dynamical problems (see the book by Wyatt [2]). Algorithms now being developed are significantly more robust than those in use just a few years ago. In this review, emphasis will be placed upon 'synthetic' quantum trajectory methods which can be used to solve the time dependent Schrodinger equation (TDSE).

Why run quantum trajectories to solve dynamical problems? Important reasons include the following: (1) Since these trajectories follow the most important regions of the evolving wave packet, efficient computational methods can be developed, especially for multidimensional problems; (2) For some applications, it may be possible to break the exponential growth in computational effort that plagues the use of traditional grid or basis function methods; (3) The trajectories provide 'classical-like' pictures showing how the process takes place. (4) New computational methods based upon the use of quantum trajectories can be developed for important processes, including quantum-classical dynamics [3], electronic non-adiabatic transitions [4], and decoherence [5].

Several previous studies have used quantum trajectories to evolve wave packets for multidimensional problems. Actually, in most cases, two degrees of freedom were involved. In the first application of the quantum trajectory method to reactive scattering, Wyatt studied the trajectory dynamics for a model collinear reaction [6]. In this formulation, reaction path curvature was included in the equations of motion for the trajectories. In a study of wave packet scattering from a barrier in a two dimensional model, Babyuk and Wyatt applied the covering function method [7] to deal with node formation in the reflected wave packet or with nodes in the initial wave packet. With this method, it was possible to evolve ensembles of quantum trajectories for long times, even for wave packets which were vibrationally excited in the initial state. By modeling the non-classical component of the momentum operator, Garashchuk and Rassolov have developed approximations to the quantum force [8]. This method has been used to compute energy resolved reaction probabilities for the collinear H+H2 reaction [9], photodissociation spectra for ICN [9], and time dependent reaction probabilities for the three-dimensional O+H2 reaction [10]. In order to alleviate problems which develop near nodes in the wave function, Kendrick introduced an artificial viscosity ('smoothing') term in the hydrodynamic equations of motion [11]. In addition, he developed a dynamical model for quantum trajectory studies of reactive scattering in systems with up to 100 modes [12].

In this study, after presenting a general classification scheme for quantum trajectories in Sec. II, equations of motion for quantum trajectories are described in Sec. III. In Sec. IV, a new adaptive hybrid scheme involving both quantum trajectories and fixed grids is described. This approach, the moving boundary truncation method [13-15], is then used to efficiently and accurately calculate reaction probabilities for the three dimensional $O(^3P)+H_2$ reaction. The quantum trajectory method [2,16], which involves the propagation of ensembles of correlated trajectories, is applied in Sec. V to a model chemical reaction involving up to 200 vibrational modes coupled to the reaction path [17-19]. Finally, Sec. VI summarizes these methods and describes some future research directions.

II. TAXONOMY OF QUANTUM TRAJECTORIES

Since there are various types of quantum trajectories, it is helpful to have a scheme for classifying them. The following scheme will be used.

  a. Analytic trajectories. These are computed using the de Broglie guidance relation, which relates the trajectory momentum, given by $\vec{p} = \vec{\nabla}S$ to the gradient of the phase (action function) of the wave function (see Sec. III). In order to run these trajectories, it is necessary to have the time dependent wave function handy. This type of calculation is used for analysis and interpretation. Valuable insights have been obtained from this type of study (for example, see Ref. 20). Analytic trajectories will be used in the hybrid method described in Sec. IV.

  b. Synthetic trajectories. These trajectories are used to solve the TDSE on-the-fly are obtained by integrating equations of motion for the hydrodynamic fields. From this information, the wave function may be computed at each point along the trajectory. The quantum trajectory method (QTM) [16], the first viable synthetic method, is based upon the propagation of an ensemble of quantum trajectories (also see Ref. 21). Spatial derivatives needed to update the trajectories and the hydrodynamic fields are obtained by local focal fitting

63

of the fields (using relatively small polynomial basis sets).

Synthetic trajectories may be further classified according to the nature of the equations of motion that are used.

Accurate synthetic trajectories. In this case, the exact equations of motion are integrated for an ensemble of trajectories, but numerical approximations arise in the fitting procedure used to compute spatial derivatives.

Approximate synthetic trajectories. These trajectories follow approximate equations of motion, including those propagated one-at-a-time via the derivative propagation method (DPM) [22]. In the DPM, equations of motion are solved for the action function and a limited number of the spatial derivatives of this function.

In addition, each of these types of synthetic trajectory may be further classified according to how the velocities of the trajectories are determined.

Bohmian trajectories. This popular type of trajectory runs at the flow velocity of the probability fluid, namely $\vec{v} = \vec{\nabla} S/m$. In principle, these trajectories are repelled by nodes in the wave function, but in practice (due to numerical inaccuracies) they may get close enough for further instabilities and inaccuracies to develop. This feature is the notorious 'node problem', which may be countered or circumvented in various ways, one of which is mentioned in Sec. VI.

Post-Bohmian trajectories. These trajectories run with non-Lagrangian velocities. The velocities might be determined prior to the trajectory propagation, or they may be determined adaptively, to account for the local dynamics. This type of trajectory was introduced into classical particle fluid dynamics in the early 1970s. The method is referred to as ALE, meaning 'arbitrary Lagrangian-Eulerian', or something 'in-between' grid points fixed in space and those moving at the Lagrange velocity.

Either of these types of trajectory may be run in real or complex space.

Real space. These quantum trajectories run with real values for both the coordinates and momentum.

Complex space. Not surprisingly, these quantum trajectories run with complex values for both the coordinates and momentum.

For this remainder of this study, we will be using analytic trajectories in Sec. IV and accurate synthetic trajectories, both Bohmian and post-Bohmian, running in real space, in Sec. V. However, we will point out that over the past several years a number of synthetic and analytic quantum trajectory calculations have been run in complex space [23].

III. EQUATIONS OF MOTION FOR QUANTUM TRAJECTORIES

To get started, we will assume a single degree of freedom, with coordinate x. The wave function is expressed in uni-polar form, $\psi(x,t) = R(x,t) \exp(iS(x,t)/\hbar)$, where the amplitude $R(x,t)$ and phase (action function)

$S(x, t)$ are real, single-valued functions, and $R(x, t) \geq 0$. Substituting into the TDSE and separating into real and imaginary parts then yields the two equations,

$$\frac{\partial \rho}{\partial t} = -\frac{\partial(\rho v_L)}{\partial x}, \tag{1}$$

$$\frac{\partial S}{\partial t} = -\frac{1}{2m}\left(\frac{\partial S}{\partial x}\right)^2 - V(x) - Q(x, t). \tag{2}$$

The first equation has the form of the classical continuity equation. The probability density and the Lagrangian flow velocity are given by

$$\rho = R^2, \qquad v_L = \frac{1}{m}\frac{\partial S}{\partial x}. \tag{3}$$

The second equation is referred to as the quantum Hamilton-Jacobi equation (QHJE). If the term denoted by Q is discarded, this equation would be the classical Hamilton-Jacobi equation. The term Q denotes the Bohm quantum potential [24], which brings quantum effects into the theory. The quantum potential, defined by

$$Q = -\frac{\hbar^2}{2m}\frac{1}{R}\frac{\partial^2 R}{\partial x^2} \tag{4}$$

can be viewed as a measure of the 'internal stress' in the probability fluid. Also, the first term on the right side of Eq. (2) is the flow kinetic energy, given by $KE = p^2/(2m) = (\partial S/\partial x)^2/(2m)$.

Equations (1) and (2) are expressed in the Eulerian frame: an observer stands at a fixed point and records the changes in the hydrodynamic fields. There are actually three important frames (or viewpoints) commonly used in hydrodynamics. These are defined below.

Eulerian frame. As mentioned above, the observer is fixed in space and records the changes taking place.

Lagrangian frame. In this case, the observer 'goes with the flow', at the local flow speed of the fluid. For wave packet dynamics, the flow velocity, nu_L, is given in Eq. (3). This frame is widely used in fluid dynamics.

Intermediate frame. Another possibility is that the observer is neither fixed in space nor moving at the Lagrangian flow velocity v_L. Rather, the velocity of the observer is 'arbitrary' and can be specified in advance of the dynamics (for example, it could be constant) or it can be determined by an algorithm during the course of the dynamics. This viewpoint was introduced in the early 1970s into classical dynamics by Hirt, Amsden, and others at the Los Alamos National Laboratory and is termed ALE, for 'arbitrary Lagrangian-Eulerian' flow.

In order to convert the previous equations of motion into a moving frame (Lagrangian or ALE), we will use the following relation. If we have a function

$f(x,t)$, Euler would determine that the rate of change at point x is $\partial f / \partial t$. However, the observer (moving at speed v) would determine a different the rate of change, denoted by df/dt. These two rates are connected by the following relation:

$$\frac{df}{dt} = \frac{\partial f}{\partial t} + v \frac{\partial f}{\partial x}.$$ (5)

If this equation is solved for $\partial f / \partial t$ and the result is substituted into Eqs. (3) and (4), we obtain the quantum hydrodynamic equations in the ALE frame. Before giving these equations, we will use the exponential form for the R-amplitude, $R = \exp(C)$. From Eqs. (3) and (4), we obtain the following equations of motion in the ALE frame,

$$\frac{dC}{dt} = -\frac{1}{2m} \frac{\partial^2 S}{\partial x^2} - \frac{1}{m} \frac{\partial C}{\partial x} \frac{\partial S}{\partial x} + v \frac{\partial C}{\partial x},$$ (6)

$$\frac{dS}{dt} = -\frac{1}{2m} \left(\frac{\partial S}{\partial x} \right)^2 - V(x) - Q(x,t) + v \frac{\partial S}{\partial x}.$$ (7)

In each of these equations, the final term arises during the conversion from the Eulerian to the ALE frame. These two equations are then integrated along each trajectory in the ensemble. Each trajectory moves according to the equation $dx/dt = v$.

In order to integrate these equations along a set of trajectories, the first and second spatial derivatives of the hydrodynamic fields are required. These derivatives are $\partial S / \partial x$, $\partial^2 S / \partial x^2$, $\partial C / \partial x$ and $\partial^2 C / \partial x^2$. and In order to evaluate these quantities at a specified time along one trajectory (at position x_0) a set of neighboring 'grid points' are selected and the fields S and C are fit to a local polynomial basis set. For example, a local cubic basis would include the terms 1, $(x - x_0)$, $(x - x_0)^2$, and $(x - x_0)^3$.

IV.   THE MOVING BOUNDARY TRUNCATION METHOD

The moving boundary truncation (MBT) method [13,14] is a time-dependent adaptive approach that has the advantages of quantum trajectory methods while significantly reducing the number of fixed grid points needed for accurate wave packet propagation. An improved version of this method [15] has been applied to the collinear $H + H_2$ reaction. Reaction probabilities were also calculated for the three dimensional $O(^3P) + H_2$ and $O(^3P) + HD$ reactions for total angular momentum $J = 0$.

The MBT method utilizes quantum trajectories on the boundaries of a set of fixed grid points. As the wave packet moves or spreads, the trajectories also move, altering the location and number of the fixed grid points such that the dynamics is accurately represented. It is important to note that the quantum trajectories do not directly influence the wave function; they simply determine which fixed grid points are utilized in the dynamics at that particular time. Indeed, the trajectories do not carry any information other than their position at each time step.

One issue that can occur is spreading or compression of the trajectories. When spreading occurs, the edges of the fixed grid may not be correctly chosen. When compression occurs, more trajectories are being propagated than are necessary to determine the edges of the set of fixed grid points. In order to deal with this, the trajectories are periodically checked to insure they are within a minimum and maximum distance of each other. Trajectories can be discarded and created as desired because all the information needed is carried by data on the fixed grid.

The MBT method was applied to the three dimensional non-rotating $O(^3P) +$ H_2 and $O(^3P) + HD$ reactions, using a $^3A'$ potential energy surface [25]. This reaction involves three arrangement channels: the reactant $O + H_2$ channel, and two product $OH + H$ channels. For the potential energy isosurface displayed in Fig. 1, the three reactant Jacobi coordinates were used; these are R (the O to H_2 distance), r (the H_2 inter-nuclear separation), and θ (measuring H_2 rotation around the R axis). There are two minimum energy paths (MEPs) corresponding to the two collinear configurations ($\theta = 0$ and $\theta = \pi$). Along these paths, the barrier height in the transition regions is 0.565 eV. The overall reaction is slightly endothermic, as the product channel along the MEPs is 0.11 eV higher in energy than the reactant channel. In the two transition regions at approximately $R = 3$ a.u., the potential surface pinches and develops minima near the two collinear configurations at $\theta = 0$ and $\theta = \pi$.

Initially, there are 2,760 trajectories divided evenly among the 60 θ divisions and placed at points $\{R, r\}$ where the density has decayed to 10^{-4} (Fig. 1a). This creates a box containing 73,800 fixed grid points. As the trajectories defining the boundary of the wave packet move, points on the underlying fixed grid are added or removed as necessary. The number of trajectories and grid points stay relatively constant until the wave packet enters the transition region, at approximately 21 fs (Fig. 1b). After the packet enters the transition region, it spreads onto the two product arrangement tubes. The trajectories continue to bring in fixed grid points on the product tubes until the transmission probability is full converged, as shown in Fig. 1c. After the wave packet enters the product tubes, both the number of trajectories and the number of grid points increase linearly until they reach their final values, 6,544 and 697,080 respectively, at the end of the propagation.

The reaction probabilities for both the MBT and the full fixed grid calculations shown in Fig. 2 are nearly in exact agreement. The results are also in good agreement with those from earlier studies [10]. Figures 2b and 2c show the reaction probabilities for the $O(^3P) + HD(v = 0, j = 0)$ reaction. Note the large difference between the probabilities for forming the OHD and OD + H

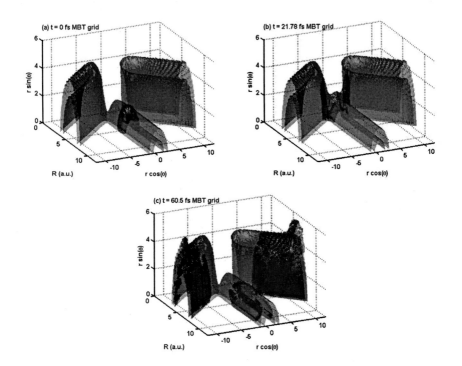

FIG. 1: Wave packet propagation for the $O(^3P) + H_2 \rightarrow OH + H$ reaction. Isosurfaces (in red) indicate the potential energy for $V = 0.75$ eV. Isosurfaces of the wave packet at the density 0.0001 are colored blue. (a) Initial wave packet. The fixed grid points used in the dynamics are contained within the blue wave packet isosurface. The potential surface breaks into two product tubes along $\theta = 0$ and $\theta = \pi$ at approximately $R = 2.5$ a.u. (b) Wave packet at 21.8 fs. The quantum trajectories have guided the wave packet correctly onto the two product tubes. (c) Wave packet after the reaction probability has converged (60.5 fs).

products. These excellent results were obtained much more efficiently than the full grid calculations; the latter take an average of 212 minutes, while the MBT calculation requires only 75 minutes, a reduction of 65%.

V. HIGH DIMENSIONAL REACTION DYNAMICS

The dynamics of ensembles containing thousands of quantum trajectories have been studied for multidimensional systems undergoing reactive scattering [17–

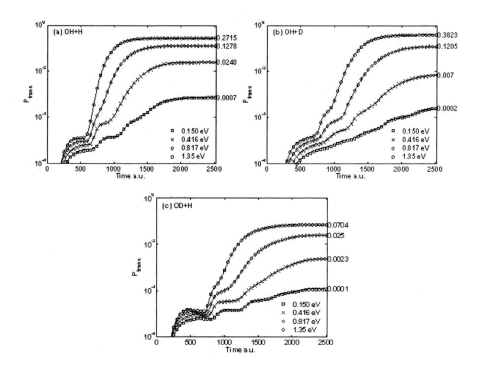

FIG. 2: (a) Reaction probabilities (on a logarithmic scale) for the $O(^3P)+H_2(v = 0, j = 0)$ reaction for various initial kinetic energies. The markers indicate the MBT results while solid lines indicate the full grid solutions. (b) The OH reaction probabilities for the reaction $O(^3P) + HD(v = 0, j = 0)$. (c) The OD reaction probabilities for the reaction $O(^3P) + HD(v = 0, j = 0)$.

19]. The Hamiltonian and equations of motion for the hydrodynamic fields were formulated in curvilinear reaction path coordinates, for the case of a planar (zero-torsion) reaction path. This method was applied to reactive systems with 50–200 harmonic vibrational modes coupled to motion along the reaction coordinate [18], and to systems with up to 25 Morse vibrational modes [19]. Dynamical results, including trajectory evolution and time-dependent reaction probabilities, were presented and power law scaling of computation time with the number of vibrational modes, denoted M, was described.

The algorithm used to propagate ensembles of quantum trajectories in multidimensional reactive systems has been described in detail [17]. An enhanced version was then developed [18] to allow for the efficient propagation of trajectory ensembles undergoing reactive scattering in multidimensional systems with

69

$M \leq 200$. The model potential energy surface used in these studies was constructed from a Gaussian barrier along the translational coordinate coupled to M harmonic oscillators. Substituting this Hamiltonian into the TDSE and introducing the polar form of the wave function, equations of motion were derived for C and S.

We will briefly present results for the scattering of an ensemble of quantum trajectories on potential surfaces involving from 50 to 200 vibrational modes. The ensemble evolution has qualitative similarities regardless of the number of vibrational modes. Projection of the trajectories onto the $(s–q_1)$ plane reveals a 'snaking' motion in the product channel since these coordinates are coupled by curvature terms. At moderate times, the leading edge of the ensemble penetrates into the region of high vibrational potential energy while the remainder of the ensemble is concentrated around the minimum of the potential. Then the tail follows into the same region while the leading edge returns back toward the region of lower vibrational energy. This type of motion repeats and continues as the transmitted packet moves further into the product valley. This phenomenon is also known as the bobsled effect [26].

Projection of 1/5 of the trajectories into the three-dimensional (s, q_1, q_2) subspace is shown in Fig. 3 for $M = 50$. For plotting purposes, the reaction coordinate has been 'stretched out', so that s and q_1 appear as rectilinear coordinates. The darkness of each ball is proportional to the value of C. Since this ensemble is a projection from 51 dimensions onto a 3D subspace, some edge trajectories carry large density while some interior ones have small densities.

The total computational time for this quantum trajectory algorithm was analyzed as a function of the number of vibrational modes. The scaling can be expressed by the relation, time $\sim M^\tau$ where τ depends upon M and lies in the range $1 \leq \tau \leq 3$. For example, $\tau = 1.04$ when $M = 50$, and $\tau = 1.56$ when $M = 200$. Extrapolation indicates that cubic scaling is expected when $M > 1000$.

VI. SUMMARY AND FUTURE DIRECTIONS

Synthetic quantum trajectories provide a viable approach for solving the TDSE for multidimensional systems. In the quantum trajectory method, an ensemble of trajectories is propagated using exact equations of motion for the hydrodynamic fields. These trajectories may move (in the Lagrangian viewpoint) at the local flow speed of the probability fluid, or (in the ALE viewpoint) at arbitrary speeds, chosen, for example, in advance of the dynamics. Spatial derivatives needed in the equations of motion are evaluated through local polynomial fitting of the data around each trajectory. Applications of this method to model chemical reactions were described in Sec. V. In these studies, as many as 200 vibrational modes were coupled to the reaction coordinate.

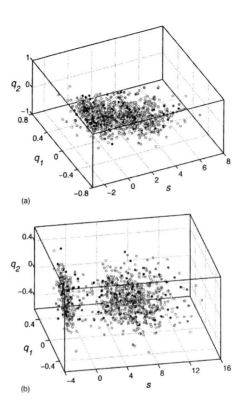

FIG. 3: Projection of quantum trajectories into the (s, q_1, q_2) subspace for $M = 50$ vibrational modes at two times: a) $t = 1400$, b) $t = 2400$. The coordinates and the time are given in a.u. The barrier is centered at $s = 0$.

In addition, a new hybrid approach, the moving boundary truncation method, was described in Sec. IV. Quantum trajectories are employed only on the boundaries of the wave packet. The packet was propagated using information carried by only those fixed grid points which within this boundary. As the packet moves, the boundary changes and points in the underlying fixed grid are added or removed as appropriate. As a result, the fixed grid is adapted to the motion of the wave packet. Using this method, accurate reaction probabilities were obtained for the three dimensional $O(^3P) + H_2$ reaction.

A new approach to quantum trajectory dynamics is being developed by Poirier [27]. In the counter-propagating wave method (CPWM), rather than starting with the usual uni-polar representation of the wave function (described in Sec. III), this approach is based upon decomposition of the wave function into a pair of counter-propagating components, each of which can be represented in polar form. In one dimension, this decomposition is

$$\psi(x,t) = \psi_+(x,t) + \psi_-(x,t) = R_+ e^{iS_+/\hbar} + R_- e^{iS_-/\hbar}. \tag{8}$$

Each component is smooth and interference free, even though $\psi(x,t)$ may be 'wildly oscillating'. These functions satisfy a pair of dynamically coupled rate equations. The function $\psi_+(x,t)$ is the 'forward-moving' component, and $\psi_-(x,t)$ is the 'reflected-component'. At the initial time, for x on the left-side of the barrier, $\psi_+(x,0)$ is the incoming wave packet and $\psi_-(x,0)$. At late times, for x on the right-side of the barrier, $\psi_+(x,t)$ is the transmitted wave packet, while for x on the left-side of the barrier, $\psi_-(x,t)$ is the reflected wave packet.

Because $\psi_+(x,t)$ and $\psi_-(x,t)$ are smooth and node-free functions, the quantum trajectory method provides an effective way to solve the coupled equations for these components. As described in Sec. V, the QTM has already been used to study reaction dynamics in systems of high dimensionality. Use of this method to solve for the counter-propagating components $\psi_\pm(x,t)$ may lead to an accurate and efficient method for studying both reactive and non-reactive scattering in systems of high dimensionality.

Acknowledgements. The Robert Welch Foundation of Houston, Texas is thanked for funding this research. In addition, I thank Brad Rowland, Chia-Chun Chou, Lucas Pettey, Julianne David, Tim Coffey, Dima Babyuk, Keith Hughes, Corey Trahan, and Courtney Lopreore for their many significant contributions to the dynamics of quantum trajectories.

---

[1] W. H. Miller, J. Chem. Phys. **125**, 084114 (2007); N. Ananth, C. Venkataraman, and W. H. Miller, J. Chem. Phys. **127**, 224104 (2006); K. G. Kay, Ann. Rev. Phys. Chem. **56**, 255 (2005); K. G. Kay, Chem. Phys. **322**, 3 (2006); J. S. Shao and E. Pollak, J. Chem. Phys. **125**, 133502 (2006); S. S. Zhang and E. Pollak, J. Chem. Theory and Comp. **1**, 345 (2005).

[2] R. E. Wyatt, Quantum Dynamics with Trajectories (Springer, New York, 2005).

[3] I. Burghardt and G. Parlant, J. Chem. Phys. **122**, 094103 (2005); I. Burghardt, J. Chem. Phys. **120**, 3055 (2004); K. H. Hughes, S. M. Parry, G. Parlant, and I. Burghardt, J. Phys. Chem. A **111**, 10269 (2007).

[4] R. E. Wyatt, C. L. Lopreore, and G. Parlant, J. Chem. Phys. **114**, 5113 (2001); C. L. Lopreore and R. E. Wyatt, J. Chem. Phys. **116**, 1228 (2002); V. Rassolov and S. Garashchuk, Phys. Rev. A **71**, 032511 (2005); S. Garashchuk, V. A. Rassolov, and G. C. Schatz, J. Chem. Phys. **123**, 174108 (2005); S. Garashchuk and V. A. Rassolov, Chem. Phys. Lett. **446**, 395 (2007).

[5] K. S. Na and R. E. Wyatt, Phys. Lett. A **306**, 97 (2002); K. Na and R. E. Wyatt, Phys. Script. **XX**, 1 (2003); A. S. Sanz and F. Borondo, Eur. Physical J. D **44**, 319 (2007).

[6] R. E. Wyatt, J. Chem. Phys. **111**, 4406 (1999).

[7] D. Babyuk and R. E. Wyatt, J. Chem. Phys. **121**, 9230 (2004); D. Babyuk and R. E. Wyatt, Chem. Phys. Lett. **400**, 145 (2004).

[8] S. Garashchuk and V. A. Rassolov, Chem. Phys. Lett. **376**, 358 (2003); S. Garashchuk and V. Rassolov, J. Chem. Phys. **118**, 2482 (2003); V. Rassolov and S. Garashchuk, J. Chem. Phys. **120**, 6815 (2004).

[9] S. Garashchuk and V. A. Rassolov, J. Chem. Phys. **120**, 1181 (2004).

[10] V. Rassolov, S. Garashchuk, and G. C. Schatz, J. Phys. Chem. A **110**, 5530 (2006); S. Garashchuk, V. A. Rassolov, and G. C. Schatz, J. Chem Phys. **124**, 244307 (2006).

[11] B. K. Kendrick, J. Chem. Phys. **119**, 5805 (2003); D. K. Pauler, B. K. Kendrick, J. Chem. Phys. **120**, 603 (2004).

[12] B. K. Kendrick, J. Chem. Phys. **121**, 2471 (2004).

[13] L. Pettey and R. E. Wyatt, Chem. Phys. Lett. **424**, 443 (2006).

[14] L. Pettey and R. E. Wyatt, Int. J. Quantum Chem. **107**, 1566 (2007).

[15] L. Pettey and R. E. Wyatt, to be published.

[16] C. L. Lopreore and R. E. Wyatt, Phys. Rev. Lett. **82**, 5191 (1999).

[17] R. E. Wyatt and D. Babyuk, Phys. Rev. E **73**, 046701 (2006).

[18] D. Babyuk and R. E. Wyatt, J. Chem. Phys. **124**, 214109 (2006).

[19] D. Babyuk and R. E. Wyatt, J. Chem. Phys. **125**, 064112 (2006).

[20] A. S. Sanz, F. Borondo, and S. Miret-Artes, Phys. Rev. B **69**, 115413 (2004); A. S. Sanz, F. Borondo, and S. Miret-Artes, Phys. Rev. B **61**, 7743 (2000); A. S. Sanz and S. Miret-Artes, J. Chem. Phys. **122**, 014702 (2005).

[21] B. K. Dey, A. Askar, and H. Rabitz, J. Chem. Phys. **109**, 8770 (1998); F. Sales Mayor, A. Askar, and H. A. Rabitz, J. Chem. Phys. **111**, 2423 (1999).

[22] C. J. Trahan, K. Hughes, and R. E. Wyatt, J. Chem. Phys. **118**, 9911 (2003); C. J. Trahan, R. E. Wyatt, and B. Poirier, J. Chem. Phys. **122**, 16104 (2005).

[23] Y. Goldfarb, I. Degani, and D. J. Tannor, J. Chem. Phys. **125**, 231103 (2006); Y. Goldfarb, J. Schiff, and D. J. Tannor, J. Phys. Chem. A **111**, 10416 (2007); Y. Goldfarb and D. J. Tannor, J. Chem. Phys. **128**, 164114 (2008); B. A. Rowland and R. E. Wyatt, J. Phys. Chem. A **111**, 10234 (2007); R. E. Wyatt and B. A. Rowland, J. Chem. Phys. **127**, 044103 (2007); C.-C. Chou and R. E. Wyatt, Phys. Rev. A **76**, 012115 (2007); A. Sanz and S. Miret-Artes, Chem. Phys. Lett. **458**, 239 (2008); C. D. Yang, Chaos Solitons and Fractals **37**, 1158 (2008); C. D. Yang, Chaos Solitons and Fractals **33**, 1073 (2007); C. D. Yang, Chaos Solitons and Fractals **32**, 315 (2007); C. D. Yang, Chaos Solitons and Fractals **30**, 342 (2006).

[24] D. Bohm, Phys. Rev. **85**, 166 (1952).

[25] S. Rogers, D. Wang, A. Kuppermann, and S. Walch, J. Phys. Chem. A **104**, 2308 (2000).

[26] R. A. Marcus, J. Chem. Phys. **45**, 4493, 4500 (1966).

[27] B. Poirier, J. Chem. Phys. **121**, 4501 (2004); C. Trahan and B. Poirier, J. Chem. Phys. **124**, 034115, 034116 (2006); B. Poirier and G. Parlant, J. Phys. Chem. A **111**, 10400 (2007).

D. Shalashilin and M. P. de Miranda (eds.)
Multidimensional Quantum Mechanics with Trajectories
© 2009, CCP6, Daresbury

Quantum Hydrodynamics for Mixed States

Keith H. Hughes and Steven M. Parry
School of Chemistry, Bangor University,
Bangor, Gwynedd LL57 2UW, UK.

Irene Burghardt
Département de Chimie, Ecole Normale Supériere, Paris, France

The hydrodynamic formulation of mixed quantum states dates back to the work of Takabayasi [1], Moyal [2] and Zwanzig [3] in the late 1940's/early 1950's and has subsequently been investigated in a number of studies [4–7]. For example, Frensley considered the hydrodynamic approach in the study of a resonant-tunneling semi-conductor diode [8] and Lill *et al.* [9] investigated the semiclassical limits of the hydrodynamic approach in quantum transport theory. More recently Burghardt *et al.* [10–12] related the hydrodynamic approach of pure states to Bohmian mechanics and later developed a novel hybrid hydrodynamic-Liouvillian approach to mixed quantum-classical dynamics [13–16] that is known as the quantum-classical moments (QCM) approach. An advantage of a hydrodynamic approach to mixed states is that the dynamics of a $2N$ dimensional density operator is reduced to N sets of equations of motion for the hydrodynamic moments. Another advantage is the straightforward way that quantum trajectories may be formulated in the Lagrangian representation. Over the last decade a great deal of effort has been dedicated to the development of numerical approaches to quantum hydrodynamics in a Lagrangian trajectory representation [17–23]. Most of these investigations relate to the Bohmian approach for pure states. However, a number of investigations [13–16] have focussed on the formulation and development of trajectories for the quantum hydrodynamics of mixed states where the hydrodynamic moments evolve along trajectories guided by a classical and hydrodynamic force.

The hydrodynamic formulation of quantum mixed states can be derived by generating momentum moments obtained by an integration over the momentum p of the Wigner phase-space distribution function $\rho_W(q, p, t)$,

$$\langle \mathcal{P}^n \rho \rangle_q = \int dp\, p^n \rho_W(q, p). \tag{1}$$

When this prescription is applied to the equation of motion of $\rho_W(q, p, t)$ an infinite hierarchy of equations of motion is obtained for the hydrodynamic moments that involves both up-coupling and down-coupling between moments of different orders.

$$\frac{\partial}{\partial t}\langle \rho \rangle_q = -\frac{1}{M}\frac{\partial}{\partial q}\langle \mathcal{P}\rho \rangle_q$$

$$\frac{\partial}{\partial t}\langle \mathcal{P}^2\rho \rangle_q = -\frac{1}{M}\frac{\partial}{\partial q}\langle \mathcal{P}^3\rho \rangle_q - 2\frac{\partial V}{\partial q}\langle \mathcal{P}\rho \rangle_q$$

$$\frac{\partial}{\partial t}\langle \mathcal{P}^n\rho \rangle_q = -\frac{1}{M}\frac{\partial}{\partial q}\langle \mathcal{P}^{n+1}\rho \rangle_q - \sum_{\substack{k=1\\ \text{odd}}}^n \binom{n}{k}\left(\frac{\hbar}{2i}\right)^{k-1}\frac{\partial^k V}{\partial q^k}\langle \mathcal{P}^{n-k}\rho \rangle_q \qquad (2)$$

The hierarchy does not converge and cannot be terminated arbitrarily at some higher moment. The hierarchy can be terminated if an appropriate closure relation may be determined. For a few cases (pure states [10] or Gaussian moments [24]) analytical closures have been established, however, in most cases approximate closure schemes for the hierarchy must be developed.

In hydrodynamics the maximum entropy approach is widely used for establishing a moment closure for the hydrodynamic equations [25–27]. The maximum entropy method provides a way of evaluating the higher moments required to terminate the hierarchy by finding a phase-space distribution function that maximises an entropy functional under the constraints that it yields the known lower moments. A fundamental requirement of the maximum entropy method is that $\rho_W(q,p) \geq 0 \quad \forall q, p$. For quantum states $\rho_W(q,p)$ can be positive or negative and so the maximum entropy method may not be the most appropriate approach in this case. An alternate approach adopted in our work that is based on the maximum entropy ansatz involves a linearisation of the maximum entropy derived $\rho_W(q,p)$ by expanding $\rho_W(q,p)$ in an orthonormal Gauss-Hermite basis.

$$\rho_W(q,p,t) = \sum_m a_m(q,t)N_m\left(\frac{\beta}{\pi}\right)^{\frac{1}{4}}H_m(\sqrt{\beta}p)\exp(-\beta p^2/2) \qquad (3)$$

The approach is similar to the Grad-Hermite approach [28] that is widely used in hydrodynamics [29–33] and differs only in the function that the expansion is based on.

A key advantage of the approach is its ability to capture both negative or positive regions of ρ_W. This is in contrast to classical approaches to hydrodynamics where the production of negative regions is a disadvantage. Another advantage of the approach is that the Hermite approach is linear and evaluation of the linear coefficients involves only a matrix multiplication at each time step.

The Hermite approach presents a dramatic improvement over a cold truncation of the moment hierarchy, and over simpler closure schemes. In view of the fact that the moment closure problem is notoriously difficult to solve [26, 27], the stability of the Hermite scheme is quite remarkable.

In future studies it is intended to apply the Hermite closure scheme to a Lagrangian trajectory representation of the quantum hydrodynamic equations of motion. Simulating quantum dynamics in a Lagrangian frame presents other difficulties that have been discussed extensively elsewhere [18, 21, 35]. However, the challenges of propagation in a Lagrangian trajectory representation cannot be confronted before a closure scheme for the moments has been established.

---

[1] T. Takabayasi, Prog. Theor. Phys. **11**, 341 (1954).
[2] J. E. Moyal, Proc. Cambridge Philos. Soc. **45**, 99 (1949).
[3] J. H. Irving and R. W. Zwanzig, J. Chem. Phys. **19**, 1173 (1951).
[4] H. Fröhlich, Physica **37**, 215 (1967).
[5] J. Yvon, J. Phys. Lettres **39**, 363 (1978).
[6] M. Ploszajczak and M. J. Rhoades-Brown, Phys. Rev. Lett. **55**, 147 (1985).
[7] L. M. Johansen, Phys. Rev. Lett. **80**, 5461 (1998).
[8] W. R. Frensley, Rev. Mod. Phys. **62**, 745 (1990).
[9] J. V. Lill, M. I. Haftel, and G. H. Herling, Phys. Rev. A **39**, 5832 (1989).
[10] I. Burghardt and L. S. Cederbaum, J. Chem. Phys. **115**, 10303 (2001).
[11] I. Burghardt and L. S. Cederbaum, J. Chem. Phys. **115**, 10312 (2001).
[12] I. Burghardt and K. B. Møller, J. Chem. Phys. **117**, 7409 (2002).
[13] I. Burghardt and G. Parlant, J. Chem. Phys. **120**, 3055 (2004).
[14] I. Burghardt, K. B. Møller, and K. H. Hughes, in *Quantum Dynamics of Complex Molecular Systems*, edited by D. A. Micha and I. Burghardt (Springer, 2006).
[15] K.H. Hughes, S. M. Parry, G. Parlant and I. Burghardt, J. Phys. Chem. A **111**, 10269 (2007).
[16] I. Burghardt, J. Chem. Phys. **122**, 094103 (2005).
[17] C. L. Lopreore and R. E. Wyatt, Phys. Rev. Lett. **82**, 5190 (1999).
[18] R. E. Wyatt, Chem. Phys. Lett. **313**, 189 (1999).
[19] R. E. Wyatt and E. R. Bittner, J. Chem. Phys. **113**, 8898 (2000).
[20] B. K. Dey, A. Askar and H. Rabitz, J. Chem. Phys. **109**, 8770 (1998).
[21] C. J. Trahan, K. H. Hughes and R. E. Wyatt, J. Chem. Phys. **118**, 9911 (2003).
[22] B. K. Kendrick, J. Chem. Phys. **119**, 5805 (2003).
[23] J. B. Maddox and E. R. Bittner, J. Phys. Chem. B **106**, 7981 (2002).
[24] I. Burghardt and K. B. Møller, J. Chem. Phys. **117**, 7409 (2002).
[25] C. D. Levermore, J. Stat. Phys. **83**, 1021 (1996).
[26] P. Degond and C. Ringhofer, J. Stat. Phys. **112**, 587 (2003).
[27] M. Junk, Math. Models Methods Appl. Sci. **10**, 1001 (2000).
[28] H. Grad, Commun. Pure Appl. Math. **2**, 331 (1949).
[29] J. V. Lill, M. I. Haftel, and G. H. Herling, J. Chem. Phys. **90**, 4940 (1989).
[30] M.K. Tippett, J. Plasma Phys. **54**, 77 (1995).
[31] M. Junk, Nonlinearity **14**, 881 (2001).
[32] M. Bisi, G. Spiga and G. Toscani, Phys. Fluids **16**, 4235 (2004).
[33] B. Qiao. X. T. He and S. P. Zhu, Europhys.Lett. **72**, 955 (2005).
[34] E. T. Jaynes, Phys. Rev. **106**, 620 (2006).
[35] K. H. Hughes and R. E. Wyatt, Chem. Phys. Lett. **366**, 336 (2002).

D. Shalashilin and M. P. de Miranda (eds.)
Multidimensional Quantum Mechanics with Trajectories
© 2009, CCP6, Daresbury

Bohmian mechanics with complex action: an exact formulation of quantum mechanics using complex trajectories

Yair Goldfarb, Ilan Degani,* Jeremy Schiff,[†] and David J. Tannor

Dept. of Chemical Physics, The Weizmann Institute of Science, Rehovot, Israel

I. INTRODUCTION

Ever since the advent of Quantum Mechanics, there has been a quest for a trajectory-based formulation of quantum theory that is exact. In the 1950s, David Bohm, building on earlier work by Madelung [1] and de Broglie [2], developed an exact formulation of quantum mechanics in which trajectories evolve in the presence of the usual Newtonian force plus an additional quantum force [3]. In recent years there has been a resurgence of interest in Bohmian mechanics (BM) as a numerical tool because of its local dynamics, which suggests the possibility of significant computational advantages for the simulation of large quantum systems [4-12]. However, closer inspection of the Bohmian formulation reveals that the non-locality of quantum mechanics has not disappeared – it has simply been swept under the rug into the quantum force.

In this work we present a variation of BM in which the quantum phase, S, is taken to be complex. This leads to a single equation for the complex phase [19], as opposed to coupled equations for real phase and real amplitude in the conventional BM. Complex phase leads to equations of motion for trajectories with complex x and p but there is a reward for this complexification – a significantly higher degree of localization than in conventional BM. We demonstrate tunneling probabilities that agree with the exact quantum mechanics down to 10^{-7}, calculated from strictly localized quantum trajectories in the sense that they do not communicate with their neighbors. We also show that wavepacket nodal patterns can be accurately described by the superposition of of contributions from

---

*Currently at: Mathematics Institute, University of Bergen, Norway.
[†]Permanent address: Dept. of Mathematics, Bar-Ilan University, Ramat Gan, Israel.

complex trajectories that start from different initial conditions in the complex plane and end at time t at the same location along the real x axis.

II. CONVENTIONAL BOHMIAN MECHANICS VS. BOHMIAN MECHANICS WITH COMPLEX ACTION

The starting point of conventional BM formulation (in 1-dimension) is the insertion of the ansatz

$$\psi(x,t) = A(x,t) \exp\left[\frac{i}{\hbar} S(x,t)\right] \tag{1}$$

in the time dependent Schrödinger equation (TDSE), where $A(x,t)$, $S(x,t)$ are *real* functions representing the amplitude and phase respectively. Separating the result into its real and imaginary parts, two PDEs are obtained

$$S_t + \frac{S_x^2}{2m} + V = \frac{\hbar^2}{2m} + V = \frac{\hbar^2}{2m}\frac{A_{xx}}{A}, \tag{2}$$

$$A_t + \frac{1}{m}A_x S_x + \frac{1}{2m}A S_{xx} = 0, \tag{3}$$

where $V(x)$ is the potential of the system. The first equation is referred to as the quantum Hamilton-Jacobi (HJ) equation for S; it differs from the classical HJ equation (the LHS) by the addition of a "hquantum potential" $Q \equiv -\frac{\hbar^2}{2m}\frac{A_{xx}}{A}$. Defining a velocity field $v(x,t) = S_x(x,t)/m$ the classical HJ equation yields Newton's equation of motion; the same process for the quantum HJ equation yields equations of motion for "quantum trajectories." Equation (3) can be reformulated as a hydrodynamic-like continuity equation for probability flow, hence Eqs. (2) and (3) are referred to as the hydrodynamic formulation of quantum mechanics. The solution of the quantum hydrodynamic equations along the quantum trajectories constitutes the conventional BM formulation.

The starting point of Bohmian mechanics with complex action (BOMCA) is the insertion of the ansatz [13–19]

$$\psi(x,t) = A(x,t) \exp\left[\frac{i}{\hbar} S(x,t)\right] \tag{4}$$

in the TDSE, where we allow the phase to be *complex*. This yields a *single* quantum HJ equation for complex S,

$$S_t + \frac{1}{2m}S_x^2 + V = \frac{i\hbar}{2m}S_{xx}, \tag{5}$$

where $Q \equiv -\frac{i\hbar}{2m}S_{xx}$ is the new quantum potential. Note that there is no expansion in powers of $\hbar$ in the derivation, hence Eq. (5) is an *exact* formulation

78

of the TDSE. It is noteworthy that for Gaussian wavepackets in potentials up to quadratic the quantum potential is independent of coordinate and therefore the quantum force vanishes. This is completely different from the case of conventional Bohmian mechanics, where for Gaussian wavepackets in quadratic potentials the quantum force is the same size as the classical force; in fact, in conventional Bohmian mechanics the quantum force is non-vanishing even for the free particle Gaussian wavepacket!

Equation (5) seems to have been first discovered by Pauli [13], who used it as the starting point for developing time-independent WKB theory. It was apparently rediscovered independently by Leacock and Padgett [15], who also reverted to a time-independent formulation to calculate eigenvalues. In recent years it has been used by several authors [16-18] as an analytical tool, but not as a constructive method to solve the TDSE with trajectories. There is also a connection to some earlier work [20-22] on a time-dependent extension of WKB. However, unlike this previous work, the present approach is formally exact, solving the TDSE using trajectories that satisfy the quantum HJ equation (Eq. (5)).

In the spirit of conventional BM our aim is to solve Eq. (5) in the Lagrangian approach, that is, along quantum trajectories. A quantum trajectory is defined by

$$\frac{dx}{dt} = v(x,t); \qquad v(x,t) = \frac{1}{m}S_x(x,t). \tag{6}$$

Unlike conventional BM, the complex value of S yields quantum trajectories $x(t;x_0)$ that evolve in the complex plane. As a consequence, the new formulation requires analytic continuation of the wavefunction and the phase to the complex plane. We consider only analytic potentials $V(x)$; therefore $v(x,t)$ is analytic in regions which do not contain nodes of $\psi(x,t)$. To obtain an equation of motion for $v(x,t)$ we take the spatial derivative of Eq. (5) and apply Eq. (6) to obtain

$$mv_t + vv_x) - \frac{i\hbar}{2}v_{xx} = -V_x(x). \tag{7}$$

Identifying the expression in the round brackets as a Lagrangian time derivative ($\frac{d}{dt} = \frac{\partial}{\partial t} + v\frac{\partial}{\partial x}$) of v, transforms Eq. (7) to a Newtonian-like equation of motion for the velocity

$$\frac{dv[x(t;t_0),t]}{dt} = \underbrace{-\frac{V_x}{m}}_{F_c/m} + \underbrace{\frac{i\hbar}{2m}v_{xx}}_{F_q/m}, \tag{8}$$

where we identify F_c, F_q as the classical and the quantum force respectively. The non-locality of quantum mechanics is manifested in the appearance of v_{xx} in the quantum force. This term prevents the first equation in (6) and Eq. (8) from being a closed set.

III.   DERIVATIVE HIERARCHY

As in conventional BM, the main difficulty lies in estimating the quantum force. We tackle this problem by taking iterated spatial partial derivatives of Eq. (8). The result can be written after a short manipulation as

$$\frac{dv^{(n)}}{dt} = -\frac{V^{(n+1)}}{m} + \frac{i\hbar}{2m}v^{(n+2)} - \tilde{g}_n; \qquad n = 0,\ldots,\infty, \qquad (1)$$

where $\tilde{g}_0 = 0$ and $\tilde{g}_n = \sum_{j=1}^{n}\binom{n}{j}v^{(j)}v^{(n-j+1)}$ for $n \geq 1$. The superscripts denote the order of a partial spatial derivative. The set of Eqs. (1) and the first equation in (6) are now an infinite but closed set that describes a *fully local* complex quantum trajectory. We may obtain a numerical approximation by truncating the infinite set at some $n = N$, thus replacing Eq. (8) with a system of $N + 1$ coupled ODEs. Since each individual equation in (1) depends on the consecutive $v^{(n+2)}$, the truncation is done by setting $v^{(N+1)} = v^{(N+2)} = 0$. The initial conditions for the $v^{(n)}$'s are given by

$$v^{(n)}(0;x_0) = \frac{1}{m}\frac{\partial^n S_x}{\partial x^n}\bigg|_{x=x_0,t=0} = \frac{\partial^n}{\partial x^n}\left(-i\hbar\frac{\psi_x}{\psi}\right)\bigg|_{x=x_0,t=0}, \qquad (2)$$

where we applied the definition from (6) together with $S = -i\hbar \ln \psi$ that follows from Eq. (4). $x_0 \in \mathbb{C}$ is an initial position of an arbitrary single trajectory. Propagation by iterative differentiation was first introduced in the context of conventional BM by Wyatt *et al.* [5,6] and by Makri *et al.* [7], where it is referred to as the DPM (Derivative Propagation Method). However, the hierarchy of ODEs is significantly simpler in BOMCA than in the context of a real-valued DPM where there are coupled equations for the amplitude and phase.

The relation $v = S_x/m$ identifies the *phase field* with an *action field* of the quantum trajectories. The equation of motion for the action along a trajectory is similar to its classical counterpart with the addition of the quantum potential

$$\frac{dS[x(t;t_0),t]}{dt} = S_t + vS_x = \frac{1}{2}mv^2 - V + \frac{i\hbar}{2}v_x. \qquad (3)$$

Having x, v and v_x, the action along a trajectory is obtained simply by adding the integral of Eq. (3) to the initial value $S(x_0,0) = -i\hbar \ln[\psi(x_0,0)]$. Inserting the action in Eq. (4) yields the value of the wavefunction $\psi[x(t;x_0),t] = \exp\{\frac{i}{\hbar}S[x(t;x_0),t]\}$ at position $x(t;x_0)$ in the complex plane. The exploration of Eq. (5) in terms of complex quantum trajectories is a novel formulation that suggests a variety of questions ranging from the implications of an approximate local quantum theory to the properties of the complex trajectories.

Two comments. 1) It is interesting to contrast the equations for $N = 1$ with classical mechanics. For $N = 1$ there is no quantum force: the equations of

80

motion are precisely the *classical* equations of motion

$$\frac{dx}{dt} = v; \qquad \frac{dv}{dt} = -\frac{V_x}{m} \qquad (4)$$

albeit for complex x and v. There is however a nonzero quantum potential that gives an additional term to the action integral (*cf.* Eq. (3)), where the term v_x fulfils

$$\frac{dv_x}{dt} = -\frac{V_{xx}}{m} - v_x^2 \qquad (5)$$

(Eq. (1) with $n = N = 1$). It is interesting to note that the defining equations for $N = 1$ (Eqs. (4–5) and Eq. (3)) have appeared previously in the literature, in the context of semiclassical methods [21–23]; we emphasize that here they emerge only as a convenient truncation to an otherwise exact quantum formulation. 2) To obtain the wavefunction on the real axis at time t_f , in principle we need to propagate a set of initial positions $\{x_{0_j}\}$ such that $\{x_j(t_f; x_{0_j})\} \in \mathbf{R}$ at a specified time t_f. Tracing back the initial positions from final positions resembles the computationally expensive "root search" problem familiar from the semiclassical literature. In multidimensional problems this can become very expensive computationally; however, we believe that certain simplifications may be possible by taking advantage of analyticity in the complex plane. This is currently being tested.

IV.   APPLICATION TO 1-D BARRIER TUNNELING

As a numerical example we consider the one-dimensional scattering of an initial Gaussian wavepacket $\psi(x,0) = (2\alpha/\pi)^{1/4} e^{-\alpha(x-x_c)^2 + \frac{i}{\hbar} p_c(x-x_c)}$ from an Eckart potential $V(x) = D/\cosh^2(\beta x)$. We take $x_c = -.7$, $\alpha = 30\pi$, $D = 40$, $\beta = 4.32$ and $m = 30$ (all units are atomic units). In Fig. 1 (left) we depict several complex quantum trajectories for the case of a wavepacket with an average translational energy $E = p_c^2/2m = 0$, for $N = 1$. Note that the complex values of x and p allow the trajectories to "tunnel" through the barrier centered at $x = 0$.

The asymptotic tunneling probability $T(E)$ is calculated by integrating the absolute square of the wavefunction for $x > 0$ at a sufficiently long time. In Fig. 1 (right) we compare the exact tunneling probabilities as a function of E with the results obtained from BOMCA and conventional BM. The exact results were computed by a split operator wavepacket propagation. The BOMCA results were calculated by propagating 50 complex quantum trajectories. The conventional BM results were calculated using the numerical formulation developed by Lopreore and Wyatt [4]. The BOMCA formulation allowed the exploration of tunneling over the whole energy range, while the conventional BM formulation

81

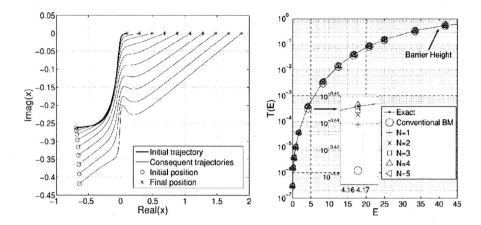

FIG. 1: Left: Several complex quantum trajectories for the scattering of an initial Gaussian wavepacket from an Eckart barrier centered around $x = 0$, where $E = p_c^2/m = 0$, $t = 1$ and $N = 1$. Note that the trajectories initiate at $\text{Re}(x_0) \simeq -.7 = x_c$ and reach $\text{Re}[x_f(x_0; t_f)] > 0$, $\text{Im}[x_f(x_0; t_f)] \simeq 0$. Hence, these trajectories "tunnel" through the barrier. Right: Comparison between the tunneling probabilities obtained by BOMCA, conventional BM and the exact results. The inset shows an enlargement of the results for $E \approx 4.17$, the lowest energy for which the conventional BM formulation was stable. Focusing on the inset, note the increasing accuracy of the numerical result as a function of N.

proved unstable at low energies ($E \lesssim 4$). Moreover, the BOMCA results are significantly more accurate than the BM results for all energies below the barrier height ($E < D$), even using just the classical equations of motion ($N = 1$). Note the improvement in the accuracy of the BOMCA results as N increases.

V. NODES AND INTERFERENCE

As can be seen from the expression for Q, the quantum potential (and consequently the quantum force) diverges at nodal regions of the wavefunction (unless A_{xx} goes to zero at the node). Numerically the difficulty is even more severe — well before a node is formed, and the amplitude of the wavefunction exhibits only nodeless ripples, the quantum trajectories are highly unstable due to rapid oscillations in the quantum force [12]. The solution of the nodal problem remains the single greatest challenge facing numerical implementation of Bohmian mechanics.

Since Bohmian formulations interpret quantum mechanics in terms of trajectories, a somewhat more natural strategy to solve the nodal problem is to apply the superposition principle directly to the contribution of the quantum trajectories as in semiclassical theory [24]. However, in conventional BM, the crossing of trajectories in configuration space is strictly prohibited [25]. This property can be seen as originating from the Bohmian interpretation of QM, in which the quantum trajectories as candidates for the actual trajectory on which a particle propagates in space. But what if we allow for trajectory crossing in BOMCA approximations, will the combined contribution of crossing trajectories accumulate to an interference pattern?

As a numerical example we reconsider the one-dimensional scattering of an initial Gaussian wavepacket from an Eckart potential with the same parameters as above. The average translational energy of the initial Gaussian is taken as $E = p_c^2/m = 10 < D$. We focus on trajectories that end up at a final time $t_f = 0.995$ at the reflected part of the wavefunction $x(t_f) < 0$. t_f is chosen as sufficiently long for the wavepacket to scatter from the barrier and interference effects to appear. The considerations developed in [21] concerning multiple root trajectories, leading to interference, can be carried over almost completely to the case of complex Bohmian mechanics, although we have found that the structure and even the number of the root branches are sensitive to N, the order of truncation.

In Fig. 2 (left) we plot three branches and six sample trajectories that end at two real positions $x_f = -1$ and $x_f = -0.05$. The branches are groups of initial positions that end at time t_f at a reflected part of the wavefunction $x_f \in [-1, -0.05]$. As we can see from the sample trajectories, to each final position at this segment of the reflected wavefunction correspond three initial positions that originate from one of the three branches. From this observation we can expect that the wavefunction would incorporate contributions from more than one branch.

In Fig. 2 (right) we present the cumulative effect of adding the results of pairs of branches, $|\psi| = |\psi_j + \psi_i|, i \neq j$. We see that rippled parts of the wavefunction are depicted with a good approximation by a proper choice of i and j. The issue of when and which branches should be add or omitted from the sum is requires a more comprehensive discussion that we leave to future publications.

VI. CONCLUSIONS

In summary we presented BOMCA, a novel formulation of Bohmian mechanics. This formulation yields simpler equations than conventional Bohmian mechanics (at the expense of complex trajectories). Moreover, BOMCA allows a direct and simple derivation of local uncoupled trajectories that may be used to reconstruct the wavefunction. The tunneling probabilities obtained by BOMCA for the scattering process were in excellent agreement with the exact results even in the extremely deep tunneling regime. We showed that even classical equations of motion with a small number of (complex) trajectories are sufficient to obtain

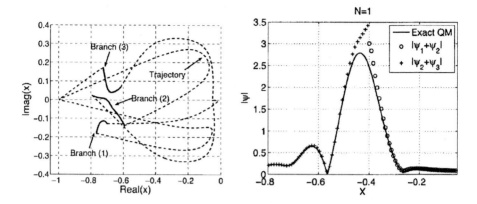

FIG. 2: Left: Three branches and six sample complex trajectories are depicted. These correspond to scattering of a Gaussian from an Eckart potential barrier using $N = 1$ BOMCA approximation (the physical parameters are given in the text). The branches are groups of initial positions that end at time $t_f = 0.995$ at a reflected part of the wavefunction $-1 < xf < -0.05$. Two sample trajectories that end at $x_f = -1$ and $x_f = -0.05$ emerge from each branch. Right: The cumulative effect of adding contributions from couples of branches $|\psi| = |\psi_j + \psi_i|, i \neq j$. Different regions of the wavefunction are depicted by different choices of i and j.

very accurate results provided that an extra, nonclassical term is added to the action integral. Moreover, we showed that wavefunction nodal patterns can be obtained very naturally by superposing amplitudes from complex trajectories that start from different initial conditions in the complex plane but reach the same real value of x at time t. It is interesting to note that BOMCA can be derived from the path integral formulation of quantum mechanics by making three modifications to the usual path integral approach: 1) incorporating the form of the initial wavefunction into the path integral; 2) allowing the stationary phase point to be complex, leading to complex trajectories; 3) allowing the path integration to be performed near, but not necessarily around, the stationary phase point. This leads to a rigorous justification for the superposition of contributions from different trajectories. Moreover, it turns out that the ODEs of higher order in N in the BOMCA hierarchy correspond precisely to higher order integrals in the exponent within the path integral formulation. Since the coupled ODEs with the BOMCA formulation are actually much easier to solve than the multiple integrals within the path integral formulation, this suggests that BOMCA may prove to be a very useful shortcut to obtaining corrections to the semiclassical evaluation of the path integral. This work was supported by the Israel Science Foundation (576/04).

[1] E. Z. Madelung, Phys. **40**, 322 (1926).

[2] L. C. R. de Broglie, Acad. Sci. Paris **183**, 447 (1926).

[3] D. Bohm, Phys. Rev. **85**, 180 (1952).

[4] C. L. Lopreore, R. E. Wyatt, Phys. Rev. Lett. **82**, 5190 (1999).

[5] C. J. Trahan, K. Hughes, R. E. Wyatt, J. Chem. Phys. **118**, 9911 (2003).

[6] C. J. Trahan, R. E. Wyatt, B. Poirier, J. Chem. Phys. **122**, 164104 (2005)

[7] J. Liu, N. Makri, J. Phys. Chem. A **108**, 5408-5416 (2004).

[8] E. R. Bittner, R. E. Wyatt, J. Chem. Phys. **113**, 8888 (2000).

[9] S. Garashchuk, V. A. Rassolov, Chem. Phys. Lett. **364**, 562-567 (2002).

[10] I. Burghardt, L. S. Cederbaum, J. Chem. Phys. **115**, 10303 (2002).

[11] E. Gindensperger, C. Meier and J. A. Beswick, J. Chem. Phys. **113**, 9369 (2000).

[12] R. E. Wyatt, *Quantum Dynamics with Trajectories: Introduction to Quantum Hydrodynamic* (Springer, 2005).

[13] W. Pauli, *Die allgemeine Prinzipien der Wellenmechanik*, in *Handbuch der Physik*, H. Geiger and K. Scheel, eds., Vol. 24, Part 1, 2nd ed. (Springer-Verlag, Berlin, 1933), pp. 83-272.

[14] K. Gottfried, *Quantum Mechanics, Volume I: Foundations* (Benjamin, New York, 1966).

[15] R. A. Leacock, M. J. Padgett, Phys. Rev. D **28**, 2491 (1983).

[16] A. S. Sanz, F. Borondo and S. Miret-Artés, J. Phys.: Condens. Matter **14**, 6109 (2002).

[17] M. V. John, Found. Phys. Lett. **15**, 329 (2002).

[18] C. D. Yang, Annals of Physics **319**, 399 (2005); Annals of Physics **319**, 444 (2005); Int. J. Quantum Chem. **106**, 1620 (2006).

[19] D. J. Tannor, *Introduction to Quantum Machanics: A Time Dependent Perspective* (University Science Press, Sausalito, 2007). The derivation of the complex HJ equation given in this book appeared in preprint versions starting in 1999.

[20] M. Boiron, M. Lombardi, J. Chem. Phys. **108**, 3431 (1998).

[21] D. Huber, E. Heller, J. Chem. Phys. **87**, 5302 (1987).

[22] D. Huber, E. Heller, R. G. LittleJohn, J. Chem. Phys. **89**, 2003 (1989).

[23] E. J. Heller, J. Chem. Phys. **62**, 1544 (1975).

[24] W. H. Miller, Adv. Chem. Phys. **25**, 69 (1974).

[25] P. R. Holland, *The Quantum Theory of Motion* (Cambridge University Press, Cambridge, 1993).

D. Shalashilin and M. P. de Miranda (eds.)
Multidimensional Quantum Mechanics with Trajectories
© 2009, CCP6, Daresbury

Quantum trajectories in phase space

Craig C. Martens,[1, *] Arnaldo Donoso,[2, †] and Yujun Zheng[3, ‡]

[1] *Department of Chemistry, University of California, Irvine,*
Irvine, CA 92697-2025, USA
[2] *Laboratorio de Física Estadística de Sistemas Desordenados, Centro de Física,*
Instituto Venezolano de Investigaciones Científicas, IVIC, Caracas, Venezuela
[3] *School of Physics, Shandong University, Jinan 250100, China*

I. INTRODUCTION

Quantum mechanics is the proper theoretical framework for describing the behavior of atoms and molecules [1, 2]. For simple systems, a direct numerical solution of the time-dependent Schrödinger equation is quite feasable, thanks to advances in both theoretical methodology and computer performance. This approach ceases to be practical for complex many-body problems, and approximate methods must be employed. A broad range of such approaches have been developed, including mean-field methods, semiclassical and mixed classical-quantum methods, phenomenological reduced descriptions, and others.

One surprisingly effective approach in many cases is to simply *ignore* quantum effects altogether and use classical mechanics to describe the motion of atoms in molecular systems. The result is the method called classical molecular dynamics (MD) [3], a commonly used tool for studying many particle systems where high temperatures, large masses, or other factors allow quantum effects in the atomic motion to be neglected. An MD simulation is performed by solving the appropriate Hamilton's or Newton's equations of motion for the particles making up the system given their mutual forces of interaction and appropriate initial conditions. An individual classical trajectory for a multidimensional problem is much easier to integrate numerically than the time-dependent wave packet of the corresponding quantum system. Unless the anecdotal information revealed by a

---

* Electronic address: cmartens@uci.edu
† Electronic address: arnaldo@ivic.ve
‡ Electronic address: yzheng@sdu.edu.cn

single trajectory is sufficient, however, collections of trajectories—*ensembles*—must in general be considered. A distribution of trajectories evolving in phase space is the most direct classical analogue of an evolving quantum wave packet, and statistical averages of dynamical variables over the classical ensemble parallel the corresponding quantum expectation values of operators.

The evolution of a classical probability distribution $\rho(q, p, t)$ in phase space is described by the classical Liouville equation [4]

$$\frac{\partial \rho}{\partial t} = \{H, \rho\}, \tag{1}$$

where q and p are the canonical coordinate and momentum, respectively, H is the system Hamiltonian, and $\{H, \rho\}$ is the Poisson bracket of H and ρ, defined as

$$\{H, \rho\} \equiv \frac{\partial H}{\partial q} \frac{\partial \rho}{\partial p} - \frac{\partial \rho}{\partial q} \frac{\partial H}{\partial p}. \tag{2}$$

In the context of classical MD, solution of the Liouville equation is accomplished by generating an ensemble of N distinct initial conditions $q_k(0)$ and $p_k(0)$ ($k = 1, 2, \ldots, N$) sampled from the given initial probability distribution $\rho(q, p, 0)$. Phase space trajectories are then computed by integrating Hamilton's equations,

$$\dot{q} = \frac{\partial H}{\partial p} \tag{3}$$

$$\dot{p} = -\frac{\partial H}{\partial q} \tag{4}$$

using the $q_k(0)$ and $p_k(0)$ as initial data. Then, aside from statistical error due to a finite N, $\rho(q, p, t)$ is given by the local phase space density of the evolving trajectories $(q_k(t), p_k(t))$ around the point (q, p). The relation between the evolution of the classical function $\rho(q, p, t)$ and the trajectory ensemble $(q_k(t), p_k(t))$ ($k = 1, 2, \ldots, N$) in phase space is illustrated schematically in the left panel of fig. 1.

In order to discuss quantum systems from an analogous ensemble perspective, we adopt a phase space representation of quantum mechanics—the Wigner representation [5–8]. Consider a one-dimensional system of mass m evolving under the influence of a potential $V(q)$. The quantum dynamics of such a system can be described by the wave function $\psi(q, t)$, which is a solution of the time-dependent Schrödinger equation [1]. An equivalent phase space description is given in terms of the Wigner function $\rho_W(q, p, t)$ [5–8]. The Wigner function is related to the density operator $\hat{\rho}$ by

$$\rho_W(q, p, t) = \frac{1}{2\pi\hbar} \int\limits_{-\infty}^{\infty} <q - \tfrac{y}{2}|\hat{\rho}(t)|q + \tfrac{y}{2}> e^{ipy/\hbar} \, dy. \tag{5}$$

87

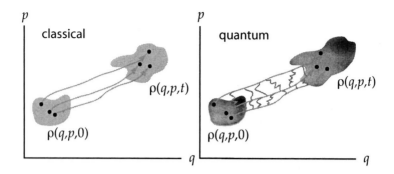

FIG. 1: A schematic representation of trajectory-based evolution of classical and quantum states in phase space. In the classical case (left), the individual trajectories evolve independently. In the quantum case (right), a trajectory-based representation unavoidably leads to a breakdown of the statistical independence of the ensemble members. A caricature of the resulting interactions is shown in the figure.

For a pure state described by the wave function $\psi(q,t)$ this becomes

$$\rho_W(q,p,t) = \frac{1}{2\pi\hbar} \int_{-\infty}^{\infty} \psi^*(q+\tfrac{y}{2},t)\psi(q-\tfrac{y}{2},t)e^{ipy/\hbar}\, dy. \tag{6}$$

The Wigner function obeys the equation of motion

$$\frac{\partial\rho_W}{\partial t} = -\frac{p}{m}\frac{\partial\rho_W}{\partial q} + \int_{-\infty}^{\infty} J(q,p-\xi)\rho_W(q,\xi,t)d\xi \tag{7}$$

where

$$J(q,p) = \frac{i}{2\pi\hbar^2} \int_{-\infty}^{\infty} \left[V(q+\tfrac{y}{2}) - V(q-\tfrac{y}{2})\right] e^{-ipy/\hbar}\, dy. \tag{8}$$

The integral in Eq. 8 can be evaluated to give

$$J(q,\eta) = \frac{4}{\hbar^2}\mathrm{Im}\left(\hat{V}(2\eta/\hbar)e^{-2i\eta q/\hbar}\right). \tag{9}$$

We stress that the Wigner representation is an exact and faithful representation of quantum mechanics; the Wigner function $\rho_W(q,p,t)$ contains the same information about observable quantities as does $\psi(q,t)$.

Equation (7) emphasizes the fundamental nonlocality of quantum mechanics: the time rate of change of ρ_W at point (q,p) depends on the value of ρ_W over a range of momentum values $\xi \neq p$.

For a potential $V(q)$ with a power series expansion in q, the integral in Eq. (7) can itself be expanded [5, 6]. In this case $J(q,p)$ becomes

$$J(q,p) = -V'(q)\,\delta'(p) + \frac{\hbar^2}{24}V'''(q)\,\delta'''(p) + \cdots,\qquad(10)$$

giving the equation of motion as a power series in $\hbar$,

$$\frac{\partial \rho_W}{\partial t} = -\frac{p}{m}\frac{\partial \rho_W}{\partial q} + V'(q)\frac{\partial \rho_W}{\partial p} - \frac{\hbar^2}{24}V'''(q)\frac{\partial^3 \rho_W}{\partial p^3} + \cdots,\qquad(11)$$

where prime denotes the derivative with respect to q. The higher order terms not shown involve successively higher even powers of $\hbar$, odd derivatives of V with respect to q, and corresponding derivatives of ρ_W with respect to p. In the classical ($\hbar \to 0$) limit, the Wigner function becomes a solution of the classical Liouville equation for probability distributions in phase space.

A probabilistic interpretation of the Wigner function is complicated by the fact that ρ_W, although always real, can assume negative values. Faithful representations of quantum mechanics *do* exist, however, that are built on positive probability distributions in phase space. An example is the Husimi representation [6], based on the Wigner function smoothed with a minimum uncertainty phase space Gaussian. We explore this representation in more detail below.

The nonlocality of quantum mechanics forbids arbitrarily fine subdivision of the quantum distribution into individual independent elements as is possible in classical mechanics, and insists that the entire state be propagated as a unified whole. If a trajectory ensemble representation of nonlocal quantum motion is to be achieved, the statistical independence of the trajectories must be given up and the individual members of the ensemble must *interact* with each other. This interdependence, or *entanglement*, of the trajectory ensemble is depicted schematically in the right panel fig. 1.

II.   METHODOLOGY

A.   Formalism

We now describe how to turn these ideas into an algorithm for simulating the time evolution of quantum systems. In particular, we sketch a method for solving the quantum Liouville equation in the Wigner representation in the context of a classical trajectory simulation [9–13]. We represent the time-dependent state of the system $\rho(q,p,t)$ as an ensemble of trajectories. In classical mechanics, the ensemble members evolve independently of each other. A quantum state, however, is a unified whole, and the uncertainty principle prohibits an arbitrarily fine subdivision and independent treatment of its constituent parts. We incorporate the non-classical aspects of quantum mechanics explicitly as a breakdown of the statistical independence of the members of the trajectory ensemble. We derive non-classical forces acting *between* the ensemble members that model the quantum effects governing the evolution of the corresponding nonstationary wave packet.

The continuous distribution function ρ is represented by a finite ensemble of trajectories,

$$\rho(q, p, t) = \frac{1}{N} \sum_{j=1}^{N} \delta(q - q_j(t))\delta(p - p_j(t)). \tag{12}$$

This ansatz is an approximate one, as the exact Wigner function ρ_W can become negative. The assumed strictly positive form of the solution in Eq. (12) thus cannot capture the full quantum dynamics in the Wigner representation. As noted above, a representation of quantum mechanics exists that is compatible with this ansatz, based on the Husimi distribution [6], a Gaussian smoothed Wigner function. Oscillations in ρ_W average out, resulting in a distribution function that has the desired non-negative property and can thus be interpreted probabilistically. In our method, we identify the continuous phase space function resulting from smoothing Eq. (12) with an equivalent positive-definite smoothing of the underlying Wigner function ρ_W. There are a number of ways to implement the smoothing in practice.

We seek a trajectory representation of quantum mechanics that includes quantum effects by *altering the motion of the trajectories themselves*. The instantaneous force acting on a particular member of the ensemble will thus depend on both the classical force $-V'(q)$ and on the phase space locations of all the other members of the ensemble. Their evolution will thus become mutually *entangled*.

Equations of motion for the trajectories must now be derived. We first note that the phase space trace of the Wigner function is conserved: $\mathrm{Tr}\,\rho_W = \int \rho\,dq\,dp = 1$, a property shared by its approximation in Eq. (12) (and the smoothed versions used in practice). In terms of the phase space flux $\vec{j} = \rho \vec{v}$, the ensemble must evolve collectively so that the continuity equation

$$\frac{\partial \rho}{\partial t} + \vec{\nabla} \cdot \vec{j} = 0 \tag{13}$$

is obeyed, where $\vec{\nabla}$ is the gradient in phase space. We exploit this continuity condition in our equations of motion by identifying the form of the current $\vec{j}$ in the Liouville equation, finding the corresponding vector field $\vec{v} = \vec{j}/\rho$, and then integrating the trajectories in phase space using $(\dot{q}, \dot{p}) = \vec{v}$.

We first consider the strict classical limit. Here, the $\hbar$-dependent terms in Eq. (11) vanish, and the phase space density obeys the classical Liouville equation [4, 14]:

$$\frac{\partial \rho}{\partial t} = -\vec{\nabla} \cdot \vec{j} = \{H, \rho\}. \tag{14}$$

By noting that $\partial\dot{q}/\partial q + \partial\dot{p}/\partial p = 0$, we can identify the phase space current vector as

$$\vec{j} = \begin{pmatrix} \partial H/\partial p \\ -\partial H/\partial q \end{pmatrix} \rho. \qquad (15)$$

Division by ρ then gives the familiar classical independent evolution of phase space trajectories under conventional Hamiltonian's equations $\dot{q} = \vec{v}_q = \partial H/\partial p$, $\dot{p} = \vec{v}_p = -\partial H/\partial q$. This occurs because of the cancellation of ρ from the expression for the phase space vector field $\vec{v}$ when $\vec{j}$ in Eq. (15) is divided by ρ.

We now turn to the quantum Liouville equation in the Wigner representation. The continuity condition involves the full equation of motion, Eq. (11). Writing the divergence of the current as

$$\vec{\nabla} \cdot \vec{j} = \frac{\partial}{\partial q}\left(\frac{\partial H}{\partial p}\rho\right)$$
$$+ \frac{\partial}{\partial p}\left(-V'(q)\rho + \frac{\hbar^2}{24}V'''(q)\frac{\partial^2\rho}{\partial p^2} + \cdots\right) \qquad (16)$$

and dividing the corresponding current by ρ, we arrive at the equations of motion for the trajectory at point (q,p):

$$\dot{q} = v_q = \frac{p}{m}$$

$$\dot{p} = v_p = -V'(q) + \frac{\hbar^2}{24}V'''(q)\frac{1}{\rho}\frac{\partial^2\rho}{\partial p^2} + \cdots. \qquad (17)$$

Note that in this case ρ *does not cancel out of the equations*. In marked contrast with the classical Hamilton's equations, the vector field now depends on the global state of the system as well as on the phase point (q,p).

A consequence of the additional ρ-dependent contribution to the force is that individual trajectory energies are not conserved.

$$\frac{dH}{dt} = \dot{q}\frac{\partial H}{\partial q} + \dot{p}\frac{\partial H}{\partial p} = \frac{p}{m}\left(\frac{\hbar^2}{24}V'''(q)\frac{1}{\rho}\frac{\partial^2\rho}{\partial p^2} + \cdots\right) \neq 0 \qquad (18)$$

This is acceptable—and in fact essential—if quantum effects are going to be represented by the method. Energy conservation is only required *on average*. It is straightforward to show from Eq. (17) that the ensemble average $< \dot{p} >= Tr(\dot{p}\rho) = - < V' >$, and thus the method obeys Ehrenfest's theorem, while the average energy $< E >= Tr(H\rho)$ is independent of time:

$$\left\langle \frac{dH}{dt}\right\rangle = \int\int \rho\frac{dH}{dt}dqdp = \int\int \frac{p}{m}\left(\frac{\hbar^2}{24}V'''(q)\frac{\partial^2\rho}{\partial p^2} + \cdots\right)dqdp = 0. \qquad (19)$$

The individual trajectories, however, can behave nonclassically—as they *must* if they are to capture the dynamics of quantum tunneling.

B. Entangled trajectory molecular dynamics

The realization of our formalism in the context of a classical molecular dynamics simulation is accomplished by generating an ensemble of initial conditions representing $\rho_W(q, p, 0)$ and then propagating the trajectory ensemble using Eq. (17). In practice, the singular distribution ρ must be smoothed to allow a faithful representation of the (analogously smoothed [6]) quantum dynamics. The nonclassical ρ-dependent force is determined in our implementation from a smooth local Gaussian representation of the instantaneous ensemble. In particular, the value of $\rho^{-1}\partial^2\rho/\partial p^2$ and terms involving higher derivatives at each phase space point (q_j, p_j) is calculated by assuming a local Gaussian approximation of ρ around $\vec{\Gamma}_j = (q_j, p_j)$:

$$\rho(q, p, t) \simeq \rho_o e^{-(\vec{\Gamma}-\vec{\Gamma}_j(t))\cdot\beta_j(t)\cdot(\vec{\Gamma}-\vec{\Gamma}_j(t))+\vec{\alpha}_j(t)\cdot(\vec{\Gamma}-\vec{\Gamma}_j(t))}. \tag{20}$$

The state $\rho(t)$ at each trajectory location (q_j, p_j) in phase space is characterized by the time-dependent parameters in the matrix β_j and vector $\vec{\alpha}_j$. We determine these numerically in practice by calculating *local* moments of the ensemble around the reference point $\vec{\Gamma}_j$ [9, 12]. These consist of sums of appropriate powers of the dynamical variables over the ensemble, weighted by a Gaussian cutoff $\phi(\vec{\Gamma}) = \exp(-\vec{\Gamma} \cdot \mathbf{h} \cdot \vec{\Gamma})$ centered at the point under consideration, where $\mathbf{h}$ is chosen to give a minimum uncertainty ϕ, consistent with the smoothing requirement for a positive quantum phase space distribution [6]. From this calculation, parameters β_j and $\vec{\alpha}_j$ can be inferred at each point $\vec{\Gamma}_j = (q_j, p_j)$. The generator of modified moments is [12]

$$\tilde{I} = \int_{-\infty}^{\infty} \int_{-\infty}^{\infty} e^{-\beta_q\xi^2 - \beta_p\eta^2 - 2\beta_{qp}\xi\eta + \alpha_q\xi + \alpha_p\eta} \phi_{h_q, h_p}(\xi, \eta)\, d\xi d\eta, \tag{21}$$

where this includes a *local Gaussian window function* ϕ:

$$\phi_{h_q, h_p}(\xi, \eta) = \exp\left(-h_q\xi^2 - h_p\eta^2\right). \tag{22}$$

The *modified* m^{th}, n^{th} moment of ξ, η is then

$$\langle \xi^{\tilde{m}}\eta^n \rangle \equiv \frac{\langle \xi^m\eta^n\phi \rangle}{\langle \phi \rangle} = \frac{\int\int \xi^m\eta^n\phi(\xi, \eta)\rho(\xi, \eta)d\xi d\eta}{\int\int \phi(\xi, \eta)\rho(\xi, \eta)d\xi d\eta}. \tag{23}$$

For ρ a local Gaussian, these moments are generated by derivatives of $\tilde{I}$:

$$\langle \xi^{\tilde{m}}\eta^n \rangle = \frac{1}{\tilde{I}} \frac{\partial^{(m+n)}}{\partial \alpha_q^m \partial \alpha_p^n} \tilde{I} \tag{24}$$

We define generalized variances and correlation:

$$\tilde{\sigma}_\xi^2 = \langle \tilde{\xi^2} \rangle - \langle \tilde{\xi} \rangle^2 \tag{25}$$

$$\tilde{\sigma}_\eta^2 = \langle \tilde{\eta^2} \rangle - \langle \tilde{\eta} \rangle^2 \qquad (26)$$

$$\tilde{\sigma}_{\xi\eta}^2 = \langle \tilde{\xi\eta} \rangle - \langle \tilde{\xi} \rangle \langle \tilde{\eta} \rangle. \qquad (27)$$

The *original* Gaussian parameters can then be reconstructed in terms of the generalized moments; for instance:

$$\alpha_p = \frac{\tilde{\sigma}_\xi^{\ 2}\langle \tilde{\eta} \rangle - \tilde{\sigma}_{\xi\eta}^{\ 2}\langle \tilde{\xi} \rangle}{\tilde{\sigma}_\xi^{\ 2}\tilde{\sigma}_\eta^{\ 2} - \tilde{\sigma}_{\xi\eta}^{\ 4}} \qquad (28)$$

$$\beta_p = \frac{\tilde{\sigma}_\xi^{\ 2}}{2(\tilde{\sigma}_\xi^{\ 2}\tilde{\sigma}_\eta^{\ 2} - \tilde{\sigma}_{\xi\eta}^{\ 4})} - h_p. \qquad (29)$$

The required modified moments can be calculated easily from the evolving ensemble:

$$\langle \tilde{\xi^m \eta^n} \rangle_k = \frac{\sum_{j=1}^N (q_j - q_k)^m (p_j - p_k)^n \phi(q_j - q_k, p_j - p_k)}{\sum_{j=1}^N \phi(q_j - q_k, p_j - p_k)}. \qquad (30)$$

The local nature of the fit allows nontrivial densities with, for instance, multiple maxima to be represented by the discrete ensemble in an accurate, efficient, and numerically stable manner.

We illustrate the general approach by considering a one-dimensional model of quantum mechanical tunneling [9, 12]. Using atomic units throughout, we consider a particle of mass $m = 2000$ moving on the potential

$$V(q) = \frac{1}{2}m\,\omega_o^2 q^2 - \frac{1}{3}bq^3, \qquad (31)$$

where $\omega_o = 0.01$ and $b = 0.2981$. This system has a metastable potential minimum with $V = 0$ at $q = 0$ and a barrier to escape of height $V^\ddagger = 0.015$ at $q^\ddagger = 0.6709$. The parameters are chosen so that the system roughly mimics a proton bound with approximately 2 metastable bound states. The dynamics are thus expected to be highly quantum mechanical.

A series of minimum uncertainty quantum wave packets and corresponding trajectory ensembles are chosen as initial states. The mean momentum $< p >= 0$ in all cases and the mean energy of the state is varied by selecting a range of initial average displacements. The trajectories are then propagated using the ensemble-dependent force given by Eq. (17). For the potential in Eq. (31), $V''' = -2b$ is constant, and the higher order terms in Eq. (17) rigorously vanish. The force then becomes

$$\dot{p}_j = -V'(q_j) - \frac{\hbar^2 b}{12}\frac{\partial^2 \rho/\partial p^2(q_j, p_j)}{\rho(q_j, p_j)} \qquad (32)$$

93

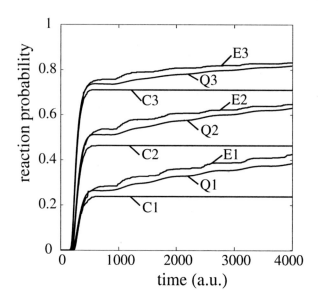

FIG. 2: Time-dependent reaction probabilities. Three initial states or ensembles are considered, and the results of the entangled trajectory ensemble simulations (E) are compared with purely classical (C) and exact quantum (Q) calculations. See the text for details.

for $j = 1, 2, \ldots, N$. The ρ-dependent factor depends on the parameters β_j and $\vec{\alpha}_j$, and thus involves summations over the entire trajectory ensemble. In terms of the local Gaussian parameters, the force becomes

$$\dot{p}_j = -V'(q_j) - \frac{\hbar^2 b}{12}(\alpha_{p,j}^2 - 2\beta_{p,j}), \qquad (33)$$

where

$$\alpha_p = \frac{\tilde{\sigma_\xi}^2 \langle \tilde{\eta} \rangle - \sigma_{\tilde{\xi}\eta}^2 \langle \tilde{\xi} \rangle}{\tilde{\sigma_\xi}^2 \tilde{\sigma_\eta}^2 - \sigma_{\tilde{\xi}\eta}^4} \qquad (34)$$

$$\beta_p = \frac{\tilde{\sigma_\xi}^2}{2(\tilde{\sigma_\xi}^2 \tilde{\sigma_\eta}^2 - \sigma_{\tilde{\xi}\eta}^4)} - h_p. \qquad (35)$$

In fig. 2, we show the time-dependent reaction probabilities $P(t)$ for three initial conditions, numbered 1–3, each corresponding to an initial minimum uncertainty wave packet or ensemble. The entangled trajectory simulations are

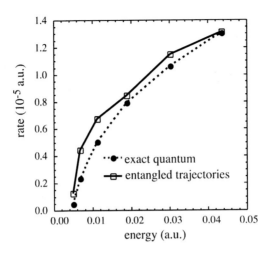

FIG. 3: Tunneling rate as a function of initial mean wave packet energy, entangled trajectory and exact quantum results.

compared with purely classical results generated with the same number of trajectories but in the absence of the quantum force and the results of numerically exact quantum wave packet calculations performed using the method of Kosloff [15].

The trajectory results shown here correspond to ensembles containing $N = 900$ trajectories. The quantum reaction probability is defined at each time as the integral of $|\psi(q,t)|^2$ from $q^{\ddagger}$ to ∞, while the classical and entangled trajectory quantities are defined as the fraction of trajectories with $q > q^{\ddagger}$ at time t. The curves are labeled C, Q, and E indicate classical, quantum, and entangled trajectory ensemble results, respectively. Case 1 corresponds to a mean energy $E_o = <\psi|\hat{H}|\psi> \simeq 0.75\, V^{\ddagger}$. For case 2, $E_o \simeq 1.25\, V^{\ddagger}$, while for case 3 $E_o \simeq 2.0 V^{\ddagger}$. Increasing the mean energy increases the short time transfer across the barrier, both classically and quantum mechanically. The classical reaction, however, ceases immediately after the first sharp rise, as the trajectories in the ensemble with energy below the barrier initially are trapped there for all time. The quantum wave packet, however, continues to escape from the metastable well by tunneling, and the reaction probability continues to grow slowly with time following the initial classical-like rise. This growth is modulated by the oscillations of the wave packet in the potential well. The entangled trajectory calculation tracks the exact quantum results quite well. Although these results slightly overestimate the exact instantaneous probability, the qualitative dynamics are described quite satisfactorily. In particular, the *non-classical* longer time growth of the reaction probability is correctly described.

In fig. 3, we examine the agreement between quantum and entangled trajectory predictions of the non-classical tunneling dynamics in more detail. The decay of the survival probability $1 - P(t)$ at times longer than the initial rapid classical decay is fit to an exponential $\exp(-kt)$ and the tunneling rate constant k thus defined is plotted in the figure as a function of mean wave packet energy. The overall correspondence is very good, especially considering that a nonzero k is a purely quantum mechanical quantity.

C. Husimi representation

The above method employs local smoothing implicitly to formulate an entangled trajectory method in the Wigner representation. We now formalize this idea by sketching a generalization of the approach that is based on a rigorous positive phase space representation of quantum mechanics: the Husimi representation [13].

The Husimi distribution is a locally-smoothed Wigner function:

$$\rho_H(q,p) = \frac{1}{\pi\hbar} \int\limits_{-\infty}^{\infty} \rho_W(q',p') e^{-\frac{(q-q')^2}{2\sigma_q^2}} e^{-\frac{(p-p')^2}{2\sigma_p^2}} \, dq' dp' \tag{36}$$

where the smoothing is over a minimum uncertainty phase space Gaussian,

$$\sigma_q \sigma_p = \frac{\hbar}{2}. \tag{37}$$

The smoothing can be represented using *smoothing operators* $\hat{Q}$ and $\hat{P}$:

$$\hat{Q} = e^{\frac{1}{2}\sigma_q^2 \frac{\partial^2}{\partial q^2}} \tag{38}$$

$$\hat{P} = e^{\frac{1}{2}\sigma_p^2 \frac{\partial^2}{\partial p^2}}. \tag{39}$$

The Husimi can then be written as a smoothed Wigner function as:

$$\rho_H(q,p) = \hat{Q}\hat{P}\rho_W(q,p). \tag{40}$$

This is related to the interesting identity:

$$e^{-a(x-x')^2} = e^{\frac{1}{4a}\frac{\partial^2}{\partial x^2}} \delta(x - x'). \tag{41}$$

We can consider the inverse *unsmoothing* operators $\hat{Q}^{-1}$ and $\hat{P}^{-1}$:

$$\hat{Q}^{-1} = e^{-\frac{1}{2}\sigma_q^2 \frac{\partial^2}{\partial q^2}} \tag{42}$$

$$\hat{P}^{-1} = e^{-\frac{1}{2}\sigma_p^2 \frac{\partial^2}{\partial p^2}}. \tag{43}$$

so that the Wigner function can be written (at least formally) as an "un-smoothed" Husimi:

$$\rho_W(q,p) = \hat{Q}^{-1}\hat{P}^{-1}\rho_H(q,p). \tag{44}$$

We can then derive an equation of motion for the Husimi distribution.

$$\frac{\partial \rho_H}{\partial t} = -\frac{1}{m}\hat{P}p\hat{P}^{-1}\frac{\partial \rho_H}{\partial q} + \int\limits_{-\infty}^{\infty} \hat{Q}J(q,\eta)\hat{Q}^{-1}\rho_H(q,p+\eta,t)\,d\xi. \tag{45}$$

Note that there are no approximations; the Husimi representation provides and *exact* description of quantum dynamics.

Powers of the coordinates and momenta become differential operators:

$$\hat{Q}q\hat{Q}^{-1} = q + \sigma_q^2 \frac{\partial}{\partial q} \tag{46}$$

$$\hat{P}p\hat{P}^{-1} = p + \sigma_p^2 \frac{\partial}{\partial p} \tag{47}$$

$$\hat{Q}q^2\hat{Q}^{-1} = q^2 + \sigma_q^2 + 2\sigma_q^2 q \frac{\partial}{\partial q} + \sigma_q^4 \frac{\partial^2}{\partial q^2}. \tag{48}$$

The Husimi equation of motion for the cubic system can then be written:

$$\frac{\partial \rho_H}{\partial t} = -\frac{1}{m}\hat{P}p\hat{P}^{-1}\frac{\partial \rho_H}{\partial q} + (m\omega_o^2 \hat{Q}q\hat{Q}^{-1} - b\hat{Q}q^2\hat{Q}^{-1})\frac{\partial \rho_H}{\partial p} + \frac{\hbar^2 b}{12}\frac{\partial^3 \rho_H}{\partial p^3} \tag{49}$$

where

$$\hat{Q}q\hat{Q}^{-1} = q + \sigma_q^2 \frac{\partial}{\partial q} \tag{50}$$

$$\hat{P}p\hat{P}^{-1} = p + \sigma_p^2 \frac{\partial}{\partial p} \tag{51}$$

$$\hat{Q}q^2\hat{Q}^{-1} = q^2 + \sigma_q^2 + 2\sigma_q^2 q \frac{\partial}{\partial q} + \sigma_q^4 \frac{\partial^2}{\partial q^2}. \tag{52}$$

Continuity conditions can then be applied in the Husimi representation, now rigorous for a positive probability distribution.

$$\frac{\partial \rho_H}{\partial t} + \vec{\nabla} \cdot \vec{j}_H = 0. \tag{53}$$

And, after a little algebra,

$$\vec{\nabla} \cdot \vec{j}_H = \frac{\partial}{\partial q}\left(\frac{p}{m}\rho_H\right) \tag{54}$$

$$+\frac{\partial}{\partial p}\left(-V'(q)\rho_H + \frac{\hbar b}{2m\omega_o}\rho_H + \frac{\hbar b q}{m\omega_o}\frac{\partial \rho_H}{\partial q} + \frac{\hbar^2 b}{4m^2\omega_o^2}\frac{\partial^2 \rho_H}{\partial q^2} - \frac{\hbar^2 b}{12}\frac{\partial^2 \rho_H}{\partial p^2}\right).$$

The phase space vector field can then be written as

$$\dot{q} = \frac{p}{m} \tag{55}$$

$$\dot{p} = -V'(q) + \frac{\hbar b}{2m\omega_o} + \frac{\hbar b q}{m\omega_o}\frac{1}{\rho_H}\frac{\partial \rho_H}{\partial q} + \frac{\hbar^2 b}{4m^2\omega_o^2}\frac{1}{\rho_H}\frac{\partial^2 \rho_H}{\partial q^2} - \frac{\hbar^2 b}{12}\frac{1}{\rho_H}\frac{\partial^2 \rho_H}{\partial p^2}. \tag{56}$$

The quantum force now contains additional terms not present in the Wigner representation quantum force. This is related to the fact that classical propagation and smoothing *do not commute*.

Because of the smoothing, the motion of a free particle motion is nonclassical in the Husimi representation!

$$\frac{\partial \rho_H}{\partial t} = -\frac{1}{m}\hat{P}p\hat{P}^{-1}\frac{\partial \rho_H}{\partial q} \tag{57}$$

or

$$\frac{\partial \rho_H}{\partial t} = -\frac{1}{m}p\frac{\partial \rho_H}{\partial q} - \frac{\sigma_p^2}{m}\frac{\partial^2 \rho_H}{\partial q \partial p}. \tag{58}$$

The extra terms due to noncommutativity of classical time evolution and smoothing. (For a harmonic oscillator, the cross terms resulting from the kinetic energy and potential energy cancel, leading to classical evolution.)

The methodology described above can be generalized to incorporate the additional terms in the equations of motion in the Husimi representation. When implemented, excellent agreement with exact results for model systems is again obtained [13]. In fig. 4, results for the cubic system are shown, indicating the level of agreement between exact quantum results, the Wigner-based method described above, and the implementation based on the positive Husimi representation.

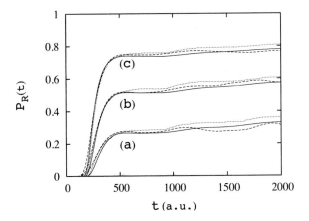

FIG. 4: Reaction probabilities vs time. Solid lines represent exact results. Fine dotted lines show results for the entangled trajectory method based on an $\hbar$ expansion of the Wigner function, as described in the text. Dashed lines present the results of this work performed in the Husimi representation. Cases a, b, and c to the initial placement of the center of the wave packet $q_0 = -0.2$ au, $q_0 = -0.3$ au, and $q_0 = -0.4$ au, respectively.

D. Integrodifferential equation form

We now return to the Wigner equation of motion in the integrodifferential form, and try to solve this directly:

$$\frac{\partial \rho_W}{\partial t} = -\frac{p}{m}\frac{\partial \rho_W}{\partial q} + \int_{-\infty}^{\infty} J(q, p-\xi)\rho_W(q,\xi,t)d\xi. \tag{59}$$

We write the divergence of the flux directly in this form:

$$\vec{\nabla} \cdot \vec{j}_W = \frac{\partial}{\partial q}\left(\frac{p}{m}\rho_W\right) - \int_{-\infty}^{\infty} J(q,\xi-p)\,\rho_W(q,\xi,t)\,d\xi. \tag{60}$$

The momentum component of the flux divergence is:

$$\frac{\partial}{\partial p}j_{W,p} = -\int_{-\infty}^{\infty} J(q,\xi-p)\,\rho_W(q,\xi,t)\,d\xi. \tag{61}$$

Integrating, we obtain

$$j_{W,p} = -\int_{-\infty}^{\infty} \Theta(q, \xi - p)\, \rho_W(q, \xi, t)\, d\xi, \tag{62}$$

where

$$\Theta(q, \xi - p) = \int_{-\infty}^{p} J(q, \xi - z)\, dz. \tag{63}$$

This can be written explicitly in terms of the potential $V(q)$:

$$\Theta(q, \xi - p) = \frac{1}{2\pi\hbar} \int_{-\infty}^{\infty} \left[V(q + \tfrac{y}{2}) - V(q - \tfrac{y}{2}) \right] \frac{e^{-i(\xi - p)y/\hbar}}{y}\, dy \tag{64}$$

The quantum trajectory equations of motion then become

$$\dot{q} = \frac{p}{m} \tag{65}$$

$$\dot{p} = -\frac{1}{\rho_W(q, p)} \int \Theta(q, p - \xi) \rho_W(q, \xi)\, d\xi. \tag{66}$$

To proceed numerically, we write the Wigner function as a superposition of Gaussians:

$$\rho_W(q, p, t) = \frac{1}{N} \sum_{j=1}^{N} \phi(q - q_j(t), p - p_j(t)), \tag{67}$$

where

$$\phi(q, p) = \frac{1}{2\pi\sigma_q\sigma_p} \exp\left(-\frac{q^2}{2\sigma_q^2} - \frac{p^2}{2\sigma_p^2} \right). \tag{68}$$

After some algebra, we find

$$\dot{p}(q, p) = -\frac{\sum_{j=1}^{N} \phi_q(q - q_j)\Lambda(q - q_j, p - p_j)}{\sum_{j=1}^{N} \phi_q(q - q_j)\phi_p(q - q_j)} \tag{69}$$

where

$$\Lambda(q - q_j, p - p_j) = \int \frac{V(q + z/2) - V(q - z/2)}{z} \exp\left[i\frac{(p - p_j)z}{\hbar} - \frac{\sigma_p^2 z^2}{2\hbar^2} \right] dz \tag{70}$$

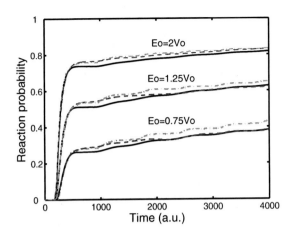

FIG. 5: Time-dependent reaction probabilities for the cubic potential system with three different initial energies $E_0 = 0.75V_0$, $E_0 = 1.25V_0$, and $E_0 = 2.0V_0$. Solid (black), dashed (blue), and dash-dotted (red) lines represent the results of exact quantum calculation, entangled trajectory simulations using the integrodifferential equation formulation, Eq. 69, and the results in ref. [9], respectively.

This can be evaluated numerically for a given potential $V(q)$.

The results of this method are shown in fig. 5, and compared with both the exact quantum results and the Wigner method based on an expansion in $\hbar$, described above. The integrodifferential equation method yields better agreement with exact results, particularly at longer times. It should be noted that this implementation incorporates the purely classical part of the equations of motion in the kernel $\Lambda(q,p)$, giving a classical mechanics where the potential $V(q)$, rather than the force $-V'(q)$ appears in the equations of motion.

III. DISCUSSION

The entangled trajectory formalism gives a unique and appealing physical picture of the quantum tunneling process. Rather than "burrowing" through the obstacle, trajectories that successfully escape the metastable well do so by "borrowing" enough energy from their fellow ensemble members to surmount the barrier. This loan is then paid back, always keeping the mean energy of the ensemble a constant.

We have described an approach to the simulation of quantum processes using trajectory integration and ensemble averaging. The general method was illustrated in the context of quantum tunneling through a potential barrier. The basis of the method is the Liouville representation of quantum mechanics and its realization in phase space *via* the Wigner function formalism. The evolution of the phase space functions is approximated by the motion of the corresponding trajectory ensembles. In the classical limit, the members of the ensemble evolve independently under Hamilton's equations of motion. When quantum effects are included, however, the corresponding "quantum trajectories" are no longer separable from each other. Rather, their statistical independence is destroyed by nonclassical interactions that reflect the nonlocality of quantum mechanics. Their time histories become interdependent and the evolution of the quantum ensemble must be accomplished by taking this entanglement into account.

[1] C. Cohen-Tannoudji, B. Diu, and F. Laloe, *Quantum Mechanics* (Wiley, New York, 1977).
[2] G. C. Schatz and M. A. Ratner, *Quantum Mechanics in Chemistry* (Prentice Hall, Englewood Cliffs, 1993).
[3] M. P. Allen and D. J. Tildesley, *Computer Simulation of Liquids* (Clarendon Press, Oxford, 1987).
[4] H. Goldstein, *Classical Mechanics* (Addison-Wesley, Reading, 1980), 2nd ed.
[5] E. P. Wigner, Phys. Rev. **40**, 749 (1932).
[6] K. Takahashi, Prog. Theor. Phys. Suppl. **98**, 109 (1989).
[7] H. W. Lee, Phys. Rep. **259**, 147 (1995).
[8] S. Mukamel, *Principles of Nonlinear Optical Spectroscopy* (Oxford University Press, Oxford, 1995).
[9] A. Donoso and C. C. Martens, Phys. Rev. Lett. **87**, 223202 (2001).
[10] A. Donoso and C. C. Martens, Int. J. Quantum Chem. **87**, 1348 (2002).
[11] A. Donoso and C. C. Martens, J. Chem. Phys. **116**, 10598 (2002).
[12] A. Donoso, Y. Zheng, and C. C. Martens, J. Chem. Phys. **119**, 5010 (2003).
[13] H. López, C. C. Martens, and A. Donoso, J. Chem. Phys. **1125**, 154111 (2006).
[14] D. A. McQuarrie, *Statistical Mechanics* (HarperCollins, New York, 1976).
[15] R. Kosloff, Ann. Rev. Phys. Chem. **45**, 145 (1994).

D. Shalashilin and M. P. de Miranda (eds.)
Multidimensional Quantum Mechanics with Trajectories
© 2009, CCP6, Daresbury

Capturing geometric phase effects
near conical intersections

Sandy Yang and Todd J. Martinez

Department of Chemistry, Beckman Institute,
and Frederick Seitz Materials Research Laboratory,
University of Illinois at Urbana-Champaign,
600 S. Mathews Ave., Urbana, IL 6180

I. INTRODUCTION

Geometric phase, also known as Berry phase [1], is a quantum mechanical concept that refers to the phase factor gained by quantum states when subjected to a cyclic adiabatic process, i.e. transport around a closed loop. Berry phase is closely related to the geometrical-topological characteristics of the local potential energy surface (PES). In most cases, the phase factor resulting from cyclic transport is zero, i.e. there is no Berry phase. However, if there exist one or more points of degeneracy enclosed by the loop, the phase can be nonzero and nontrivial. This appears particularly in the theory of conical intersections [2] between two or more electronic states. Conical intersections are familiar in the context of the Jahn-Teller effect, but they are now known to be considerably more general since there are many examples of "accidental" conical intersections, i.e. ones which are not determined by symmetry.

We are interested in the study of Berry phase specifically because conical intersections are ubiquitous in chemical systems and especially important in photochemical reaction mechanisms which necessarily involve transitions between multiple electronic states [3] The full multiple spawning (FMS) method has been developed [4] for simulating quantum dynamics involving nonadiabatic transitions between various potential energy surfaces. The total FMS wavefunction is constructed from a Born-Huang sum of products. Standard basis sets and quantum chemical methods are used to represent the electronic wavefunction in each term. The nuclear wavefunction is expanded as a coherent superposition of frozen Gaussians, similar to the CCS method of Shalashilin and Child [5]. A unique aspect of FMS is the adaptive nature of the nuclear basis set, i.e., "spawning." The spawning technique was introduced to increase the size of the nuclear basis set when the wavefunction experiences nonadiabatic transitions near avoided crossings or conical intersections. It has also been used to describe tunneling effects [6]. Recently, a new spawning technique called optimal spawning has been constructed and implemented in FMS. By maximizing the matrix element coupling parent and child basis functions, FMS can describe nonadiabatic transitions more accurately and efficiently, which has significant implications for ab initio calculations. Moreover, optimal spawning has been found to capture the geometric phase effect near conical intersections better than previous spawning methods. In this article, we first summarize the FMS method and different spawning algorithms. Then we apply these spawning methods to a two-state two-mode conical intersection model, paying particular attention to the geometric phase effect.

II. EQUATIONS OF MOTION AND SPAWNING TECHNIQUE

Both the electrons and the nuclei are treated quantum mechanically and on a consistent basis in *ab initio* multiple spawning (AIMS), which is based on the full multiple spawning (FMS) method for nonadiabatic dynamics. Special attention must be paid to the interface of the quantum mechanical treatment of the electrons and that of the nuclei because of the tension between the locality of quantum chemistry and the global character of the time-dependent nuclear Schrödinger equation. This tension is relieved in FMS by using phase-space localized basis functions to describe the nuclei. Each of these basis functions carries an electronic label in FMS and an entire electronic wavefunction in AIMS, i.e. these are actually vibronic basis functions. The localized nature of the basis functions enables the use of approximations to evaluate the required integrals and in principle these approximations can be improved as necessary. The multiconfigurational total wavefunction in FMS is written in terms of electronic and nuclear wavefunctions, $\phi_I(\mathbf{r}; \mathbf{R})$ and $\chi_I(\mathbf{R}; t)$, respectively:

$$\psi = \sum_I \chi_I(\mathbf{R}; t)\phi_I(\mathbf{r}; \mathbf{R}), \tag{1a}$$

$$\chi_I(\mathbf{R}; t) = \sum_{m=1}^{N_I(t)} c_m^I(t)\chi_m^I(\mathbf{R}; \bar{\mathbf{R}}_m, \bar{\mathbf{P}}_m, \gamma_m^I, \alpha_m^I). \tag{1b}$$

The subscript I indexes the electronic state, vectors $\mathbf{r}$ and $\mathbf{R}$ denote the electronic and nuclear coordinates respectively, c_m^I is a time-dependent complex amplitude associated with each individual trajectory basis function χ_m^I, and $N_I(t)$ is the number of nuclear basis functions on electronic state I at time t, whose value may change when a new trajectory is spawned. The trajectory basis functions (TBFs) χ_m^I are written as a multidimensional product of one-dimensional frozen Gaussians [7] parameterized by width α_m^I, phase γ_m^I and centroid phase space variables $\bar{R}_m^I$ and $\bar{P}_m^I$. The phase space variables evolve classically on a single electronic potential energy surface, according to the electronic label carried by

104

the TBF. Although the Gaussian basis function parameters evolve classically, quantum mechanical effects are treated because the time-dependent Schrdinger equation is solved to obtain the time-evolution of the complex coefficients in Eq. (1). In order to solve for the time evolution of the amplitudes c_m^I, one requires the overlap matrix

$$\mathbf{S}_{mn}^{IJ} = \langle \chi_m^I | \chi_n^J \rangle \delta_{IJ} \qquad (2)$$

to account for the nonorthogonal character of the TBFs and also matrix elements of the right-acting time derivative

$$\dot{\tilde{S}}_{mn}^{IJ} = \langle \chi_m^I | \frac{\partial}{\partial t} \chi_n^J \rangle \delta_{IJ} \qquad (3)$$

which express how the nonorthogonality of the TBFs changes in time. We have assumed that the electronic states are orthonormal in Eqs. (2) and (3). With these definitions, the equations of motion for the complex coefficients are:

$$\frac{d\mathbf{C}^I}{dt} = -i \left(S^{II} \right)^{-1} \left\{ \left(\mathbf{H}^{II} - i\dot{\tilde{\mathbf{S}}}^{II} \right) \mathbf{C}^I + \sum_{J \neq I} \mathbf{H}^{IJ} \mathbf{C}^J \right\}. \qquad (4)$$

The spawning procedure is one of the unique aspects of FMS, and the adaptive addition of TBFs during nonadiabatic events is an important part of the method's accuracy and efficiency. Trajectory basis functions on one electronic state are allowed to spawn new trajectories on another electronic state only when they enter a region of significant nonadiabatic coupling (defined with the use of a numerical threshold). The nonadiabatic coupling vector is used to help determine when spawning might be needed and along which direction the momentum vector should be adjusted:

$$\mathbf{d}^{IJ} \equiv \left\langle \phi_I(\mathbf{r}; \mathbf{R}) \left| \frac{\partial}{\partial \mathbf{R}} \right| \phi_J(\mathbf{r}; \mathbf{R}) \right\rangle_r. \qquad (5)$$

Once a trajectory enters a spawning region as dictated by the magnitude of the vector $\mathbf{d}^{IJ}$, the TBF is propagated (uncoupled from other TBFs in the simulation) until it reaches the end of the spawning region, i.e. until the magnitude of the nonadiabatic coupling vector falls below the numerical threshold value. A new basis function is created, i.e. "spawned," on the coupled electronic state and this new TBF is then *backward-propagated* to the time when the parent TBF entered the spawning region. This new "child" TBF is then added (with zero amplitude) to the bundle of TBFs and the simulation continues. This procedure for adding spawned TBFs guarantees that they are in the right place at the right time to be populated by the solution of the nuclear Schrödinger equation. There are two important aspects of this procedure. First, the new TBF is generally at most weakly coupled to other TBFs when it appears in the basis set. This is because the spawning procedure is set up to guarantee that it will be important, i.e. strongly coupled to the parent TBF, only later after its addition to the simulation. Secondly, the coupling of the child TBF to other TBFs in the simulation will usually rise and then fall as the parent and child approach each other and then recede. This allows for the development of coherence between the parent and child TBFs, which is prerequisite for population transfer. Thus, the numerical threshold which defines the spawning region is generally chosen to be quite low, and the spawning procedure is a means for predicting where child TBFs need to be located later in time.

An important question which remains unanswered in the above description is where in phase space the child TBF should be placed. We demand that the parent and child TBFs have the same classical energy. This ensures that even when the TBFs are all distant and uncoupled (which will inevitably happen for realistic basis set sizes in high dimensionality) the average classical energy of the TBFs will be conserved. We also desire the coupling between the parent and child TBFs to be maximized, since this implies that the child basis function will be important in the solution of the time-dependent Schrödinger equation. Considering the maximization of the parent-child coupling and the classical energy constraint leads to an overcomplete set of equations for the phase space location of the child TBF. In general, such a set of equations does not have a unique solution, and can be solved only in a least-squared sense. This leads to the various spawning techniques we now discuss. It is important to realize at the onset that the FMS method is exact in the limit of a complete basis set of TBFs. Thus, the spawning procedures can be viewed as a means of improving convergence when one is far from a complete basis set (which is the usual case in practice). Thus, results become insensitive to the details of the spawning procedure as the number of TBFs used increases. However, there could be large differences in the accuracy and efficiency of different methods for practically relevant basis sets and this is the motivation for investigating different possible approaches.

The two simplest classes of solutions for the location of the child TBF are the *position-preserving* and *momentum-preserving* spawns. In these solutions, either the child TBF's position or momentum is fixed to that of the parent while the conjugate variable is adjusted to equalize classical energy between parent and child trajectories. Here we consider the position-preserving type of spawn paired with a pure momentum jump,

$$\mathbf{P}^I_{\text{new}} = \mathbf{P}^I_{\text{old}} - D\hat{\mathbf{d}}^{IJ}, \tag{6}$$

where $\mathbf{P}^I_{\text{new}}$ is the centroid momentum vector of the newly spawned child, $\mathbf{P}^I_{\text{old}}$ is that of the parent, and $\hat{\mathbf{d}}^{IJ}$ is a unit vector directed along the nonadiabatic coupling defined in Eq. (5). The scalar value D is chosen such that the total classical energy of the child is identical to that of the parent. For a one-dimensional problem, momentum jumps are uniquely defined and position-preserving spawns lead to the same adjustment used in surface hopping [8].

In principle, it could happen that the electronic state to which a spawn should occur is classically inaccessible, i.e. no value of D in Eq. (6) can satisfy the classical energy constraint. In surface hopping, such failures are known as frustrated hops. Many have tried to tease out the full implications of frustrated hops [9–11]. Recently, these frustrated hops were identified as essential to guarantee the proper equilibrium state at long time [9]. In FMS, however, frustrated spawns are often not a serious problem. In surface hopping, the "hops" are the vehicle by which electronic population transfer takes place. In contrast, spawning is important in that it allows nonadiabatic transitions to occur, but spawning itself does *not* dictate the statistical balance of population among the various electronic surfaces — this is instead determined by the solution of the time-dependent Schrödinger equation in the adaptive basis set of TBFs.

Nevertheless, one might want to ensure that spawning occurs even when no position-preserving spawn satisfying the classical energy constraint is available. A simple means of doing this is to allow quenching to the energy shell in these cases. Of course, this is no longer strictly a position-preserving spawn, since it is the position of the basis function which is modified (after removing all momentum along the nonadiabatic coupling vector) to satisfy the classical energy constraint. There are two obvious choices of descent direction, both of which perform reasonably well: the nonadiabatic coupling vector, or the negative of the gradient (steepest descent). For one-dimensional problems, the two approaches are obviously identical. There has not yet been a systematic study to determine which one performs better in high dimensional problems. If the nonadiabatic coupling vector $\hat{\mathbf{d}}^{IJ}$ is chosen, then the momentum adjustment is followed by a position shift that minimizes the functional

$$E^{\text{child}}\left(\mathbf{P}_{\text{adjusted}}, \mathbf{R}_{\text{parent}} + \gamma \cdot \hat{\mathbf{d}}^{IJ}\right) - E^{\text{parent}}\left(\mathbf{P}_{\text{parent}}, \mathbf{R}_{\text{parent}}\right), \qquad (7)$$

where γ is determined by optimization. In cases where position adjustment is required in addition to the momentum adjustment, the maximum overlap between parent and child is necessarily diminished. This implies also that the maximum Hamiltonian element between parent and child will be smaller than usual, and hence there is a bias against effectively populating these spawned TBFs. We believe this diminished population transfer is a key physical component of detailed balance, but we will not explore this issue further here.

Here we introduce a third class of spawning algorithms, which attempts to blend the position-preserving and momentum-preserving spawns in a manner that treats all spawning events equivalently. Heller and coworkers [12] have previously noted the importance of hybrid jumps in a phase space theory of nonadiabatic transitions and this partially inspires our proposal here. In this new "optimal spawning" algorithm, we choose the phase space location of the child to minimize the functional:

$$\lambda E_{\text{diff}} - \left(V_{\text{pc}}^{IJ}\right)^2, \qquad (8)$$

where E_{diff} is the difference in the classical energy of the parent and child, V_{pc}^{IJ} is the off-diagonal potential energy matrix element coupling the parent and child, and λ is a Lagrange multiplier which must be determined. The formulation given here is appropriate when a diabatic representation of the electronic states is used, as will be done in the examples below. However, the extension to an adiabatic representation is straightforward. In practice, we solve the constrained optimization problem using a sequential penalty method, meaning that the Lagrange multiplier is increased steadily during the solution procedure. This is a standard method for solving the nonlinear programming problem implicit in Eq. (8). For a fixed value of λ, minimization pushes the energy gap toward zero while maximizing the coupling as a function of $\mathbf{R}_{\text{child}}$ and $\mathbf{P}_{\text{child}}$. Sequentially increasing λ steadily raises the penalty for energy non-conservation, while tracking changes in the coupling maximum as smoothly as possible. Each minimization cycle (for fixed λ) is performed with standard conjugate gradient techniques.

III. DISCUSSION

In the simulations presented here, the initial target wavefunction is chosen to be a single multidimensional Gaussian. Propagation is performed on diabatic potential energy surfaces. To maximize overlap between the initial FMS wavepacket and the initial target wavefunction, the complex amplitude of each trajectory in the bundle is determined by projection:

$$c_m^I(0) = \sum_{n=1}^{N_I(0)} \left(S^{-1} \right)_{mn}^{II} \langle \chi_n^I(t=0) | \Psi_{t=0}^{\text{target}} \rangle. \tag{9}$$

The phase space location of each initial TBF is drawn randomly from the Wigner distribution corresponding to the target wavefunction. We reject initial TBFs whose energy expectation value is not within 10% of the exact quantum mechanical energy. Results are reported for three different spawning methods — strict p-jump, standard, and optimal spawning. Strict p-jump refers to spawning with momentum adjustment along the nonadiabatic coupling vector. If the resulting child trajectory does not satisfy the classical energy conservation constraint after the momentum adjustment, it is not spawned. This is the most similar scheme to surface hopping, and has in fact never been used in past FMS simulations. The standard spawning algorithm involves momentum adjustment, and if necessary quenching to the energy shell in order to satisfy the classical energy conservation constraint. This is the algorithm in general use in most FMS simulations. Finally, the optimal spawning method allows hybrid position-momentum jumps, as described in the previous section. Numerically exact quantum results used as reference are obtained with the fast Fourier transform (FFT) method [13].

The model problem we use to investigate the performance of the different spawning methods is a two-dimensional, two-state conical intersection model originally introduced by Ferretti and coworkers [14]. This model describes a collinear triatomic ABA and provides a useful test bed for comparison of nonadiabatic simulation schemes. The potential energy contribution to the Hamiltonian is written as

$$V_{11}(X, Y) = \frac{1}{2}k_x(X - X_1)^2 + \frac{1}{2}k_y Y^2 \tag{10a}$$

$$V_{22}(X, Y) = \frac{1}{2}k_x(X - X_2)^2 + \frac{1}{2}k_y Y^2 + \Delta \tag{10b}$$

$$V_{12}(X, Y) = \gamma Y e^{-\alpha(X-X_3)^2 - \beta Y^2} \tag{10c}$$

where the subscripts label diabatic electronic states. The minima of the parabolic surfaces are located at $X_1 = 4$ and $X_2 = 3$ bohr. The interstate coupling is controlled by the parameter γ (set to 0.01 in atomic units). We use the same model parameters as Ferretti, and refer the reader to the original paper for full details [14]. The initial wavepacket starts on the diabatic state $|1\rangle$ with zero initial momentum and the total simulation time corresponds roughly to one half-period along the X coordinate.

We place the initial target wavepacket at $X = 5.2, Y = 0$ (represented with 9 initial TBFs as described above) on diabatic state $|1\rangle$. This corresponds to an energy which is just slightly above that of the conical intersection. This low energy case is challenging numerically, because most trajectories will have insufficient kinetic energy to spawn near the intersection point. The electronic population dynamics for this case is shown in Fig. 1. The accuracy of the predicted population transfer increases as one moves from strict momentum-jumps, to standard spawning, and finally to optimal spawning.

Optimal spawning allows newly spawned basis functions to be located further away from their parent trajectories than the alternative spawning procedures do, and such a difference is more noticeable if additional displacement is required to conserve energy in the case of frustrated spawns. This may be helpful in cases where a new trajectory needs to jump a large distance in coordinate space, e.g., tunneling through a barrier. Additional details, however, are beyond the scope of the current paper. The importance of allowing such full surface jumps in phase space is demonstrated in Fig. 2, where the reduced density $\rho(Y, t)$ for diabatic state $|2\rangle$ is plotted at several times. Comparison between numerically exact results (FFT) and various spawning techniques shows that optimal spawning best captures the double-peak in the wavefunction which comes from the linearity of the coupling around the intersection point. As pointed out by Ferretti [14], the presence of the node at $Y = 0$ is a manifestation of Berry's phase and is sensitive to the correct treatment of quantum interference.

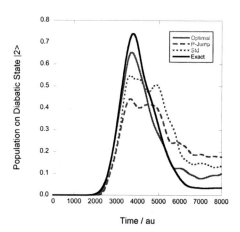

FIG. 1: Comparison of population on diabatic state $|2\rangle$ as a function of time for numerically exact and spawning simulations. The initial wavepacket is placed at $X = 5.2, Y = 0$ on diabatic state $|1\rangle$.

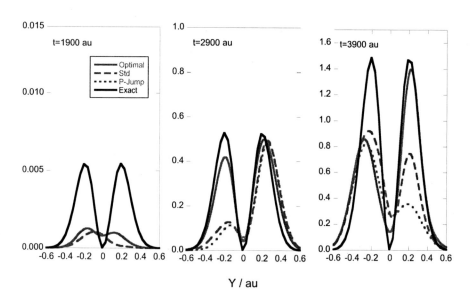

FIG. 2: Comparison of reduced density along Y coordinate on diabatic state $|2\rangle$ from exact and spawning methods at various times (see Fig. 1). Optimal spawning is best able to describe the depletion of density at $Y = 0$ which is a signature of passage through a conical intersection.

IV. CONCLUSIONS

Berry phase is an intrinsically quantum mechanical effect, arising because of the *sign* of the coupling between multiple electronic states. This sign manifests itself as a phase factor and leads to interference effects that cannot be described classically. Here, we have shown that this strongly quantum mechanical effect can be described by the full multiple spawning method. Furthermore, it is described more accurately with a new spawning algorithm for adaptive basis set expansion that we have termed "optimal spawning." Optimal spawning places new basis functions at phase space locations that maximize the coupling to the existing basis set while maintaining a classical notion of energy conservation. Because FMS is guaranteed to be numerically exact for a complete basis set, one expects that the method will become insensitive to the details of the spawning procedure once the basis set is large enough. This is indeed observed in the test cases presented here (results not shown). However, in practice one desires to accelerate convergence as much as possible in order to limit computational expense and thus the efficiency of the spawning procedure is very important. It is possible that the advantages of optimal spawning will increase with dimensionality, since it is less likely that heuristic procedures like the position and momentum jump will be close to the optimal spawning location in high dimensional cases. Verification of this conjecture will have to await further studies, but it is remarkable that already noticeable improvement can be seen in the two-dimensional case, where the phase space is only four-dimensional and therefore the spawning locations predicted by the different methods are likely rather close to each other. Furthermore, as shown here, the interference associated with the geometric phase effect is much better modeled using the optimal spawning method. Finally, we point out that the optimal spawning procedure does away completely with any notion of "frustrated spawns." Although we have not found these to be a serious problem for the spawning method (as discussed above), the optimal spawning procedure is more satisfying than previous spawning procedures because there is simply no such thing as a "frustrated spawn." Thus, there is no need to treat these cases in any special way, e.g. by steepest descent procedures. The optimal spawning procedure reduces to simpler approaches such as the momentum-jump in appropriate limits, but it remains efficient even in cases where both position and momentum require adjustment (e.g., tunneling phenomena). Therefore, we have a sophisticated and robust way to allow any phase space point to be chosen statistically for the newly spawned basis function in the nonadiabatic coupling region, which in turn helps to capture the geometrical phase change near the conical intersections.

Acknowledgments. This work was supported by the National Science Foundation (CHE-07-19291).

[1] M. V. Berry, Proc. R. Soc. London, Ser. A **392**, 45 (1984).
[2] D. R. Yarkony, Rev. Mod. Phys. **68**, 985 (1996).
[3] B. G. Levine and T. J. Martnez, Annu. Rev. Phys. Chem. **58**, 613 (2007).
[4] M. Ben-Nun and T. J. Martnez, Adv. Chem. Phys. **121**, 439 (2002).
[5] D. V. Shalashilin and M. S. Child, Chem. Phys. **304**, 103 (2004).
[6] M. Ben-Nun and T. J. Martnez, J. Chem. Phys. **112**, 6113 (2000).
[7] E. J. Heller, J. Chem. Phys. **75**, 2923 (1981).
[8] J. C. Tully, J. Chem. Phys. **93**, 1061 (1990).
[9] P. V. Parandekar and J. C. Tully, J. Chem. Theory Comput. **2**, 229 (2006).
[10] A. W. Jasper and D. G. Truhlar, Chem. Phys. Lett. **369**, 60 (2003).
[11] J. Fang and S. Hammes-Schiffer, J. Phys. Chem. A **103**, 9399 (1999).
[12] E. J. Heller, B. Segev, and A. V. Sergeev, J. Phys. Chem. B **106**, 8471 (2002).
[13] D. Kosloff and R. Kosloff, J. Comput. Phys. **52**, 35 (1983).
[14] A. Ferretti, G. Granucci, M. Persico, and G. Villani, J. Chem. Phys. **104**, 5517 (1996).

D. Shalashilin and M. P. de Miranda (eds.)
Multidimensional Quantum Mechanics with Trajectories
© 2009, CCP6, Daresbury

Quantum dynamics using Gaussian wavepackets: the vMCG method.

G. A. Worth*

School of Chemistry, University of Birmingham, Birmingham, B15 2TT, U.K.

The *variational multi-configurational Gaussian* (vMCG) method is in principle a full quantum dynamics method able to solve the time-dependent Schrödinger equation exactly. It is derived from the well-established *multi-configuration time-dependent Hartree* (MCTDH) wavepacket propagation algorithm [1–3], through the G-MCTDH extension [4, 5]. The MCTDH method has been applied to a variety of problems, and has proved itself able to treat larger systems than are accessible to normal grid-based wavepacket methods. Particularly striking examples are found in studies on non-adiabatic systems using the simple vibronic-coupling model Hamiltonian [6] where up to 24 modes have been included [7], whereas standard methods are usually limited to 4 or fewer modes.

The power of the MCTDH method comes from the use of a time-dependent basis set to describe the dynamical modes, known as single-particle functions. These functions have coupled variational equations of motion and move so as to optimally describe the true evolving wavepacket. This keeps the basis-set small and describes only the region of space occupied by the wavepacket, which saves effort. In addition it converges on the exact numerical result. This allows approximate calculations to be made with a small basis set which can be improved by adding functions until the property of interest is converged.

G-MCTDH replaces the single-particle functions for a mode with parametrised functions, of which Gaussian functions are a suitable example. The parameters for the functions also follow variational equations of motion, and the theory is still a full quantum dynamics method. The practical requirement of solving the required integrals, however, introduces approximations - for example Gaussians allow the use of a local harmonic approximation (LHA). Thus we tend to refer to G-MCTDH as a mixed quantum – semi-classical approach as it no longer converges on the full numerical result.

In the limit that only Gaussian functions are used, we obtain a wavefunction described by a superposition of "Gaussian wavepackets" (GWPs). This

---

*Electronic address: g.a.worth@bham.ac.uk

is termed vMCG, and has characteristics in common with the semi-classical GWP propagation methods. G-MCTDH thus covers the complete spectrum of quantum dynamics, from grid based through mixed quantum - semi-classical to semi-classical GWP methods.

Most methods that use Gaussian basis functions use GWPs that follow classical trajectories. This makes the theories simple, easy to interpret, and resulting algorithms easy to implement. The G-MCTDH (and thus vMCG) Gaussian functions do not follow classical trajectories and the GWPs are directly coupled. As a result, the coverage of configuration space is better and convergence faster. The pay-off though is the need to solve difficult, coupled equations of motion. Integrating the GWP equations of motion is complicated by stability and numerical problems caused by the strong coupling between parts of the system. This meant that early calculations were unable to attain convergence and were extremely sensitive to numerical parameters. A recently developed integrator, using a conjugate space of orthonormal functions, seems to have cured many of the problems [8].

As a mixed method, G-MCTDH is ideal for system - bath problems, in which a part of the system of interest can be thought of as reasonably harmonic and only weakly coupled to a part which is strongly quantum mechanical. The latter is treated using grid-based quantum dynamics and the former with GWPs [9]. An example of this approach applied to a benchmark problem is the calculation of the absorption spectrum of the pyrazine molecule [8].

Despite its good convergence properties, it will be difficult to converge the vMCG method for a strongly quantum mechanical system due to the huge number of basis functions required. In many cases, though, fully converged results are not required and the convergence properties of vMCG make them very attractive as with only a few functions the correct qualitative behaviour of quantum systems is recovered [5, 10].

An area of growing interest in which the vMCG method can be used is direct dynamics. Here, the potential energy surface is calculated on-the-fly using a quantum chemistry program as and when it is required by the evolving functions [11]. This not only saves the tedious effort of first calculating the potential function before any dynamics can be studied, but also has the potential to treat larger systems than using an analytic potential function as only relevant parts of the space are searched. Direct dynamics vMCG (DD-vMCG) is reviewed in Ref. 12.

vMCG Theory

The G-MCTDH wavefunction ansatz is

$$\Psi(Q_1,\ldots,Q_f,t) = \sum_{j_1=1}^{n_1} \cdots \sum_{j_p=1}^{n_f} A_{j_1\ldots j_p}(t) \prod_{\kappa=1}^{p-n} \varphi_{j_\kappa}^{(\kappa)} \prod_{\kappa=n+1}^{p} g_{j_\kappa}^{(\kappa)} \tag{1}$$

where $A_{j_1\ldots j_p}(t)$ are the expansion coefficients, $\varphi_{j_\kappa}^{(\kappa)}(Q_\kappa)$ are the single-particle functions for the κth mode, and $g_{j_\kappa}^{(\kappa)}(Q_\kappa)$ the GWP basis (or any suitable set of parametrised functions). The single-particle functions are in turn described by a time-independent basis set, such as a discrete variable representation (DVR) [2, 13]:

$$\varphi_{j_\kappa}^{(\kappa)}(Q,t) = \sum_{\alpha} c_{j\alpha}(t)\chi_\alpha(Q) \quad , \tag{2}$$

while the Gaussian functions are defined by

$$g_j(\mathbf{Q},t) = \exp\left(\mathbf{Q}^T \boldsymbol{\zeta}_j \mathbf{Q} + \mathbf{Q}^T \boldsymbol{\xi}_j + \eta_j\right) \quad . \tag{3}$$

Note that the coordinates for the GWP are written here in a vector. Three different sets of equation of motion are then obtained from a variational solution of the time-dependent Schrödinger equation:

$$i\dot{A}_j = \sum_{lk} S_{jk}^{-1}\left(\langle\Phi_k|H|\Phi_l\rangle - i\langle g_k|\frac{\partial}{\partial t}g_l\rangle\right) A_l \tag{4}$$

$$i\dot{\varphi}^{(\kappa)} = \left(1 - P^{(\kappa)}\right)\left(\rho^{(\kappa)}\right)^{-1}\langle\mathbf{H}\rangle^{(\kappa)}\varphi^{(\kappa)} \tag{5}$$

$$i\dot{\boldsymbol{\Lambda}} = \mathbf{C}^{-1}\mathbf{Y} \quad . \tag{6}$$

The first if for the expansion coefficients, the second for the single-particle functions and the third for the GWP parameters collected together as a vector. For a derivation and full explanation of the terms see Ref. 4.

For vMCG only Eq. (4) and Eq. (6) are relevant. For the expansion coefficients, the evolution depends on the Hamiltonian matrix in the GWP basis (for vMCG the configuration function Φ_J is simply the Gaussian function g_j), on the overlap of the GWP basis through the overlap matrix, S, and its time-derivative. The matrix $\mathbf{C}$ and vector $\mathbf{Y}$ required for the evolution of the GWP parameters are functions of moments of the Hamiltonian and overlap matrix.

On purpose, the GWPs have been written in the general form Eq. (3) so as not to bias the method towards any notion of underlying classical behaviour. Note that in principle it is possible to use either *thawed* or *frozen* GWPs, depending on whether the width matrix $\boldsymbol{\zeta}$ is included in the evolving parameters or not. It

115

has been found, however, that frozen GWPs result in a more stable and efficient propagation. The connection to the more common, Heller-form for a GWP can be made using the relationship

$$\xi_{j\alpha} = -2\zeta_{j\alpha}q_{j\alpha} + ip_{j\alpha} \tag{7}$$

where $(q_{j\alpha}, p_{j\alpha})$ are real functions describing the position and momentum of the centre of a function j for degree of freedom α.

Using this relationship equations for motion for the center of vMCG GWPs can be obtained. These are found to be strongly coupled and non-classical. However, if the basis set is **complete**, i.e.

$$P = \sum_{ij} |g_i\rangle S_{ij}^{-1} \langle g_j| = 1 \tag{8}$$

then

$$\dot{q}_{j\alpha} = \frac{p_{j\alpha}}{m_\alpha}$$

$$\dot{p}_{j\alpha} = -V'_{j\alpha} - \frac{4\zeta_{j\beta}^2}{m_\beta}q_{j\alpha} + \sum_{\beta \neq \alpha} V''_{j\alpha\beta}q_{l\beta}$$

and some classical structure starts to emerge. Furthermore, for coherent states in a harmonic potential, the width can be taken as

$$\zeta_{j\alpha} = \frac{m_\alpha \omega_\alpha}{2} \quad ; \quad V''_\alpha = m_\alpha \omega_\alpha^2$$

and the GWPs follow classical trajectories [8].

The properties of the vMCG method are exemplified in the results shown in Fig. 1. These plots show the results of calculations on the 4-dimensional Henon-Heiles potential of Brewer [14]. The left hand panel (a) shows that the converged spectrum is obtained using only a few hundred GWPs rather than the 1000s needed by classical trajectory based semi-classical methods. The right hand panel, (b), shows how the coupling between the GWPs leads to the correct description of tunnelling, a quantum mechanical phenomenon that cannot be described using classical trajectory based methods. The calculation here used a 1-dimensional unbound potential and described a wavefunction using 2 GWPs. The initial conditions set up the wavefunction with a Gaussian with energy below the barrier and on the other side of the well from it. This meant that effectively one GWP was initially populated and placed in the desired position. The classical trajectory from this point is shown in bold on the lower figure as an oscillating function. In the vMCG calculation, the initially populated GWP follows close to this trajectory, but as shown in the upper panel the energy drops and the trajectory is damped. This energy loss is taken up by the initially unpopulated GWP that escapes the well by "going over" the barrier. The ability of vMCG to also describe the behaviour of non-adiabatic state-crossing has also been demonstrated [8, 10].

116

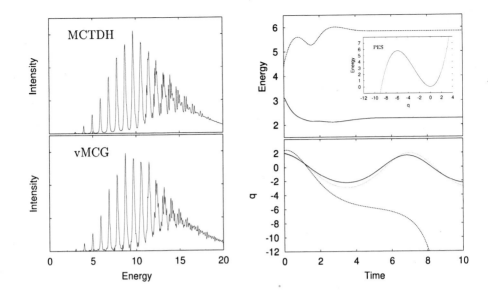

FIG. 1: The vMCG method applied to the four-dimensional Henon-Heiles potential. (a) The spectrum. The MCTDH calculation is the exact result obtained using grid-based wavepacket propagation, while vMCG used two sets of 25 2-dimensional GWPs. (b) Tunnelling through a barrier. The inset shows the potential, and the upper panel the energy of two GWPs. The total energy is below the barrier. The lower panel shows the trajectories of the GWPs, compared to the classical trajectory for the initial conditions in bold. Taken from [5]

Acknowledgements. Irene Burghardt derived the original G-MCTDH equations of motion and is involved in the implementation of the method in a development version of the Heidelberg MCTDH code [15]. Benjamin Lasorne is responsible for the implementation of the direct dynamics code. Hans-Dieter Meyer and Mike Robb have been influential in solving various problems involved with the implementation of the method.

[1] H.-D. Meyer, U. Manthe and L. S. Cederbaum, Chem. Phys. Lett. **165** (1990) 73.

[2] M. H. Beck, A. Jäckle, G. A. Worth and H.-D. Meyer, Phys. Rep. **324** (2000) 1.

[3] H.-D. Meyer, F. Gatti and G. A. Worth, eds., High dimensional quantum dynamics: Basic Theory, Extensions, and Applications of the MCTDH method (VCH, Weinheim, Germany, 2008), in press.

[4] I. Burghardt, H.-D. Meyer and L. S. Cederbaum, J. Chem. Phys. **111** (1999) 2927.

[5] G. Worth and I. Burghardt, Chem. Phys. Lett. **368** (2003) 502.

[6] G. A. Worth, H.-D. Meyer, H. Köppel, L. S. Cederbaum and I. Burghardt, Int. Rev. Phys. Chem. **27** (2008) 569.

[7] A. Raab, G. Worth, H.-D. Meyer and L. S. Cederbaum, J. Chem. Phys. **110** (1999) 936.

[8] I. Burghardt, K. Giri and G. A. Worth, J. Chem. Phys. **129** (2008) 174104.

[9] I. Burghardt, M. Nest and G. A. Worth, J. Chem. Phys. **119** (2003) 5364.

[10] G. A. Worth, M. A. Robb and I. Burghardt, Farad. Discuss. **127** (2004) 307.

[11] G. A. Worth and M. A. Robb, Adv. Chem. Phys. **124** (2002) 355.

[12] G. A. Worth, M. A. Robb and B. Lasorne, Mol. Phys. **106** (2008) 2077.

[13] J. C. Light, I. P. Hamilton and J. V. Lill, J. Chem. Phys. **82** (1985) 1400.

[14] M. L. Brewer, J. Chem. Phys. **111** (1999) 6168.

[15] G. A. Worth, M. H. Beck, A. Jäckle, I. Burghardt, , B. Lasorne and H.-D. Meyer, The MCTDH Package, Development Version 9.0, (2008).

D. Shalashilin and M. P. de Miranda (eds.)
Multidimensional Quantum Mechanics with Trajectories
© 2009, CCP6, Daresbury

Coupled Coherent States and other Gaussian-based techniques for quantum propagation from the time-dependent variational principle

Dmitrii V. Shalashilin*
*School of Chemistry, Bangor University,
Bangor, Gwynedd LL57 2UW, UK.*

Irene Burghardt
*Département de Chimie, Ecole Normale Supérieure,
24 rue Lhomond, F-75231 Paris Cedex 05, France*

I. INTRODUCTION

It is well known that the time dependence of a wave function $\Psi(\alpha_1, \alpha_2, \ldots, \alpha_n)$ is simply that of its parameters, and equations for the "trajectories" $\alpha_n(t)$ can be worked out from the variational principle

$$\delta S = 0 \tag{1}$$

by minimizing the action $S = \int L dt$ of the Lagrangian

$$L(\alpha_1^*, \alpha_2^*, \ldots, \alpha_n^*, \alpha_1, \alpha_2, \ldots, \alpha_n) =$$
$$= \langle \Psi(\alpha_1^*, \alpha_2^*, \ldots, \alpha_n^*) | i\frac{\hat{\partial}}{\partial t} - \hat{H} | \Psi(\alpha_1, \alpha_2, \ldots, \alpha_n) \rangle \tag{2}$$

with respect to the parameters of the wave function [1,2]. Everywhere in this article the time derivative operator

$$i\frac{\hat{\partial}}{\partial t} = \frac{i}{2} \left(\frac{\overrightarrow{\partial}}{\partial t} - \frac{\overleftarrow{\partial}}{\partial t} \right) \tag{3}$$

---

*Electronic address: d.shalashilin@leeds.ac.uk

119

is taken as a half sum of two parts acting on the ket $i\frac{\partial}{\partial t}$ or on the bra $-i\frac{\partial}{\partial t}$, respectively.

The variational principle (1) straightforwardly leads to the Lagrange equations of motion

$$\frac{\partial L}{\partial \alpha_l} - \frac{d}{dt}\frac{\partial L}{\partial \dot{\alpha}_l} = 0, \tag{4}$$

and an adjoint equation for the complex conjugate. Therefore the remarkable fact shown first in the Ref. 2 is that the dynamical equations obtained from the Lagrangian exhibit a symplectic structure, similarly to the equations of classical mechanics.

The goal of this article is to systematically apply the variational principle (1,2) and the Lagrange equations (4) to the wave function expressed as a superposition of Frozen Gaussian (FG) wave packets also known as Coherent States (CS).

II. THEORY

First let us apply variational principle to function expressed by a single frozen Gaussian CS as

$$|\Psi\rangle = a|z\rangle \tag{5}$$

where CS $|z\rangle$ the coordinate representation coherent states are Gaussian wave packets

$$\langle x|z\rangle = \left(\frac{\gamma}{\pi}\right)^{1/4}\exp\left(-\frac{\gamma}{2}(x-q)^2 + \frac{i}{\hbar}p(x-q) + \frac{ipq}{2\hbar}\right) \tag{6}$$

with q and p representing the position and the momentum of the wave packet

$$z = \frac{\gamma^{1/2}q + i\hbar^{-1}\gamma^{-1/2}p}{\sqrt{2}} \qquad z^* = \frac{\gamma^{1/2}q - i\hbar^{-1}\gamma^{-1/2}p}{\sqrt{2}} \tag{7}$$

Parameter γ represents the width of the CS and is constant for a Frozen Gaussian CS. The Lagrangian then becomes

$$L = \langle\Psi|i\frac{\partial}{\partial t} - \hat{H}|\Psi\rangle = i\left[\frac{a^*\dot{a}}{2} - \frac{a\dot{a}^*}{2}\right]\langle z|z\rangle + i\left[\frac{z^*\dot{z}}{2} - \frac{z\dot{z}^*}{2}\right]a^*a - a^*aH_{\mathrm{ord}}(z,z^*) \tag{8}$$

where $\langle z|z\rangle = 1$, and according to (15)

$$\langle\Psi|\hat{H}|\Psi\rangle = \langle az|\hat{H}|az\rangle = a^*a\langle z|z\rangle H_{\mathrm{ord}}(z,z^*) = a^*aH_{\mathrm{ord}}(z,z^*) \tag{9}$$

and the solution of Lagrange equations can be easily found both for a and z yielding the trajectory of z, which obeys the Hamilton's equation

$$\dot{z} = -i\frac{\partial H_{\mathrm{ord}}(z, z^*)}{\partial z^*} \qquad (10)$$

and familiar solution for the amplitude

$$a = a(0)\exp(iS) \qquad (11)$$

where

$$S = \int \left[i\frac{\dot{z}z^* - \dot{z}^*z}{2} - H_{\mathrm{ord}}(z, z^*) \right] dt \qquad (12)$$

is the action.

Now let us consider a more generic wave function represented as a superposition of several CS

$$|\Psi\rangle = \sum_{\ell=1}^{N} a_\ell |z_\ell\rangle \qquad (13)$$

Applying variational principle in exactly the same way as above leads to a set of coupled equations for the derivatives of the wave function parameters $\alpha = (a_1 \ldots a_N, z_1 \ldots z_N)$, which can be written as a system of linear equations for the time derivatives

$$A_\alpha \dot{\alpha} = b_\alpha \qquad (14)$$

When resolved the equations for the classical variables z include forces acting on classical variables from quantum amplitudes and vice-versa. The exact form of the matrix A_α and right hand side b_α can be found in [3]. The Eqs. (14) are simply the Lagrange equation (4) equivalent to those of G-MCTDH/vMCG methods.

Let us now notice that we are not obliged to apply the variational principle to all parameters of the wave function (13). While an "optimal" time evolution will only be obtained for the subset of variational parameters, reasonable assumptions can be introduced for the remaining set of non-variational parameters. For example, we are free to choose the CS trajectories $z_i(t)$ and obtain Lagrange equations of motion to the amplitudes only. It seems reasonable to choose trajectories $z_i(t)$ which are optimal for a single CS, *i.e.* obey Hamilton's equation (10) obtained by applying the variational principle to the single CS wave function (5). It is also convenient to present the amplitudes as

$$a_j = d_j \exp(iS_j) \qquad (15)$$

where S is the action (12). Then the equations for a smooth preexponential factor d rather than for the rapidly oscillating amplitude a. The results are the familiar equations of the CCS theory (see, $e.g.$, Eq. (85) in Ref. [6]),

$$\sum_j \langle z_\ell | z_j \rangle \dot{d}_j \exp(iS_j) = -i \sum_j \Delta^2 H'_{\ell j} d_j \exp(iS_j) \qquad (16)$$

where

$$\Delta^2 H'_{\ell j} = \langle z_\ell | z_j \rangle \delta^2 H'_{\ell j} \qquad (17)$$

and

$$\delta^2 H'_{\ell j} = \left[H_{\mathrm{ord}}(z_\ell^*, z_j) - H_{\mathrm{ord}}(z_j^*, z_j) - i(z_\ell^* - z_j^*)\dot{z}_j \right] \qquad (18)$$

which in CCS becomes

$$\delta^2 H'_{\ell j} = \left[H_{\mathrm{ord}}(z_\ell^*, z_j) - H_{\mathrm{ord}}(z_j^*, z_j) - (z_\ell^* - z_j^*)\frac{\partial H(z_j^*, z_j)}{\partial z_j^*} \right] \qquad (19)$$

Thus the CCS equations for the amplitudes will be represented as a system of linear equations

$$A_d \dot{d} = b_d \qquad (20)$$

which is again a Lagrange equation.

Instead of choosing CS trajectories $z_i(t)$ and applying the variational principle to the amplitudes let us now assume certain "trajectories" $a_i(t)$ for the amplitude oscillations and apply the variational principle to the CS phase space positions z_i only.

$$A_z \dot{z} = b_z \qquad (21)$$

The equations (21) represent a peculiar possibility to make the Frozen Gaussian approximation [7] (Eq.(11)) exact at the expense of coupling trajectories via equations obtained from the variation of the classical z variable only. This can be done by imposing the "trajectories" of the quantum amplitudes, as the solution (11) that would be optimal for a single CS wave function, and applying the variational principle to z only. This approach , which we call Coupled Coherent States Trajectories (CCST) is opposite to the CCS method, where the trajectories of the classical variables z were set and the variational principle was applied to the amplitudes.

III. DISCUSSION AND CONCLUSIONS

In this article we used the variational principle Eq. (1) to derive various forms of equations for the evolution of the parameters of the wave function (13). The wave function has been chosen to be a superposition of Frozen Gaussian Coherent States carrying quantum amplitude. Then CS phase space positions z and their quantum amplitudes a were treated on the same footing as "quasi-classical" variables. Their trajectories were determined from Lagrange equations. The derivation allows easy comparison of different methods.

The idea that the oscillations of quantum amplitudes are mathematically equivalent to those of a system of coupled classical oscillators is not new (see for instance [2]), but in the present approach the quantum oscillations of a are also coupled with the oscillations of the classical variables z. This slightly unorthodox view may lead us in new directions. For example, it is appealing to apply the methods of classical statistical mechanics to the Lagrange equation (4) in which classical and quantum "oscillators" are treated at the same classical-like level of description, determined by the symplectic structure of the variational parameter dynamics [2].

---

[1] S. I. Sawada, R. Heather, B. Jackson, H. Metiu, J. Chem. Phys., **83**, 3009 (1985), S. I. Sawada, H. Metiu, J. Chem. Phys., **84**, 227 (1986).
[2] P. Kramer and M. Saraceno, *Geometry of the Time-Dependent Variational Principle in Quantum Mechanics* (Springer, NewYork, 1981), A. K. Kerman and S. E. Koonin, Ann. Phys. **100**, 332 (1976), D. J. Rowe, A. Ryman, and G. Rosensteel, Phys. Rev. A, **22**, 2362 (1980), J. Broeckhove, L. Lathouwers, E. Kesteloot, and P. V. Leuven, Chem. Phys. Lett., **149**, 547 (1988), A. D. McLachlan, Mol. Phys. **8**, 39 (1964).
[3] D. V. Shalashilin and I. Burghardt J. Chem. Phys. **129**, 084104 (2008).
[4] I. Burghardt, H.-D. Meyer, and L. S. Cederbaum, J. Chem. Phys., **111**, 2927 (1999).
[5] G. A. Worth and I. Burghardt, Chem. Phys. Lett. **368**, 502 (2003), I. Burghardt, M. Nest, and G.A. Worth, J. Chem. Phys. **119**, 5364 (2003), I. Burghardt, K. Giri, and G. A. Worth, to be submitted.
[6] D. V. Shalashilin and M. S. Child, Chem. Phys., **304**, 103 (2004).
[7] E. J. Heller, J. Chem. Phys., **75** 2923 (1981).

D. Shalashilin and M. P. de Miranda (eds.)
Multidimensional Quantum Mechanics with Trajectories
© 2009, CCP6, Daresbury

The G-MCTDH method: correlated system-bath dynamics using Gaussian wavepackets

I. Burghardt,[1,][*] R. Martinazzo,[2] F. Martelli,[1,][2] and G. A. Worth[3]

[1]*Département de Chimie, Ecole Normale Supérieure,*
24 rue Lhomond, 75231 Paris cedex 05, France
[2]*Department of Physical Chemistry and Electrochemistry,*
University of Milan, Via Golgi 19, 20133 Milan, Italy
[3]*School of Chemistry, University of Birmingham, Birmingham, UK*

I. INTRODUCTION

The G-MCTDH (Gaussian-based multiconfiguration time-dependent Hartree) method [1–4] provides a general variational framework for combining a multi-configurational form of the wavefunction (or density operator) with the use of parametrized time-dependent basis functions, and more specifically with a Gaussian basis. G-MCTDH was proposed in 1999 as a hybrid quantum-semiclassical variant of the parent MCTDH method [6–9], specifically adapted to the treatment of system-environment type problems. At that point in time, MCTDH itself had started to produce impressive results for comparatively high-dimensional systems. The most prominent example is the 24-mode calculation by Raab et al. [10] for the non-adiabatic dynamics of the pyrazine molecule at the S_2-S_1 conical intersection; this calculation has since served as a benchmark for various approximate quantum dynamics methods. Despite the outstanding efficiency of the method, MCTDH still encounters the exponential scaling problem which is at the root of the limitations inherent in the standard propagation schemes. G-MCTDH is one of the variants of the original MCTDH method that have been designed to further improve the scaling properties and move towards very high-dimensional systems. (Other approaches include, e.g., the multi-layer MCTDH scheme [12, 13]).

Here, we examine the current status of the G-MCTDH method as applied to system-bath type problems. According to [1], hybrid configurations are em-

---

[*]Electronic address: irene.burghardt@ens.fr

ployed which combine fully flexible MCTDH-type single particle functions for a small number of "system" degrees of freedom with multi-dimensional Gaussian functions for a – potentially large – number of bath degrees of freedom. As summarized below, this strategy has been successfully applied to various system-environment type situations, including vibrational relaxation and decoherence [3] as well as multidimensional nonadiabatic dynamics at conical intersections [4, 5]. Our recent study of the pyrazine S_2-S_1 benchmark system [4] shows that convergence can be obtained for the full 24-dimensional quadratic vibronic coupling model [10], using a 4 + 20 mode hybrid scheme. Applications further include recently developed effective-mode formulations within a linear vibronic coupling model [14, 15]. A key feature of all applications is that system-bath correlations are correctly accounted for.

Further, the method has been applied as a purely Gaussian-based approach [2] – denoted vMCG (variational multiconfigurational Gaussian wavepackets) – in direct dynamics calculations using on-the-fly electronic structure calculations to provide the potential energy surfaces [11], see the contribution by G. A. Worth in this volume.

Finally, we compare below with other variational and non-variational schemes using moving Gaussian basis sets, showing that G-MCTDH yields several generalized coherent-state methods a special cases. These include the Coupled Coherent States (CCS) method by Shalashilin and Child [16, 17] and the Local Coherent State Approximation (LCSA) by Martinazzo and collaborators [18]. A series of approximations can thus be derived which represent the quasi-classical bath dynamics to varying degrees of accuracy.

II. G-MCTDH THEORY

In the following, a brief outline is given of the G-MCTDH approach, see Refs. 1–4. The formal structure underlying the method is very general and results from the application of a time-dependent variational principle (here, in the Dirac-Frenkel form [8, 19–24]) to a parametrized wavefunction. In practice, Gaussian basis functions are a very convenient choice, due to the quasi-classical dynamics associated with Gaussian wavepackets, along with the fact that analytical expressions can be given for the matrix elements appearing in the equations of motion.

A. Wavefunction ansatz

Similarly to the parent MCTDH method [6–8] the G-MCTDH variant [1–3] uses a multiconfigurational wavefunction ansatz. For coupled electronic states, the wavefunction takes the form $|\Psi\rangle = \sum_{s=1}^{r} \Psi^{(s)}|s\rangle$, with components

$$\Psi^{(s)}(\mathbf{r}_1, \ldots, \mathbf{r}_P, t) = \sum_J A_J^{(s)}(t)\Phi_J^{(s)}(\mathbf{r}_1, \ldots, \mathbf{r}_P, t) \tag{1}$$

where the configurations $\Phi_J^{(s)}$ correspond to Hartree products composed of a class of "primary" modes ($\kappa = 1, \cdots, M$) and a class of "secondary" modes ($\kappa = M+1, \cdots, P$) [1, 3, 4]

$$\Phi_J^{(s)}(\mathbf{r}_1, \ldots, \mathbf{r}_P, t) = \prod_{\kappa=1}^{M} \varphi_{j_\kappa}^{(\kappa s)}(\mathbf{r}_\kappa, t) \prod_{\kappa=M+1}^{P} g_{j_\kappa}^{(\kappa s)}(\mathbf{r}_\kappa, t) \tag{2}$$

Here, the $\varphi_j^{(\kappa s)}$ represent the general time-dependent single particle functions (SPFs) of the standard MCTDH method [8] while the $g_j^{(\kappa s)}$ are time-dependent Gaussian wavepackets (GWPs),

$$g_j^{(\kappa s)}(\mathbf{r}_\kappa, t) = \exp[\mathbf{r}_\kappa \cdot \mathbf{a}_j^{(\kappa s)}(t) \cdot \mathbf{r}_\kappa + \boldsymbol{\xi}_j^{(\kappa s)}(t) \cdot \mathbf{r}_\kappa + \eta_j^{(\kappa s)}(t)] \tag{3}$$

with the set of complex parameters $\Lambda_j^{(\kappa s)}(t) = \{\mathbf{a}_j^{(\kappa s)}(t), \boldsymbol{\xi}_j^{(\kappa s)}(t), \eta_j^{(\kappa s)}(t)\}$ where $\mathbf{a}_j^{(\kappa s)}$ is a complex symmetric matrix, $\boldsymbol{\xi}_j^{(\kappa s)}$ is a complex vector, and $\eta_j^{(\kappa s)}$ is a complex number. Using the relation $\boldsymbol{\xi} = -2\mathbf{a} \cdot \mathbf{q} + i\mathbf{p}$, the Gaussian form Eq. (3) can be re-written so as to conform to the expression familiar from the work by Heller [25–27], where $(\mathbf{p}, \mathbf{q})$ are real quantities referring to the time-dependent center position and momentum. Starting from the form Eq. (3), we will distinguish "thawed" Gaussians (TG) whose width matrix $\mathbf{a}_j^{(\kappa s)}$ is taken as a time-dependent variational parameter, from "frozen" Gaussians (FG) [26], whose width matrix is fixed. In the present applications, we focus on FG functions which are as a rule more robust numerically than TG functions. Note that each of the modes, or "particles" κ can be multidimensional. Indeed a key aspect of both MCTDH and G-MCTDH is the combination of (potentially many) degrees of freedom in such multidimensional particles.

B. Dynamical equations

Equations of motion for the time-dependent coefficients $A_J^{(s)}$, time-dependent SPFs $\varphi_j^{(\kappa s)}$, and time-dependent GWP parameters $\Lambda_j^{(\kappa s)}$ of the ansatz Eqs. (1)–(3) can be derived *via* the Dirac-Frenkel variational principle, $\langle \delta\Psi|H - i\partial/\partial t|\Psi\rangle = 0$ [1]. This leads to coupled equations for all components of the wavefunction ansatz, as briefly summarized here.

126

1. Expansion coefficients

The dynamical equation for the coefficient vector $\boldsymbol{A}$ is obtained as follows [1],

$$i\dot{\boldsymbol{A}}^{(s)} = [\boldsymbol{S}^{(s)}]^{-1}\left[\sum_{s'}\boldsymbol{H}^{(ss')} - i\boldsymbol{\tau}^{(s)}\,\delta(s-s')\right]\boldsymbol{A}^{(s')} \tag{4}$$

involving the time dependent overlap matrix $S_{jl}^{(\kappa s)} = \langle g_j^{(\kappa s)}|g_l^{(\kappa s)}\rangle$ as well as the differential overlap $\tau_{jl}^{(\kappa s)} = \langle g_j^{(\kappa s)}|\dot{g}_l^{(\kappa s)}\rangle = \sum_\alpha S_{jl}^{(\kappa s,0\alpha)}\dot{\lambda}_{l\alpha}^{(\kappa s)}$. The latter plays a role similar to the constraint operator of standard MCTDH [8] and reflects the dynamical coupling between the coefficients and GWP parameters.

2. Primary-mode single-particle functions

With regard to the SPFs of the "primary" subspace, the dynamical equations keep the same form as in conventional MCTDH [1],

$$i\dot{\boldsymbol{\varphi}}^{(\kappa s)} = \left(\hat{1} - \hat{P}^{(\kappa s)}\right)\left[\boldsymbol{\rho}^{(\kappa s)}\right]^{-1}\sum_{s'}\hat{H}^{(\kappa,ss')}\boldsymbol{\varphi}^{(\kappa s')} \tag{5}$$

with the projector $\hat{P}^{(\kappa s)}$, the reduced density matrices $\boldsymbol{\rho}^{(\kappa s)}$, and the matrix of mean-field Hamiltonian operators $\hat{H}_{jl}^{(\kappa,ss')}$ [6–8]. Due to the projector $(\hat{1} - \hat{P}^{(\kappa s)}) = (\hat{1} - \sum_j |\varphi_j^{(\kappa s)}\rangle\langle\varphi_j^{(\kappa s)}|)$, for $\kappa = 1,\ldots,M$, Eq. (5) captures the portion of the evolution which takes one out of the space defined by the instantaneous basis set.

3. Secondary-mode parametrized functions

Finally, the dynamics of the Gaussian parameter vector $\boldsymbol{\Lambda}^{(\kappa s)}$ in the "secondary" subspace is determined by the following equation [1],

$$i\dot{\boldsymbol{\Lambda}}^{(\kappa s)} = \left[\boldsymbol{C}^{(\kappa s)}\right]^{-1}\boldsymbol{Y}^{(\kappa s)} \tag{6}$$

where the r.h.s. involves the inverse of the matrix $\boldsymbol{C}$ multiplied by the vector $\boldsymbol{Y}$,

$$C_{j\alpha,l\beta}^{(\kappa s)} = \rho_{jl}^{(\kappa s)}\langle\frac{\partial g_j^{(\kappa s)}}{\partial\lambda_{j\alpha}^{(\kappa s)}}\Big|(\hat{1} - \hat{P}^{(\kappa s)})\Big|\frac{\partial g_l^{(\kappa s)}}{\partial\lambda_{l\beta}^{(\kappa s)}}\rangle \tag{7}$$

$$Y_{j\alpha}^{(\kappa s)} = \sum_{s'}\sum_l\langle\frac{\partial g_j^{(\kappa s)}}{\partial\lambda_{j\alpha}^{(\kappa s)}}\Big|(\hat{1} - \hat{P}^{(\kappa s)})\hat{H}_{jl}^{(\kappa,ss')}\Big|g_l^{(\kappa s')}\rangle \tag{8}$$

The dimensionality of these quantities is $n_\kappa \times n_p$, where n_κ is the number of GWPs and n_p is the number of parameters associated with a given Gaussian particle. Eqs. (7)–(8) again involve a projector $\hat{P}^{(\kappa s)} = \sum_{jl} [S^{(\kappa s)}]_{jl}^{-1} |g_j^{(\kappa s)}\rangle\langle g_l^{(\kappa s)}|$ for $\kappa = M+1, \ldots, P$, which now takes into account the non-orthogonality of the basis functions. All matrix elements of Eqs. (7)–(8) are calculated in terms of Gaussian moments, using a local harmonic approximation for the potential [1–3].

For a single, multidimensional Gaussian in a given electronic state s and moving in a mean field generated by the primary modes, the classical-like equations of motion by Heller [25–27] are recovered. In the general case, the multiconfigurational form leads to a "non-classical" coupling between the Gaussian functions, which significantly modifies the trajectories as compared with a purely classical evolution.

C. Why $i\dot{\Lambda} = C^{-1}Y$?

The structure of Eqs. (6)–(8) for the parameter evolution results from the application of the variational principle to a parameter-dependent wavefunction. As pointed out in [19, 20, 22], these equations exhibit a symplectic structure – very similar to the Hamilton's equations of classical mechanics. This structure follows from the analogy of the quantum Lagrangian $L = \langle H \rangle - i\langle \psi | (\partial \psi / \partial \lambda_\alpha) \rangle \dot{\lambda}_\alpha$ and the classical Lagrangian $L = H - p\dot{q}$. In this sense, the Gaussian parameter dynamics is indeed pseudo-classical, and reduces to the classical equations of motion if applied to a single GWP. From a more general perspective, Ref. 28 points out that the dynamics of both the expansion coefficients and wavefunction parameters is formally treated on the same footing by the variational approach.

D. Comparison to other methods

G-MCTDH uses the most general realization of a multiconfigurational, variational approach involving parametrized basis functions. The method includes several other approaches as special cases, notably the variational Gaussian wavepacket method by Sawada and Metiu [29, 30] and the recently developed local coherent state approximation (LCSA) by Martinazzo et al. [18]. This latter method can in fact be considered as a "selected configurations" version of G-MCTDH, with a wavefunction ansatz of the form Eq. (1) but a restricted set of configurations $\Phi_j^{(s)} = \varphi_j^{(\kappa s)} g_j^{(\kappa' s)}$, where each bath configuration is attached to a given system configuration carrying the same index j. This leads to a diagonal form of the C matrix [18], i.e.,

$$\tilde{C}_{j\alpha,l\beta}^{(\kappa s)} = \delta_{jl} \rho_{jl}^{(\kappa s)} \langle \frac{\partial g_j^{(\kappa s)}}{\partial \lambda_{j\alpha}^{(\kappa s)}} \Big| (\hat{1} - \hat{P}_l^{(\kappa s)}) \Big| \frac{\partial g_l^{(\kappa s)}}{\partial \lambda_{l\beta}^{(\kappa s)}} \rangle \tag{9}$$

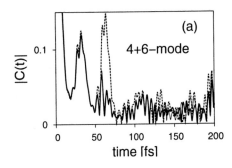 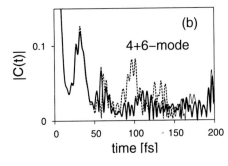

FIG. 1: Convergence properties of 4+6-mode G-MCTDH hybrid calculations for the second-order vibronic coupling model for the pyrazine molecule (reproduced from Ref. 4). (a) The results of two G-MCTDH calculations are compared with the standard MCTDH (exact) result. The first G-MCTDH calculation (dashed line) employs the same number of particles as compared with the standard MCTDH calculation (thin solid line). The second calculation (bold solid line) has an augmented GWP basis in the secondary subspace (i.e., 20 instead of 5-8 functions per particle), and can be considered converged. (b) For comparison, a vMCG calculation (dashed line) with 20 GWPs per particle is shown; here, the converged hybrid G-MCTDH calculation (bold solid line) and reference MCTDH calculation (thin solid line) are also reproduced. The vMCG calculation is significantly harder to converge than the G-MCTDH hybrid calculations.

where $\hat{P}_l^{(\kappa s)} = |g_l^{(\kappa s)}\rangle\langle g_l^{(\kappa s)}|$. Approximations based on the LCSA zeroth-order picture could be promising in future developments of the G-MCTDH algorithm.

Furthermore, several methods which involve non-variational, classically evolving Gaussian basis sets can be understood as special cases of the full variational approach. These include, in particular, the coupled coherent states (CCS) method of Shalashilin and Child and the Full Multiple Spawning (FMS) method by Martínez and collaborators [31–33], which introduces the added feature of an adaptive basis set.

III. APPLICATION: PYRAZINE VIBRONIC COUPLING MODEL

Applications of the G-MCTDH method to several system-bath type problems have been described in Refs. 3–5. These applications include vibrational energy relaxation and decoherence [3], typically involving 20-60 explicit bath modes, as well as non-adiabatic dynamics according to linear and quadratic vibronic coupling models [4, 5], again involving around 20-30 modes. In these examples, the dynamics was shown to be very close to the exact MCTDH results.

Here, we focus on our recent results for the 24-mode second-order vibronic

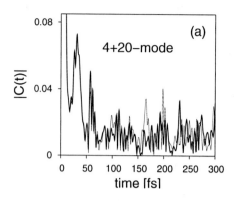 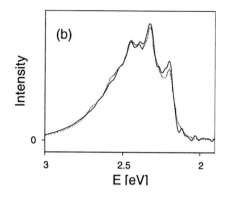

FIG. 2: G-MCTDH 24-mode calculation for the model by Raab et al. [10], according to Ref. 4. (a) Autocorrelation function for the G-MCTDH calculation (bold trace) using 6962400 configurations and 1644 MB memory as compared with a standard MCTDH calculation (thin trace) using 10966760 configurations and 2614 MB memory. Both calculations are near convergence. (b) Comparison of the spectrum obtained by Fourier transformation from a G-MCTDH autocorrelation function (full line) with the experimental spectrum of Ref. 34 (dotted line).

coupling model for the pyrazine molecule [4]. This model has been employed in the benchmark calculations by Raab et al. [10]; due to its marked anharmonicity, this model poses a challenge for both standard MCTDH and G-MCTDH. In Ref. 4, we have used improved MCTDH calculations as a reference, and carried out G-MCTDH calculations in a comparable convergence domain.

Since a subset of four modes are strongly coupled to the electronic subsystem, we use a 4+20 mode system-bath type partitioning which fits naturally into the G-MCTDH concept. In Ref. 4, we have successively tested G-MCTDH for 4-mode and 10-mode reduced models, as well as the full (4+20)-dimensional model. We report here on selected results of this study, see Figs. 1 and 2 which illustrate the convergence properties of the G-MCTDH calculations.

IV. CONCLUSIONS

The calculations for the highly anharmonic pyrazine system illustrate the feasibility of the G-MCTDH method, with the use of typically 10-20 basis functions per GWP "bath" mode, as compared with 3-10 SPFs per mode in the reference MCTDH calculations. The larger number of basis functions is not surprising, given that the FG functions used here are highly constrained as compared with the fully flexible single-particle functions of standard MCTDH. If the most strongly coupled "system" modes are treated as GWP particles as

130

well, convergence is much harder to achieve. For the reduced 4-mode system, we have shown [4] that the all-Gaussian vMCG approach requires of the order of 100 basis functions per GWP mode. The use of G-MCTDH as a hybrid method is therefore a good strategy to obtain accurate calculations in high-dimensional systems that allow a system-bath type partitioning.

Given that the numerical difficulties associated with time-dependent Gaussian basis sets are well known from previous work, the stability and efficiency of the G-MCTDH algorithm hinges on several aspects including (i) the use of normalized FG functions ("coherent state gauge") as compared with non-normalized functions or of TG functions, (ii) the regularization of singularities when encountered in the evolution of the S and C matrices, and (iii) the adaptation of the integration scheme to the rapid phase oscillations that are manifest in the time-dependent S matrix [4]. Further improvements could involve suitable approximations to the inversion of the C matrix, which would be based upon the LCSA approximation – i.e., a diagonal form of the C matrix – as a zeroth-order scheme, as well as the possibility of eliminating rapidly oscillating phase factors, by analogy with a similar strategy used in the CCS approach (see Ref. 28 for a discussion of this aspect). Variational Gaussian basis sets should thus provide a route to accurate quantum propagation in many dimensions.

Acknowledgements. We thank Dmitry Shalashilin for many insightful discussions.

[1] I. Burghardt, H.-D. Meyer, and L. S. Cederbaum, J. Chem. Phys. **111**, 2927 (1999).

[2] G. A. Worth and I. Burghardt, Chem. Phys. Lett. **368**, 502 (2003).

[3] I. Burghardt, M. Nest, and G. A. Worth, J. Chem. Phys. **119**, 5364 (2003).

[4] I. Burghardt, K. Giri, and G. A. Worth, J. Chem. Phys. **129**, 174104 (2008).

[5] I. Burghardt and G. A. Worth, Quantum dynamical modeling of ultrafast processes in complex molecular systems: multiconfigurational system-bath dynamics using Gaussian wavepackets, in *Femtochemistry and Femtobiology–Ultrafast Events in Molecular Science*, edited by M. M. Martin and J. T. Hynes, Elsevier, 2004.

[6] H.-D. Meyer, U. Manthe, and L. S. Cederbaum, Chem. Phys. Lett. **165**, 73 (1990).

[7] U. Manthe, H.-D. Meyer, and L. S. Cederbaum, J. Chem. Phys. **97**, 3199 (1992).

[8] M. H. Beck, A. Jäckle, G. A. Worth, and H.-D. Meyer, Phys. Rep. **324**, 1 (2000).

[9] G. A. Worth, H.-D. Meyer, H. Köppel, L. S. Cederbaum, and I. Burghardt, Int. Rev. Phys. Chem. **27**, 569 (2008).

[10] A. Raab, G. A. Worth, H.-D. Meyer, and L. S. Cederbaum, J. Chem. Phys. **110**, 936 (1999).

[11] G. A. Worth, M. A. Robb, and I. Burghardt, Faraday Discuss. Chem. Soc. **127**, 307 (2004).

[12] H. Wang and M. Thoss, J. Chem. Phys. **119**, 1289 (2003).

[13] I. R. Craig, H. Wang, and M. Thoss, J. Chem. Phys. **127**, 144503 (2007).

[14] L. S. Cederbaum, E. Gindensperger, and I. Burghardt, Phys. Rev. Lett. **94**, 113003 (2005).

[15] H. Tamura, E. R. Bittner, and I. Burghardt, J. Chem. Phys. **126**, 021103 (2007).

[16] D. V. Shalashilin and M. S. Child, J. Chem. Phys. **114**, 9296 (2001).

[17] D. V. Shalashilin and M. S. Child, Chem. Phys. **304**, 103 (2004).

[18] R. Martinazzo, M. Nest, P. Saalfrank, and G. Tantardini, J. Chem. Phys. **125**, 194102 (2006).

[19] P. Kramer and M. Saraceno, *Geometry of the Time-Dependent Variational Principle in Quantum Mechanics*, Springer-Verlag, Berlin Heidelberg New York, 1981.

[20] D. J. Rowe, A. Ryman, and G. Rosensteel, Phys. Rev.A **22**, 2362 (1980).

[21] A. D. McLachlan, Mol. Phys. **8**, 39 (1964).

[22] J. Broeckhove, L. Lathouwers, E. Kesteloot, and P. V. Leuven, Chem. Phys. Lett. **149**, 547 (1988).

[23] P. A. M. Dirac, Proc. Cambridge Philos. Soc. **26**, 376 (1930).

[24] J. Frenkel, *Wave Mechanics*, Clarendon, Oxford, 1934.

[25] E. J. Heller, J. Chem. Phys. **62**, 1544 (1975).

[26] E. J. Heller, J. Chem. Phys. **75**, 2923 (1981).

[27] S.-Y. Lee and E. J. Heller, J. Chem. Phys. **76**, 3035 (1982).

[28] D. V. Shalashilin and I. Burghardt, J. Chem. Phys. **129**, 084104 (2008).

[29] S.-I. Sawada, R. Heather, B. Jackson, and H. Metiu, J. Chem. Phys. **83**, 3009 (1985).

[30] S. Sawada and H. Metiu, J. Chem. Phys. **84**, 227 (1986).

[31] T. J. Martínez, M. Ben-Nun, and R. D. Levine, J. Phys. Chem. **100**, 7884 (1996).

[32] M. Ben-Nun and T. J. Martínez, J. Chem. Phys. **112**, 6113 (2000).

[33] M. Ben-Nun and T. J. Martínez, Adv. Chem. Phys. **121**, 439 (2002).

[34] I. Yamazaki, T. Murao, T. Yamanaka, and K. Yoshihara, Faraday Discuss. Chem. Soc. **75**, 395 (1983).

D. Shalashilin and M. P. de Miranda (eds.)
Multidimensional Quantum Mechanics with Trajectories
© 2009, CCP6, Daresbury

Local Coherent-State approximation
to system-bath quantum dynamics

R. Martinazzo,[1,*] I. Burghardt,[2] F. Martelli,[3] and M. Nest[4]

[1] *Dept. of Physical Chemistry and Electrochemistry,*
University of Milan, Golgi 19, 20113, Milan, Italy
[2] *Dept. de Chemie, Ecole Normal Superieure,*
24 rue Lhomond, f-75231 Paris cedex 05, France
[3] *Dept. de Chemie, Ecole Normal Superieure,*
24 rue Lhomond, f-75231 Paris cedex 05,
France (on leave from Dept. of Physical Chemistry
and Electrochemistry, University of Milan)
[4] *Institute für Chemie, Universität Potsdam,*
Karl-Liebknecht-Strasse 24-25, 14476 Potsdam, Germany

I. INTRODUCTION

System-bath dynamical problems arise naturally in chemical physics, e.g. when studying reactions in condensed phase or gas-surface processes. They represent one of the most challenging issues in current rate theories, especially when the need of a quantum description arises, as in the case of inherently quantum systems (e.g. hydrogen atom transfer in biologically relevant environments), and/or of low temperature media (e.g. the cold surfaces of the interstellar dust grains).

Our way to tackle this kind of problems is a 'brute-force' approach in which one follows the energy-conserving dynamics of a system coupled to a finite-size bath, and observes the dissipative dynamics (of the *system*) for times less than the Poincaré recurrence time. Such a (unitary) description of the total system+bath has been recently become a possible alternative [1–3] to open-system quantum dynamical approaches[4, 5] thanks to recent advances in quantum simulations of large systems. In this context, the main issue is the size of the bath (or, more properly, the average frequency spacing) which sets the limiting time

---

*Electronic address: rocco.martinazzo@unimi.it

scale for observing dissipative behaviour: in typical situations, a few ps process requires thousands of degrees of freedom, and this is beyond current computational possibilities, even for the Multi-Configuration Time-Dependent Hartree (MCTDH) method [6, 7], the most efficient, exact quantum dynamical method currently available. In order to make progress in this direction, some of the present authors have recently introduced a set of approximations, collectively named as Local Coherent-State approximation (LCSA) [8], to the unitary dynamics of a typical system-bath problem. The approximations are mainly in the bath description, whose dynamics is usually of no direct relevance, in the same spirit as in the reduced density operator approach. The resulting 'LCSA' approach turns out to be a selected-configuration MCTDH variant which closely resembles the so-called Gaussian-MCTDH [9–11] method, see below.

II. THEORY

We started by considering a typical system-bath hamiltonian which had been used for a long time to model dissipation (e.g. see Ref. 12–19), namely

$$H = H^{sys} + \sum_{k=1}^{F} \hbar\omega_k(a_k^\dagger a_k + \frac{1}{2}) - \sum_{k=1}^{F}(\lambda_k^\dagger a_k + \lambda_k a_k^\dagger) \tag{1}$$

where H^{sys} is the subsystem Hamiltonian, the second term on the r.h.s. is the Hamiltonian describing a harmonic bath and the third term represents the system-bath coupling, which was assumed to be linear in the bath coordinates but arbitrary in the subsystem coordinates; $a_k^\dagger, a_k$ are the usual harmonic oscillator (HO) raising/lowering operators. We can generalize it by writing

$$H = H^{sys} + H^{env}(..q_k p_k..; \mathbf{x}) \tag{2}$$

where H^{env} is an 'environment' Hamiltonian (now comprising the coupling with the system) which is supposed to be *local* in system coordinates $\mathbf{x}$ and approximately *harmonic* in the bath degrees of freedom $(..q_k, p_k..)$. In this way one can include anharmonic bath oscillators, coupling between bath modes, etc... Our approximations come from the following observations concerning the Hamiltonian of Eq. (2): (i) coupling to the bath is local in subsystem coordinates, and (ii) the bath is approximately harmonic. Then, focusing on a wavefunction description appropriate for the $T = 0$ K case, point (i) suggests the use of subsystem Discrete-Variable-Representation (DVR) states in expanding the wavefunction for the total system, i.e.

$$|\Psi\rangle = \sum_\alpha C_\alpha |\xi_\alpha\rangle |\Phi_\alpha\rangle \tag{3}$$

where $\{|\xi_\alpha\rangle\}$ is a DVR set for the subsystem coordinates, and $|\Phi_\alpha\rangle$ are the resulting *local* bath states, one for each grid point α used to cover the relevant subsystem configuration space. In addition, point (ii) suggests that a product of HO coherent states (CSs) could be appropriate to describe the resulting *local* bath states, i.e.

$$|\Phi_\alpha\rangle = |z_\alpha^1\rangle |z_\alpha^2\rangle .. |z_\alpha^F\rangle := |Z_\alpha\rangle$$

The result is that the bath dynamics is described by a set of coupled, pseudoclassical trajectories $z_\alpha^k = z_\alpha^k(t)$, one for each bath degree of freedom k *and* system grid point α. The system dynamics is contained in the time evolution of the amplitude coefficients C_α, which make an important part of the system reduced density matrix $(\rho_{\alpha\beta} = C_\alpha^* C_\beta \langle Z_\beta | Z_\alpha \rangle$ in the underlying DVR).

At finite temperature $T > 0$ K an analogous approach is possible as long as the initial system+bath density operator ρ^{sb} can be written in the form

$$\rho^{sb} = \sum_i p_i |\Psi_i^{LCSA}\rangle \langle \Psi_i^{LCSA}| \tag{4}$$

where each $|\Psi_i^{LCSA}\rangle$ is a vector of LCSA form (eq. 3), which then undergoes the *same* energy-conserving time-evolution of the $T = 0$ K case. This is the case, for example, when the initial density operator $\rho^{sb}(0)$ can be factorized as $\rho^{sb}(0) = \rho^{sys}(0) \otimes \rho_\beta^{bath}(0)$ and $\rho_\beta^{bath}(0)$ is a thermal density operator of a harmonic bath at temperature $k_B T = \beta^{-1}$. Indeed, using the CS representation of such thermal density operator, a Monte Carlo sampling of the resulting (bath) phase-space integral easily provides the set of 'realizations' of eq.4.

Equations of motion

Equations of motion can be derived with the help of the Dirac-Frenkel variational principle, using C_α and z_α^k as dynamical variables. When using conventional phase factors for the CSs (what we can call the "standard gauge") they take the following form.

The "system equation" is a kind of Schrödinger-Langevin equation

$$i\hbar \dot{C}_\alpha = \sum_\beta H_{\alpha\beta}^{damp} C_\beta + v_\alpha^{eff} C_\alpha$$

in which the elements of the system DVR hamiltonian are *damped* by the overlap between bath states, $H_{\alpha\beta}^{damp} = H_{\alpha\beta}^{sys} \langle Z_\alpha | Z_\beta \rangle$. The local, effective potential, $v^{eff} = v^{lmf} + v^{gauge}$, contains a 'local mean-field' potential

$$v_\alpha^{lmf} = \langle Z_\alpha | H^{env}(\mathbf{x}_\alpha) | Z_\alpha \rangle = H_{ord}^{env}(..z_\alpha^{k*}, z_\alpha^k, ..; \mathbf{x}_\alpha)$$

135

(here H_{ord}^{env} is the environment hamiltonian operator expressed in terms in $a_k^\dagger, a_k$ and normally ordered, i.e. with all $a_k^\dagger$'s on the left of a_k's) and a 'gauge' potential

$$v_\alpha^{gauge} = -i\hbar \sum_{k=1}^F \langle z_\alpha^k | \dot{z}_\alpha^k \rangle = \hbar \sum_{k=1}^F \text{Im}(z_\alpha^{k*} \dot{z}_\alpha^k)$$

which can be explicitly written down with the bath equations below.

The "bath equations" are pseudoclassical equations

$$i\hbar C_\alpha \dot{z}_\alpha^k = \sum_\beta H_{\alpha\beta}^{damp}(z_\beta^k - z_\alpha^k)C_\beta + C_\alpha \frac{\partial H_{ord}^{env}}{\partial a_k^\dagger}(..z_\alpha^k z_\alpha^{k*}, ..; \mathbf{x}_\alpha)$$

containing a 'classical, local force'

$$\dot{z}_{\alpha,class}^k = -\frac{i}{\hbar} \frac{\partial H_{ord}^{env}}{\partial a_k^\dagger}(..z_\alpha^k z_\alpha^{k*}, ..; \mathbf{x}_\alpha)$$

and a 'quantum' one

$$\dot{z}_{\alpha,quant}^k = -\frac{i}{\hbar C_\alpha} \sum_\beta H_{\alpha\beta}^{damp}(z_\beta^k - z_\alpha^k)C_\beta$$

coupling CSs of the *same* degree of freedom at *different* grid points. The latter is essential for a quantum, though approximate, description of the bath dynamics. The above gauge potential can then be easily written down with the help of the matrix

$$\Gamma_{\alpha\beta} = \sum_{k=1}^F z_\alpha^{k*} z_\beta^k$$

which is also useful to evaluate the CSs overlaps, $\langle Z_\alpha | Z_\beta \rangle = exp(\Gamma_{\alpha\beta} - \Gamma_{\alpha\alpha}/2 - \Gamma_{\beta\beta}/2)$. For a derivation of the equations see Ref. 8, and notice that, in general, $[a, f_{ord}(a^\dagger, a)] = \partial f_{ord}(a^\dagger, a)/\partial a^\dagger$.

General properties

The above equations have some interesting properties. Some of them arise from the use of the Dirac-Frenkel variational principle. Norm and energy conservation are guaranteed with our *ansatz* (since it is also an allowed variation) and can be used in practice to check the quality of the propagation. More generally, the solutions of the LCSA equations define a hamiltonian flow in the space of the parameters, i.e. the equations have a symplectic structure that can be

136

used to set up a *robust* propagation scheme. We'll come back to this point in Section IV.

Other properties arise from the LCSA *ansatz* itself. The bath dynamics is reduced to a set of trajectories, whose number scales linearly with the bath dimensions. This means that the method itself has a power-low scaling with such dimensions, the exponent of this scaling depending on the interaction between bath modes. For bath modes coupled to the system only (e.g. with the hamiltonian of Eq. 1) *linear* scaling has been observed and model simulations with tens of thousands of bath degrees of freedom have been performed on modest computers [8]. This good scaling property is in common with mixed quantum-classical methods, which however fail to correctly represent the system-bath correlations. In LCSA a number of trajectories is used for each bath degree of freedom, and they are coupled to each other by the building up of the (quantum) correlation. Note also that in our case the system 'wavefunction' (the amplitude coefficients) enters *linearly* in the bath equations, and therefore phase factors do play a role in the classical dynamics, apart from an overall phase factor.

Coupled trajectories arise in a number of closely related approaches, namely the Coupled-Coherent-State method of Shalashilin and Child [20–23] and the Gaussian-MCTDH method of Burghardt, Worth and coworkers [9–11]. The latter, in particular, is strongly connected with LCSA. The two approaches share a conventional, 'exact' description of some interesting degrees of freedom and an approximate, CS description of other, less interesting degrees of freedom. Indeed, as a matter of fact, the G-MCTDH equations [9] reduce to LCSA ones under suitable constraints (e.g. see Appendix B of Ref. 8). The main difference between the two is that in LCSA *all* the configurations are orthogonal to each other, as a consequence of the presence of a different DVR state in each of them. This leads to considerable simplifications in the resulting equations (see above, in particular, the bath equations), at the price of a reduced accuracy.

Finally, one interesting property about the pseudo-classical description of the bath degrees of freedom is that it suits well to induce *dissipative* dynamics into the total system. This can be accomplished by adding a suitably designed friction coefficient η to the bath equations, mimicking the presence of a *secondary* (infinite, memory-less) bath. More formally, it can be shown that applying the LCSA approximation to a system+bath+secondary bath configuration, a classical approximation to the secondary bath dynamics, and standard assumptions (Ohmic bath in the continuum limit) a friction coefficient appears in the LCSA equations for the system+bath degrees of freedom[28] (e.g. see Appendix A of Ref. 8). This possibility has been exploited, especially in conjunction with the need of removing numerical instabilities of the method without altering the system dynamics. We call such a modified version of our approach the 'damped' LCSA variant, for obvious reasons.

III. APPLICATIONS

The method has been applied to a number of model problems, ranging from tunneling to vibrational relaxation and sticking dynamics, and the results have been compared with those of exact, Multi-Configuration-Time-Dependent-Hartree calculations in systems with up to 80 bath oscillators. A detailed account of such a comparison is given in Ref. 8. Here we merely summarize the main results.

When the method is applied to problems with small dimensional baths (e.g. an oscillator coupled to few HO bath oscillators) it performs rather well, and the results are in close agreement with exact ones. This is particularly true for 1D bath problems, in which LCSA is free of the (local) Hartree approximation, thereby suggesting that constraining the local bath states to be CSs is a reasonably good approximation. The correct treatment of system-bath correlation is evident in the test problem of a double well system coupled bilinearly to a harmonic oscillator[24]. Fig.1 shows, for example, the behavior of the tunneling splitting for different values of the coupling strength c, compared to exact results. Notice for comparison that a time-dependent self-consistent field approach to this problem would badly fail in describing the tunneling dynamics at all but very small coupling strengths [24].

Application of the method to large-dimensional baths show the main limitation of the present approach. The vibrational relaxation dynamics of an anharmonic oscillator coupled to a 50D bath, as described by standard LCSA, is in only qualitative agreement with converged MCDTH calculations. A detailed analysis suggests that this is more probably due to *numerical* difficulties than to real limitations of the LCSA approach. For example, time-reversal invariance is lost after a few tens of fs, discrepancies increase in weaker-coupled systems (long time dynamics), and, in general, long-time results show some dependence on numerical parameters (e.g. the grid spacing defining the Colbert-Miller DVR used in the calculations). This is a much more subtle problem that it seems at first sight; as an example, we notice that our integrator (a standard Runge-Kutta 4-th order one) allows very good norm and energy conservation. Though some improvement has been recently found by employing better-suited DVR sets (in particular, the Potential-Optimized DVR set based on the eigenvectors of the system hamiltonian)[25], the working strategy at present is to use the damped version of LCSA. The fictitious friction coefficient η of the previous Section can be optimized with a minimum effort without reference to any benchmark result, and turns out be essentially a bath property. The use of such a 'trick' allows one to get results in very good agreement with exact ones in an extremely cheap way, see Fig. 2. Likewise, one can 'stabilize' the bath dynamics in tunneling problems without affecting the system dynamics, as we have shown in Fig.1 and observed in other, large dimensional tunneling problems.

One interesting feature of the 'damped' version of LCSA is that the intro-

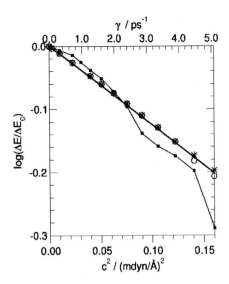

FIG. 1: A double-well system coupled to a 1D harmonic bath oscillator: tunneling splitting as a function of the coupling strength. Bold lines for exact results, square symbols for standard LCSA. Very good results can be obtained by employing the damped version of LCSA (stars), even when the fictitious damping is turned on for the first 0.1 ps only (empty circles). Here, damping helps in removing an 'initialization' problem, see Ref. 8 for details.

duction of a friction coefficient η, by inducing an overall dissipative dynamics, completely removes the bath recurrence problem. This is shown in Fig.3 where different discretizations of the same bath (i.e. which preserve the spectral density $J(\omega)$) give the same (essentially exact) results for times much larger than their corresponding recurrence times.

Thus, the introduction of a simple damping coefficient in the pseudoclassical bath equations seems to solve the numerical instability problems, and introduce nice features in the method. This, however, cannot be the final solution. This is clear, for example, when considering a sticking dynamics (i.e. by using the bath to model a surface). In this case, the standard version of LCSA works reasonably well, and correctly reproduces the energy transfer. However, when looking at detailed quantities such as the sticking probability it is clear that dynamics does not proceed 'smoothly', see Fig.4. The bad break here is that when we introduce the damping coefficient we do stabilize the bath dynamics but at the price of having no more sticking (!). This is clearly due to the important role that low-frequency bath oscillators play in the dynamics: the use of a frequency dependent damping coefficient can improve the situation, but this seems to be a

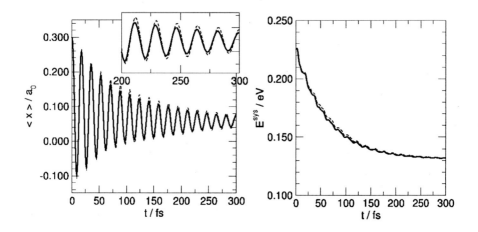

FIG. 2: Average position (left) and system energy (right) for a 50D vibrational relaxation dynamics with relaxation time $\gamma^{-1} = 50$ fs. Full lines for converged MCTDH results, and dashed lines for (damped) LCSA calculations. The latter take ~ 1 min on a standard desktop computer.

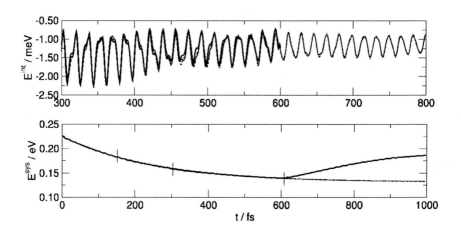

FIG. 3: A vibrational relaxation dynamics showing the removal of the recurrence problem when the damped version of LCSA is used. Bold lines for MCTDH calculations with 80 bath modes, solid, dashed and dotted lines for LCSA calculations with 20,40, and 80 modes. Vertical bars mark the corresponding 'nominal' recurrence times. Top: average interaction energy. Bottom: average system energy.

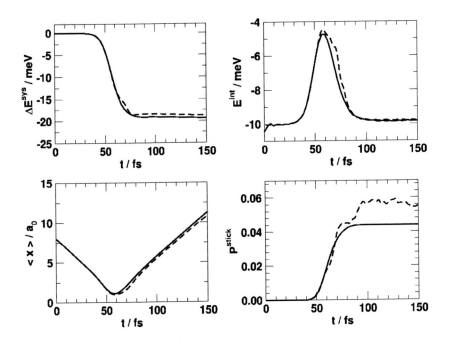

FIG. 4: A model sticking dynamical problem, describing a H atom colliding with a 50D-mode surface at a collision energy of 200 meV. Average system energy loss (ΔE^{sys}), interaction energy (E^{int}), position ($<x>$) and sticking probability (P^{stick}) as a function of time. Solid lines for MCTDH results, dashed lines for LCSA.

too *ad hoc* procedure. For this reason, we have been currently looking for much more *robust* propagation algorithms than the ones we have adopted so far. This motivated a deeper understanding of the properties of the working equations, as it is sketched in the following Section.

IV. HAMILTONIAN FLOWS

The results obtained so far were based on 'brute-force' solution of the first-order LCSA equations of motion. However, a good propagator should take care of preserving their (non-evident) features, namely their *symplectic* structure. Indeed, it has been known for some time[26, 27] that *any* variational quantum method (under quite mild regularity conditions) can be recast in the form of a symplectomorphism on a symplectic manifold. This means in practice that rather than using a brutal time discretization one can better approximate the short-time dynamics of the system by a composition of (simple) symplectic maps in order to keep trace of this extraordinary property. In the following we summarize the important points in this respect, leaving an ampler discussion to a forthcoming paper.

Let's first briefly introduce the concept of hamiltonian flows in generic symplectic manifolds. A symplectic manifold is a differentiable manifold equipped with a *closed, non-degenerate* 2-form ω. In a coordinate system x^i it can be written as $\omega = \sum_{i,j>i} \omega_{ij} dx^i dx^j$. Here dx^i are the fundamental 1-forms, that is $dx^i(\mathbf{v}) = v^i$ for any tangent vector $\mathbf{v}$ in a given point $\mathbf{x}$, and the product of differentials is the so-called 'wedge' product. Non-degeneracy means in practice that ω_{ij} is non-singular everywhere in the manifold[29], and this allows one to set up a one-to-one map between tangent and *co*-tangent vectors (1-forms). That is, for a given 1-form $\alpha = \sum \alpha_i dx^i$ there is an associated vector field $\mathbf{X}_\alpha$ such that $\alpha(\mathbf{v}) = \omega(\mathbf{X}_\alpha, \mathbf{v})$, and its *flow*, defined by the curves $\dot{x}^i = X_\alpha^i$. Then, given a smooth function H (which can be called a hamiltonian) and its 1-form dH the flow induced by its associated vector field $\mathbf{X}_H$ (what can be called a hamiltonian flow) conserves the function itself, $dH(\mathbf{X}_H) = \omega(\mathbf{X}_H, \mathbf{X}_H) = 0$. Closedness ($d\omega = 0$ where d is the 'exterior' derivative) means that these properties can be 'transported' along the manifold, and guarantees that the symplectic form ω itself is invariant under any hamiltonian flow (formally $\mathcal{L}_{X_H} \omega = 0$, $\mathcal{L}_Y$ being the Lie derivative along the vector field $\mathbf{Y}$. This forms the basis for Liouville's theorem).

In our context, it is worth noticing that a 'variational' method can be defined with the help of the *time-dependent variational principle*, namely $\delta S = 0$. Here the action $S = \int_{t_1}^{t_2} dt\, L$ is given by the (real) Lagrangian[26, 27]

$$L = \frac{i\hbar}{2} \frac{\langle \Psi | \dot{\Psi} \rangle - \langle \dot{\Psi} | \Psi \rangle}{\langle \Psi \mid \Psi \rangle} - \frac{\langle \Psi \mid H \mid \Psi \rangle}{\langle \Psi \mid \Psi \rangle}$$

The time dependent variational principle gives back the time-dependent Schrödinger equation when $|\Psi\rangle$ is allowed to vary in the whole space, without constraints. It is implied by the Dirac-Frenkel one. The converse is also true when $i |\delta\Psi\rangle$ is an allowed variation for any possible variation $|\delta\Psi\rangle$.

Then, a general symplectic structure can emerge when (smoothly) introducing a set of variational parameters $\mathbf{x}$, $|\Psi\rangle = |\Psi(\mathbf{x})\rangle$, forming a coordinate system in the manifold of the 'sample' space. This can be made up, for example, by the real and the imaginary parts of a set of n complex parameters, such as our $\{..C_\alpha..z_\alpha^k..\}$. In terms of this parametrization,

$$L = \sum_{i=1}^{n} \dot{x}^i Z_i(\mathbf{x}) - \mathcal{H}(\mathbf{x})$$

142

where

$$Z_i = \frac{i\hbar}{2\langle\Psi\,|\,\Psi\rangle}\left(\left\langle\Psi\,\middle|\,\frac{\partial\Psi}{\partial x^i}\right\rangle - \left\langle\frac{\partial\Psi}{\partial x^i}\,\middle|\,\Psi\right\rangle\right)$$

are the components of a 1-form $\alpha = -\sum Z_i dx^i$, and $\mathcal{H}(\mathbf{x}) = \langle\Psi(\mathbf{x})|H|\Psi(\mathbf{x})\rangle\,/\,\langle\Psi(\mathbf{x})|\Psi(\mathbf{x})\rangle$. A closed 2-form can then be defined as $\omega = d\alpha$, and it is non-degenerate if $\omega_{ij} = \partial Z_i/\partial x^j - \partial Z_j/\partial x^i$ is non-singular. In this case, the 2-form $\omega = \sum\omega_{ij}dx^i dx^j$ provides the symplectic structure we need.

Indeed, the equations of motion defined by the time-dependent variational principle follow by the above Lagrangian in the form

$$\sum \dot{x}^i\omega_{ij} = \frac{\partial\mathcal{H}}{\partial x^j}$$

or equivalently, for a generic tangent vector $\mathbf{v}$,

$$\sum \dot{x}^i\omega_{ij}v^j = \omega(\dot{\mathbf{x}},\mathbf{v}) = \sum\frac{\partial\mathcal{H}}{\partial x^j}dx^j(\mathbf{v}) = d\mathcal{H}(\mathbf{v})$$

It follows that if ω is a symplectic form, the 'variational flow' *is* the hamiltonian flow of the hamiltonian $\mathcal{H}(\mathbf{x})$, i.e. $\dot{\mathbf{x}} = \mathbf{X}_\mathcal{H}$. The variational equations can also be written with the help of Poisson brackets

$$\dot{x}^i = \{H, x^i\}$$

which are defined by $\{f,g\} = \omega(\mathbf{X}_g, \mathbf{X}_f)$ for any two smooth functions f and g. In a coordinate system they are given explicitly by

$$\{f,g\} = \sum\frac{\partial f}{\partial x^i}\frac{\partial g}{\partial x^j}\xi^{ij}$$

where ξ^{ij} is the matrix inverse of ω_{ij}.

A detailed analysis of the LCSA case [25] reveals that the relevant form ω is indeed non-degenerate in the whole parameter space where none of the amplitude coefficients C_α is zero. This is consistent with the *ansatz* of Eq. 3 since when one the C_α vanishes the associated CSs z_α^k are irrelevant for the dynamics.

V. SUMMARY

In this paper an account has been given of the current status of what we have called the Local Coherent-State Approximation, and its related quantum dynamical approach to system-bath problems. An attempt has been made to show its merits and present limitations. On the one hand, we have shown that the method can be very accurate and extremely cheap, very nice features for possible realistic applications. On the other hand, we have also shown that numerical stability problems have been preventing straightforward application of the approach. In an attempt to overcome these difficulties, we have also sketched our ongoing search of a robust propagation scheme.

143

Acknowledgements   Gian Franco Tantardini and Peter Saalfrank are greatly acknowledged for their continuous and active involvement in the project.

---

[1] M. Nest and H.-D. Meyer, J. Chem. Phys. **119**, 24 (2003).

[2] I. Burghardt, M. Nest, and G. A. Worth, J. Chem. Phys. **119**, 5364 (2003).

[3] H. Wang and M. Thoss, J. Chem. Phys. **119**, 1289 (2003).

[4] H.-P. Breuer and F. Petruccione, *The theory of open quantum systems* (Oxford, Oxford, 2002).

[5] U. Weiss, *Quantum dissipative systems*, vol. 13 of *Series in Condensed Matter Physics* (World Scientific, 2008).

[6] M. H. Beck, A. Jackle, G. A. Worth, and H.-D. Meyer, Phys. Rep. **324**, 1 (2000).

[7] H.-D. Meyer and G. Worth, Theor. Chem. Acc. **109**, 251 (2003).

[8] R. Martinazzo, M. Nest, P. Saalfrank, and G. F. Tantardini, J. Chem. Phys. **125**, 194102 (2006).

[9] I. Burghardt, H.-D. Meyer, and L. S. Cederbaum, J. Chem. Phys. **111**, 2927 (1999).

[10] G. A. Worth and I. Burghardt, Chem. Phys. Lett. **502**, 368 (2003).

[11] G. A. Worth, M. A. Robb, and I. Burghardt, Faraday Discuss. **127**, 307 (2004).

[12] R. J. Rubin, J. Math. Phys. **1**, 309 (1960).

[13] J. R. Senitzky, Phys. Rev. **119**, 670 (1960).

[14] R. Zwanzig, J. Chem. Phys **32**, 1173 (1960).

[15] R. Zwanzig, J. Stat. Phys. **9**, 215 (1973).

[16] S. A. Adelman and J. D. Doll, J. Chem. Phys. **64**, 2375 (1976).

[17] J. C. Tully, J. Chem. Phys. **73**, 6333 (1980).

[18] A. O. Caldeira and A. J. Leggett, Ann. Phys.(N.Y.) **149**, 374 (1983).

[19] E. Cortes, B. J. West, and K. Lindeberg, J. Chem. Phys. **82**, 2708 (1985).

[20] D. V. Shalashilin and M. S. Child, J. Chem. Phys. **119**, 1961 (2003).

[21] D. V. Shalashilin and M. S. Child, J. Chem. Phys. **121**, 2563 (2004).

[22] D. V. Shalashilin and M. S. Child, J. Chem. Phys. **122**, 224108 (2005).

[23] D. V. Shalashilin and M. S. Child, J. Chem. Phys. **122**, 224109 (2005).

[24] N. Makri and W. H. Miller, J. Chem. Phys. **87**, 5781 (1987).

[25] R. Martinazzo (unpublished).

[26] A. K. Kerman and S. E. Koonin, Annals of Physics **100**, 332 (1976).

[27] P. Kramer and M. Saraceno, *Geometry of the time-dependent variational principle in quantum mechanics*, vol. 140 of *Lecture Notes in Physics* (Springer-Verlag, Berlin Heidelberg New York, 1981).

[28] The same applies to finite temperature cases where, as expected, both a friction *and* a fluctuating term appear in the LCSA equations of each realization of eq.4.

[29] This condition restricts the analysis to even dimensional manifolds.

D. Shalashilin and M. P. de Miranda (eds.)
Multidimensional Quantum Mechanics with Trajectories
© 2009, CCP6, Daresbury

Bipolar quantum trajectory simulations: trajectory surface hopping and path integral Monte Carlo

J. B. Maddox and B. Poirier*

*Department of Chemistry and Biochemistry,
Texas Tech University, Box 41041,
Lubbock, Texas, 79409-1061, USA*

I. INTRODUCTION

In recent years a set of "counter-propagating wave methods" (CPWMs) [1–8] have been developed for solving the time-independent (TISE) and time-dependent (TDSE) Schrödinger equations. These methods and the theory behind them were originally introduced as a means of reconciling certain conceptual disparities and computational short-comings between exact quantum trajectory methods (QTMs) [9] based on the de Broglie-Bohm theory [10–12] and semiclassical theory/calculations [13–19]. Thus far, the CPWMs have been successfully applied to a wide variety of quantum mechanical phenomena, including the zero-point motion and classical correspondence of stationary bound states [1], barrier tunneling associated with stationary scattering states [2–5], partial transmission and reflection probabilities in nonadiabatic scattering systems [6], nonstationary wavepacket dynamics [7], and multi-dimensional dynamics (both stationary and nonstationary) [8].

The theoretical and computational details of the CPWMs for different applications are quite diverse; however, the underlying theme involves a two-term, so-called "bipolar," decomposition of the quantum mechanical wavefunction,

$$\psi = \psi_+ + \psi_-, \tag{1}$$

where the $\psi_\pm$ components correspond to traveling waves moving in opposite directions. In the context of stationary scattering states (the topic addressed in this paper) the CPWM determines a bipolar decomposition where $\psi_\pm$ may be

---

*Electronic address: `bill.poirier@ttu.edu`

interpreted in terms of the incident/transmitted/reflected waves from scattering theory. Each of the bipolar components is associated with a set of trajectories constituting a Lagrangian manifold (LM) in phase space [19–22]. In one-dimensional (1D) scattering problems ψ_+ and ψ_- are associated with a family of right and left moving trajectories, respectively. By design, this idea is analogous to the situation in semiclassical theory where the Wentzel-Kramers-Brillouin (WKB) wave solutions, which may be regarded as an approximate bipolar decomposition, are associated with right/left moving classical trajectories [13]. The CPWM, however, is an exact method and the LMs associated with $\psi_\pm$ are not necessarily classical.

In principle, the decomposition in Eq. (1) is far from unique, and one challenge of the CPWM is to determine a suitable bipolar decomposition such that: (a) the total wavefunction is an exact solution of the Schrödinger equation; (b) the individual components are smooth and have well-defined semiclassical analogs; (c) the associated trajectories are well-behaved; and (d) the overall method is computationally tractable for a wide variety of systems and parameters. Section II briefly reviews the CPWM for stationary scattering states, where it is shown that the method basically involves transforming the TISE for ψ into a time-*dependent* pair of coupled total differential equations for $\psi_\pm$. The evolution of $\psi_\pm$ in time may be regarded as kind of nonequilibrium relaxation dynamics, in a moving reference frame determined by the bipolar LMs. By virtue of the coupling between the bipolar components, $\psi_\pm(t)$ eventually relax to a steady state, such that Eq. (1) gives the desired stationary solution of the TISE.

In the remainder of this paper we present several new algorithms for solving the CPWM equations of motion. Previous implementations have relied upon propagating $\psi_\pm$ along interdependent trajectories, *i.e.*, trajectories that communicate and share information with one another, albeit only locally. The new algorithms represent a departure from that strategy in that we aim to solve the CPWM equations exactly, or at least approximately, using completely *independent* trajectories—propagated numerically without reference to, or communication with, the other trajectories in the ensemble. The goal of this approach is to construct robust computational methods suitable for execution on massively parallel computer architectures, similar in spirit to existing classical trajectory simulations [23], and thereby, greatly increasing the dimensionality of the physical systems that can be addressed using exact quantum dynamics. In doing so we develop several new concepts surrounding the CPWM which have not been previously examined. These include the notion of trajectory surface hopping, where bipolar trajectories are allowed to stochastically hop between the bipolar LMs in a manner similar to traditional surface hopping schemes for describing nonadiabatic electronic transitions in mixed quantum/classical simulations [24–28]. A path integral representation of the CPWM is also developed and the resulting computational methods incorporate a Monte Carlo importance sampling scheme for the bipolar paths. We present detailed accuracy and convergence benchmarks for a 1D potential barrier, and discuss the viability of these new methods towards multi-dimensional scattering problems.

II. BACKGROUND

A. Basic Theory

To clarify the basic operation of the CPWM, we consider a 1D scattering problem consisting of a particle with mass m, energy E, and position x, incident from the left upon some potential energy barrier $V(x)$. For simplicity, $V(x)$ is assumed to be a smooth function that converges to zero asymptotically, $i.e.$, $\lim_{x \to \pm\infty} V(x) = 0$. Note that these restrictions are not required to apply the CPWM; however, the time evolution equations are somewhat more complicated when they are not satisfied [5]. We adopt a standard left-incident normalization convention such that the boundary conditions on the bipolar components are given by

$$\psi_+(x \to -\infty, t) = \exp[i(\sqrt{2mE}\,x - Et)/\hbar] \qquad (2)$$
$$\psi_-(x \to +\infty, t) = 0 \qquad (3)$$

For these boundary conditions, the ψ_+ component corresponds to the incident and transmitted waves, in the left and right asymptotic regions, respectively, while ψ_- represents the reflected wave. In Refs. [3, 5] it was shown that a bipolar decomposition possessing the attributes discussed in Sec. I is obtained as the steady state solutions of the following coupled total differential equations

$$\frac{d\psi_\pm}{dt} = \frac{i}{\hbar}\left(E - V\right)\psi_\pm - \frac{i}{\hbar}V\psi_\mp \qquad (4)$$

where t represents a pseudo-time variable and d/dt is the total time derivative

$$\frac{d\psi_\pm}{dt} = \frac{\partial\psi_\pm}{\partial t} \pm v\frac{\partial\psi_\pm}{\partial x} \qquad (5)$$

acting in the reference frame of a free particle with velocity $v = \sqrt{2E/m}$; note that the reference frames for ψ_+ and ψ_- are moving to the right and left, respectively, with equal but opposite constant velocities $\pm v$. The fact that we have total time derivatives here implies a pair of auxiliary equations of motion for trajectories in the two bipolar reference frames

$$\frac{dx_\pm}{dt} = \pm v, \qquad (6)$$

which in this particular case have a simple linear time dependence $x_\pm(t) = \pm vt + x_\pm(0)$ where $x_\pm(0)$ is the initial position. The time evolution of the

147

bipolar components is implicitly defined along these trajectories $\psi_\pm[x_\pm(t), t]$ in a hydrodynamic-like fashion. This is quite similar to the situation in QTM methods; however, in that approach the trajectories themselves are dependent upon the wavefunction, *i.e.*, the so-called "pilot-wave" concept [12].

Several interesting flux relationships are obtained from Eq. (4). Defining the bipolar component probability densities and probability current densities as $\rho_\pm = |\psi_\pm|^2$ and $j_\pm = \pm v\rho_\pm$, respectively, we then have an expression for the conservation of the total combined probability density [3]

$$\frac{\partial\rho_+}{\partial t} + \frac{\partial j_+}{\partial x} = -\left(\frac{\partial\rho_-}{\partial t} + \frac{\partial j_-}{\partial x}\right), \tag{7}$$

a relation between the probability lost/gained by the right and/or left moving reference frames

$$\frac{d\rho_\pm}{dt} = \pm\frac{2V}{\hbar}\text{Im}[\psi_+^*\psi_-], \tag{8}$$

and a steady state relation,

$$\frac{\partial\rho_+}{\partial x} = \frac{\partial\rho_-}{\partial x}, \tag{9}$$

which states that at long times, the $\rho_\pm$ are equal, apart from a constant (in this case, the transmission probability). Note that Eqs. (8) and (9) are only valid for the special case of constant velocity trajectories, although similar expressions can be obtained for other bipolar decompositions—*e.g.*, for asymptotically asymmetric potentials [5]. The transmission, P_T, and reflection, P_R, probabilities at a given energy are usually the most important properties to be calculated from the stationary state; these are given by

$$P_T = \rho_+(x \to +\infty, t \to +\infty) \tag{10}$$
$$P_R = \rho_-(x \to -\infty, t \to +\infty) \tag{11}$$

in terms of the long time limit of the asymptotic bipolar densities. These relations are subject to the condition of asymptotically symmetric potentials and the left incident normalization of Eq. (2). In Section III, we will use Eq. (8) to define the rates for a particle to hop from one bipolar LM to another. For now we make a short digression to describe how Eq. (4) has been solved previously, to obtain P_T and P_R.

B. Plane wave propagator (PWP)

The first step in solving Eq. (4) involves selection of an appropriate numerical scheme for integrating the CPWM equations over time. This task can be approached in several ways, and the particular method of choice depends a great deal on the desired level of accuracy versus computational expense. Previous studies have employed various strategies such as simple first-order (forward Euler) time integration [5] and fourth-order Runge-Kutta methods [3]. Since our ultimate aim here is focused on the development of new methods for application in high-dimensions, we favor simplicity and speed as opposed to high accuracy; therefore, we have elected to employ methods that are first-order with respect to an appropriately chosen fixed time-step size, Δt.

In practice, the bipolar components are calculated on a discrete space-time grid that moves with time. Since the two bipolar LMs consist of constant velocity trajectories moving in opposite directions, it is quite natural to think in terms of equally spaced grid points. To begin, we define an interaction region $x_L \leq x \leq x_R$ (such that the potential at the boundaries $V(x_L) = V(x_R) \approx 0$ is sufficiently small) and a finite number, N, of equally spaced grid points, $\{x_i\}$ such that $x_1 = x_L$, $x_N = x_R$, and the space-step size is $\Delta x = x_{i+1} - x_i = (x_L - x_R)/(N-1)$. These points define the positions at which the bipolar components are to be evaluated as a function of time, $i.e.$, $\psi_{\pm,i}(t) = \psi_\pm(x_i, t)$. For a given space-step size Δx, there is a natural time-step size $\Delta t = \Delta x/v$, such that after one time step, the grid points will be coincident with their initial positions but displaced by a single grid point: $x_\pm(\Delta t) = x_i \pm v\Delta t = x_{i\pm 1}$. Smaller time-step sizes may be used; however, this implies that the grid points associated with $x_\pm$ will not be coincident after one time step. Although this can be easily handled with interpolation methods and would allow for greater accuracy, for the present purpose we prefer to avoid the extra programming overhead, and simply use the natural time-step size above. One consequence of this choice is that we will have to use many more grid points to obtain the same level of accuracy that has been achieved with previous numerical implementations of the CPWM [5].

Previous studies utilizing this space-time grid have employed the so-called "plane-wave-propagator" (PWP) representation [5] of the first-order bipolar solutions of Eq. (4), $i.e.$,

$$
\begin{aligned}
\psi_\pm(x_{i\pm 1}, t + \Delta t) &= e^{iE\Delta t/\hbar}\psi_\pm(x_i, t) - \\
&\quad \frac{i\Delta t}{\hbar}V(x_i)\left[\psi_+(x_i, t) + \psi_-(x_i, t)\right],
\end{aligned} \tag{12}
$$

with boundary conditions

$$
\psi_{+,1}(t + \Delta t) = e^{-iE\Delta t/\hbar}\psi_{+,1}(t) \quad \text{and} \tag{13}
$$

$$
\psi_{-,N}(t + \Delta t) = 0, \tag{14}
$$

at the grid edges of the interaction region. In this interdependent trajectory implementation, these expressions are applied recursively, starting from an initial guess, $\psi_{+,i}(0) = e^{imvx_i/\hbar}$ and $\psi_{-,i}(0) = 0$. Equation (4) are relaxation equations, as a result of which the initial conditions are largely immaterial, vis-à-vis the final steady-state solutions that are obtained; however, the number of

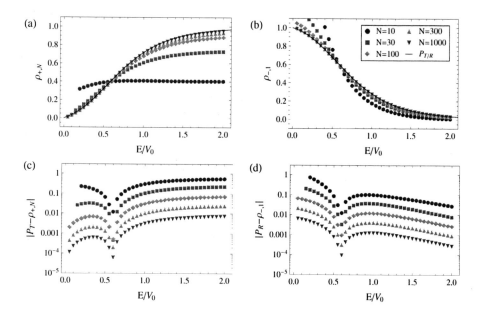

FIG. 1: (color online) Accuracy benchmarks for the CPWM applied to the Eckart A potential barrier (V_0=0.0018 hartrees). The results shown here were obtained using the PWP algorithm described in Section II B. The calculated (a) transmission $\rho_{+,N}$ and (b) reflection $\rho_{-,1}$ probabilities are plotted as a function of E/V_0 for different numbers of grid points N and compared with the (solid lines) analytical probabilities $P_{T/R}$. The absolute errors of the calculated transmission and reflection probabilities are shown in (c) and (d), respectively.

time steps required is affected by this choice [3]. Once a steady state has been reached, successive applications of Eqs. (12)-(14) introduce no further changes to the corresponding bipolar densities $\rho_{\pm,i}$, though the phase of $\psi_\pm(t)$ continues to evolve as $\exp(-iE\Delta t/\hbar)$. The transmission and reflection probabilities of the scattering state are then estimated as $P_T \approx \rho_{+,N}$ and $P_R \approx \rho_{-,1}$, respectively.

To gauge the accuracy of the CPWM, we calculate the transmission and reflection probabilities for a particle with mass m=2000 a.u., incident upon a symmetric Eckart barrier potential

$$V(x) = V_0 \operatorname{sech}^2(\alpha x) \qquad (15)$$

where V_0=0.0018 hartree is the barrier height, α=3.0 bohr^{-1} determines the barrier width, and the interaction region boundaries are taken to be $x_R=-x_L=2.0$ bohr. This set of parameters has been previously referred to as the "Eckart A" system [3, 5]. In Figure 1 we present accuracy benchmarks for the PWP algorithm where the calculated results are compared against analytical theory [4, 29].

150

These results will serve as a comparison for the new algorithms to be developed in the next sections. Figure 1(a) shows the calculated transmission probability $\rho_{+,N}$ for different numbers of grid points N, as a function of the ratio E/V_0; the solid line marks the analytical results. Clearly the error decreases as the number of grid points increases. Also note that there is a cross-over from positive to negative errors at roughly $E/V_0=0.6$. Similar trends are observed for the calculated reflection probabilities $\rho_{-,1}$ shown in Figure 1(b). The absolute errors in the transmission and reflection are plotted on a log scale in panels (c) and (d), respectively. The cusp-like feature in the absolute errors reflects the fact that the calculated results cross the analytical curves in that region so that the apparent decrease in the error is somewhat artificial. In practice the transmission and reflection do not exactly add to unity as they should. By renormalizing the raw values the absolute error can be decreased by roughly half an order of magnitude.

In the next several sections we approach the problem of scattering from a different perspective. Our intent is to develop a computational strategy which captures quantum mechanical effects exactly, or approximately, using independent classical-like trajectories. The results of the PWP algorithm will serve as a reasonable benchmark for judging the quality of these new methods.

III. BIPOLAR TRAJECTORY SURFACE HOPPING (BTSH)

A. Hopping rates in nonadiabatic and bipolar dynamics

The notion of describing quantum phenomena using classical trajectories is familiar in the context of mixed quantum/classical simulations that fall under the category of surface hopping methods [24, 30–33]. In such methods, a system of nuclear degrees of freedom is represented by an ensemble of classical trajectories evolving on potential energy surfaces determined by the system's electronic states. Quantum effects associated with nuclear motion, such as zero-point motion and tunneling are inherently neglected while quantum effects associated with the electronic degrees of freedom such as nonadiabatic electronic transitions, electronic coherence, mixed state dynamics, and Stuckelberg oscillations are more or less correctly represented [24, 34]. The nuclear motion is generally smooth, and classical-like, apart from sudden changes in velocity (magnitude and/or direction) associated with instantaneous electronic transitions which cause the nuclear system to jump between adiabatic potential surfaces; these "hops" become more pronounced in the vicinity of avoided crossings where the nonadiabatic coupling between two or more electronic states is more intense. The hopping dynamics associated with a single trajectory occurs stochastically, and by averaging over the ensemble, one can obtain transmission and reflection probabilities corresponding to each state in the electronic manifold. While such methods are well developed and have proven to be extremely powerful tools for a wide range of systems, they remain somewhat unsatisfactory for the following reasons: (1) P_R is poorly reproduced, implying that there is likely significant error at low energies; (2) they can not be applied to single-surface dynamics; and (3) they are not exact. Moreover, there is generally no way to gauge the validity of neglecting quantum effects in the nuclear motion without resorting to a direct comparison with a fully quantum mechanical treatment, which becomes less feasible as the dimensionality of the problem increases.

In Ref. [6] a CPWM was developed for nonadiabatic systems with multiple electronic states, and it was demonstrated for several simple 1D multisurface systems that the CPWM provides numerically exact results consistent with conventional fully quantum methods. This involves a generalization of the theory and numerical algorithm described in Sec. II to include a distinct bipolar decomposition and associated pair of bipolar LMs for each electronic state in the system. The bipolar equations of motion and associated flux relationships are augmented by nonadiabatic coupling terms that lead to density flow among the various bipolar components for the different electronic states. The dynamical evolution of the bipolar components in these multisurface problems is similar to the single surface case, in that relaxation dynamics give rise, in the limit of long times, to steady state solutions for all of the bipolar components. One can then calculate the transmission and reflection probabilities for each adiabatic potential surface in the system, as described above.

It would be computationally beneficial to formulate the CPWM such that the bipolar trajectories could be decoupled from one another, in a manner similar to the independent trajectory assumption that is implicit to traditional surface hopping methods. To demonstrate one possible realization of this strategy, we make use of the flux relationships given in Sec. II A. Here, we will not explicitly address the issue of electronic transitions; however, we will formulate a method which captures quantum effects in the nuclear dynamics in terms of a trajectory ensemble that includes hopping dynamics between the $+$ and $-$ LMs associated with the bipolar CPWM components for single-surface dynamics. In this way, intrastate hopping is used to represent the dynamics of nuclear degrees of freedom and is very similar to interstate hopping dynamics in surface hopping methods.

Specifically, Eq.(8) relates the probability density lost/gained by a trajectory on one LM to the probability gained/lost by a trajectory on the opposite LM. We can use this to define a spatially dependent hopping rate between the LMs in a manner that is analogous to the hopping rates between adiabatic potential surfaces. These hopping rates may be defined as

$$R_{-\leftarrow+} = -\frac{1}{\rho_+}\frac{d\rho_+}{dt} \quad \text{and} \quad R_{+\leftarrow-} = -\frac{1}{\rho_-}\frac{d\rho_-}{dt} \tag{16}$$

where $R_{-\leftarrow+}$ is the rate of probability per unit time for a trajectory to hop from the $+$ LM to the $-$ LM, and vice versa for $R_{+\leftarrow-}$. The similarity between the

152

bipolar hopping rates of Eq. (16) and Tully's nonadiabatic hopping probabilities defined in Eq. (14) and (15) of Ref. [24] is quite striking. In both instances, the hopping rate contains a term of the form

$$R \propto \frac{2V_{ij}}{\hbar} \frac{\text{Im}[\psi_i^* \psi_j]}{|\psi_i|^2} \qquad (17)$$

where ψ_i and ψ_j represent generic amplitudes and V is a potential energy factor associated with intercomponent coupling. In Tully's case, the amplitudes are associated with electronic coherences and V is an off-diagonal diabatic intersurface coupling term. In the bipolar context, however, the amplitudes correspond to transmitted/reflected waves associated with nuclear motion, which are coupled via the scattering potential. These similarities are interesting especially in light of the fact that the two cases encompass completely different quantum effects, i.e., electronic transitions versus reactive scattering. Moreover, this suggests that both phenomena may be treated on a more or less equal footing, e.g., in a bipolar treatment of multisurface dynamics [6].

B.   Bipolar surface hopping algorithm

Below we describe a computational strategy for dealing with scattering systems, albeit without electronic transitions, that is very similar in design to traditional nonadiabatic surface hopping methods. First though, in Figure 2, we present an analysis of the bipolar densities and hopping rates for three stationary states of the Eckart A potential, corresponding to energies E that are below (50%), equal to (100%), and above (150%) the barrier height V_0. Panels (a) and (b) show the converged, long-time-limit densities ρ_+ and ρ_-, respectively, for the three scattering states and the inset of (b) shows the total densities $\rho = |\psi_+ + \psi_-|^2$. Immediately we can see that the component densities $\rho_\pm$ are much smoother than the total density ρ. It is also clear that the right asymptote of ρ_+ reflects the fact that the transmission increases as the energy increases. Similarly, the left asymptote of ρ_- shows that the reflection decreases with increasing energy, as expected. In panels (c) and (d) we plot the hopping rates $R_{-\leftarrow+}$ and $R_{+\leftarrow-}$, respectively. At lower energy, we observe that $R_{-\leftarrow+}$ is enhanced while $R_{+\leftarrow-}$ is diminished, and at higher energy the converse of this is true. In other words, if the energy is large, then a trajectory evolving on the + LM has a tendency to stay on the + LM; however, if it does hop to the − LM, then there is an enhanced probability that it will hop back to the + LM. Ultimately, this would lead to an overall increase in the transmission probability. At low energies, the situation is reversed, and a trajectory initially on the + LM has tendency to hop to the − LM and is more likely to stay there, thus, leading to an increase in the overall reflection probability.

To demonstrate how Eq. (16) can be used in practice in the context of an

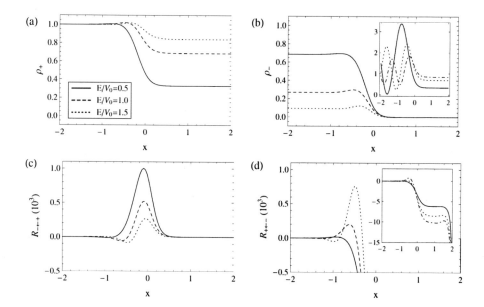

FIG. 2: The densities of the bipolar components (a) $\rho_+ = |\psi_+|^2$ and (b) $\rho_- = |\psi_-|^2$ are plotted as a function position x for several energy values. The inset of (b) shows the corresponding total densities $\rho = |\psi_+ + \psi_-|^2$. The hopping rates $R_{-\leftarrow+}$ and $R_{+\leftarrow-}$ are shown in (c) and (d), respectively. Note that in terms of the BTSH algorithm, negative rates mean a 0% chance of hopping. The inset of (d) shows a wider view of $R_{+\leftarrow-}$ showing the position dependence at the right boundary of the interaction region.

independent trajectory scheme, we have developed a numerical algorithm that calculates transmission and reflection probabilities from an ensemble of independent, hopping, constant velocity trajectories. This method is referred to as the analytical bipolar trajectory surface hopping (BTSH) method; the term "analytical" is used here to reflect the fact that the method requires that the problem has been previously solved. In other words, the bipolar components must be computed in advance, and the results here are merely meant to serve as a "proof of concept," demonstrating that the CPWM approach can be developed in a manner which mimics the operation of surface hopping algorithms. Ultimately, however, we desire a "synthetic" method, which constructs the bipolar components autonomously. Our efforts in this regard will follow in a later section, but the analytical BTSH algorithm is a useful conceptual milestone, and establishes preliminary accuracy and convergence benchmarks. For this purpose we return to the Eckart A system, using the previously discussed PWP solutions for the bipolar components as input.

Given the steady state bipolar components $\psi_\pm$, one can calculate the LM hopping rates as a function of x over the desired interaction region. An ensemble of trajectories is then constructed where each trajectory starts off on the $+$ LM (with velocity $+v = \sqrt{2E/m}$) at the left boundary x_L of the interaction region, and will terminate at either the right boundary x_R on the $+$ LM or at x_L on the $-$ LM. Throughout the course of its evolution the trajectory may undergo any number of hops between the $\pm$ LMs. The hopping dynamics is simulated as follows: trajectories proceed with constant velocity ($+v$ or $-v$) in a step-wise fashion. At each step a pseudo-random number ζ is generated; if the trajectory is on the $+$ LM, then a hop to the $-$ LM will occur if $\zeta \le \Delta t R_{-\leftarrow+}$ (hopping probability), and the trajectory then changes direction and follows the $-$ LM; otherwise, it will continue along the $+$ LM. Similarly, if a trajectory is on the $-$ LM, then it will hop to the $+$ LM if $\zeta \le \Delta t R_{+\leftarrow-}$. Note that a negative hopping rate means a 0% chance of hopping. In general, the hopping probabilities are fairly small and a large number of hops is not likely; the algorithm described above is of the "fewest switches" variety [24]. Furthermore, the hopping probabilities vanish asymptotically; hence, all trajectories inevitably wind up at one of the grid boundaries, and it is therefore impossible to encounter a situation where a trajectory becomes trapped inside the interaction region forever. The transmission and reflection probabilities are estimated as the fraction of trajectories that exit the grid at x_R and x_L, respectively.

Figure 3 summarizes the results for the Eckart A system obtained with the analytical BTSH algorithm. The bipolar components used to construct the hopping probabilities are taken from the PWP calculations described in Section II B. The accuracy of the bipolar components is effectively determined by the number of grid points N used in the PWP calculations. This has been verified for Eckart A over a wide range of values for E and N. For each combination of E and N, we perform 100 BTSH trials involving an ensemble of n trajectories. We have performed the calculations for several different values of n to determine the statistical convergence of the BTSH algorithm. At the end of each trial we tally the fraction of transmitted trajectories n_T/n and reflected trajectories n_R/n; by averaging over the number of trials we obtain the statistical accuracy and convergence of n_T/n and n_R/n as a function of n, N, and E. In Figure 3(a) we show the absolute errors of the BTSH transmission probabilities after 100 trials with $n=10^5$ trajectories per trial. Note the reflection errors are identical to the transmission errors since the BTSH method inherently preserves the normalization of the transmission/reflection probabilities. The errors relative to exact analytical results are plotted as a function of E/V_0 for several values of N. Beyond $n = 1000$, the accuracy of each BTSH calculation is independent of the number of trajectories, with the error comparable to that of the corresponding PWP calculation, suggesting that convergence with respect to n has been achieved. Figure 3(b) shows the standard deviation of the BTSH transmission probabilities over 100 trials for different numbers of trajectories n for $N=1000$. The figure clearly shows that the convergence of the method follows a $1/\sqrt{n}$

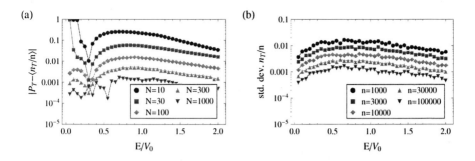

FIG. 3: (color online) Accuracy and convergence benchmarks for the analytical BTSH algorithm (Sec. III) applied to the Eckart A potential system. (a) The absolute errors of the average transmission probability $\langle n_T/n \rangle$ ($n=10^5$ paths), relative to analytical theory P_T, are plotted as a function of E/V_0 for different numbers of grid points N. As expected, the errors associated with the BTSH are comparable to the PWP algorithm shown in Figure 1. (b) Standard deviation of the transmission probability ($N=100$) for different numbers of paths n. The BTSH converges to the PWP results with a $1/\sqrt{n}$ scaling.

power law dependence, and we have also verified that the convergence of the BTSH is independent of the number N (at least for $N \geq 30$).

While the results obtained with the analytical BTSH method are encouraging—in the sense that they do demonstrate the possibility of utilizing hopping between LM and statistical averaging as a means of accurately describing quantum effects—as a practical tool, this approach is found lacking, because the solution of the bipolar components must be known in advance. We have attempted several strategies to convert the basic ideas of the BTSH into a synthetic method, *i.e.*, one that determines the bipolar component solutions on-the-fly using independent trajectories, without any *a priori* knowledge. Unfortunately, none of these ideas have proven successful in that endeavor, and it would seem that a direct application of the hopping rates in Eq. (16) may not be possible, though these ideas may be reconsidered in future publications. For the moment, we formulate an alternative strategy based upon a path integral representation of the CPWM equations, which we have found to be more successful, as described in the next section.

156

IV. BIPOLAR PATH INTEGRAL MONTE CARLO (BPIMC)

A. Discretized paths

In this section, we develop a path integral representation of the CPWM. To see how this works, it useful to recast the propagation step of the PWP algorithm as a matrix–vector operation. Indeed, there are many ways one could imagine doing this; however, we have elected to use the following conventions: a single step of the PWP algorithm is given by the matrix–vector product

$$\mathbf{\Psi}_{+-}(t + \Delta t) = \mathbf{U} \cdot \mathbf{\Psi}_{+-}(t) \tag{18}$$

where $\mathbf{\Psi}_{+-}(t)$ is a single column vector containing *both* bipolar components, and has the form

$$\mathbf{\Psi}_{+-}(t) = \begin{pmatrix} \psi_{+,1}(t) \\ \psi_{-,1}(t) \\ \vdots \\ \psi_{+,N}(t) \\ \psi_{-,N}(t) \end{pmatrix} \tag{19}$$

We can imagine that each grid point in the interaction region, i, is represented by a spinor, consisting of the two bipolar components $\psi_{\pm,i}$, which are then stacked on top of one another to give a large column vector. Because the PWP equations contain only nearest-neighbor coupling, the time evolution operator $\mathbf{U}$ is found to be a sparse, block tri-diagonal matrix

$$\mathbf{U} = \begin{pmatrix} \tilde{u}_L & \tilde{u}_{-,2} & \tilde{0} & \cdots & & \tilde{0} \\ \tilde{u}_{+,1} & \tilde{0} & \tilde{u}_{-,3} & \ddots & & \vdots \\ \tilde{0} & \tilde{u}_{+,2} & \ddots & \ddots & & \tilde{0} \\ \vdots & & \ddots & \ddots & \tilde{0} & \tilde{u}_{-,N} \\ \tilde{0} & & \cdots & \tilde{0} & \tilde{u}_{+,N-1} & \tilde{u}_R \end{pmatrix} \tag{20}$$

where $\tilde{u}_{L/R}$, $\tilde{u}_{\pm,i}$, and $\tilde{0}$ are all 2×2 blocks. Specifically, $\tilde{0}$ is a 2×2 zero matrix and the two nonzero diagonal blocks $\tilde{u}_{L/R}$ represent the boundaries of the interaction region, and contain simple time-evolving phase factors

$$\tilde{u}_L = \begin{pmatrix} e^{-iE\Delta t/\hbar} & 0 \\ 0 & 0 \end{pmatrix} \text{ and } \tilde{u}_R = \begin{pmatrix} 0 & 0 \\ 0 & e^{-iE\Delta t/\hbar} \end{pmatrix} \tag{21}$$

This particular choice for the boundary blocks supports the both left and right incident boundary conditions. A distinction is made by choosing an appropriate initial condition for the vector $\boldsymbol{\Psi}_{+-}$. The sub- and super-diagonal blocks have the form

$$\tilde{u}_{+,i} = \begin{pmatrix} F_i & C_i \\ 0 & 0 \end{pmatrix} \quad \text{and} \quad \tilde{u}_{-,i} = \begin{pmatrix} 0 & 0 \\ C_i & F_i \end{pmatrix}, \tag{22}$$

respectively, with elements given by

$$F_i = e^{iE\Delta t/\hbar} + C_i \quad \text{and} \quad C_i = -\frac{i\Delta t}{\hbar}V(x_i) \tag{23}$$

One can evaluate the bipolar components at any time-step by making successive matrix vector products

$$\boldsymbol{\Psi}_{+-}(t + M\Delta t) = \mathbf{U}^M \cdot \boldsymbol{\Psi}_{+-}(t) \tag{24}$$

where M is the desired number of time steps.

The propagator matrix $\mathbf{U}$ has some very interesting properties, and also because it is very sparse, the matrix–vector products are amenable to specialized numerical algorithms which can be efficiently parallelized. These considerations will be addressed in a future paper, but for now we focus on how successive matrix–vector products can be interpreted as a sum over a set of restricted "paths." These CPWM paths are restricted in the sense that only moves between nearest neighbor grid points are allowed during a single time step, as shown in Figure 4(a). This is much more restrictive than, for example, a set of discrete Feynman paths—which connect *any* two positions over a single time step—as in the conventional path integral Monte Carlo (PIMC) approach [35–38]. Given N discrete grid points and M time steps, there are only $2^M N$ allowed bipolar CPWM paths, as opposed to the N^M discrete PIMC paths.

Let us consider paths connecting the point x_1 and x_N—i.e., the paths that contribute to the transmission amplitude $\psi_{+,N}$, if the initial condition is taken to be $\psi_{+,i}(0) = \delta_{i0}$; $\psi_{-,i} = 0$. This situation is shown in Figure 4(b). The shortest such path gives a contribution of $\psi_{+,N}^{(N-1)} = F_{N-1}\cdots F_1$ to the total amplitude $\psi_{+,N}$ at x_N. The superscript $(N-1)$ denotes the fact that it takes $N-1$ time steps to generate this path. The next set of shortest paths connecting x_1 and x_N involve a single-step detour along the $-$ LM that can occur at any grid point i in the interaction region. There are $N-1$ such paths, which give a combined contribution of $\psi_{+,N}^{(N+1)} = \sum_i C_{+,i}C_{-,i+1}F_{+,N-1}\cdots F_1$ to $\psi_{+,N}$, but precisely two time steps later than the shortest path. In order to combine the amplitudes associated with these two contributions, we must account for the time-delay by multiplying one of the contributions by an appropriate phase-factor. Other (longer) paths may be similarly constructed. The matrix multiplication operations involving $\mathbf{U}$ can then be viewed as a convenient way of adding together the amplitudes for paths initiating at x_1 at different times, but terminating at a given position x_i at a given final time, and keeping track of the associated phase factors/time delays.

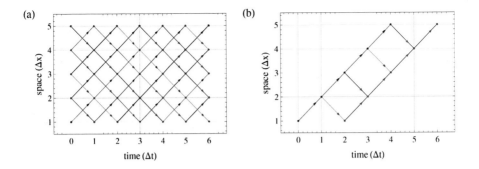

FIG. 4: (color online) Constant velocity CPWM trajectories/paths for $N=5$ grid points as a function of time steps. (a) Trajectories on the +LM (blue) move upward in this figure while trajectories on the -LM (red) move downward. In the PWP algorithm, the whole set of $\pm$ trajectories is propagated simultaneously along with the bipolar components $\psi_\pm$. The $\pm$ trajectories communicate with each other at the end of each time step. The PWP trajectories do not change direction, so additional trajectories are introduced and deleted at the grid boundaries each new time step, in order to populate the full set of grid points across the interaction region. (b) Selected BPIMC paths that contribute to the transmission amplitude, $\psi_{+,N}$. The path (blue) connecting grid point 1 to grid point 5 contains no "hops" and is the shortest possible path between the grid edges. Other paths (red) which hop twice in a row (once to the $-$ LM, and then right back again to the $+$ LM) arrive at grid point 5 exactly two time steps later.

B.   Bipolar path integral Monte Carlo algorithms

The matrix representation of the CPWM is useful, and we expect that numerical algorithms based upon sparse matrix algebra will be very efficient for problems involving relatively few degrees of freedom. For very large systems, however, it is appealing to develop an algorithm capable of reproducing the CPWM results to any desired level of accuracy, using importance sampling to sum over a selected subset of paths. To accomplish this, we appeal to Monte Carlo integration methods [37]. In principle such methods are not so hindered by the dimensionality of the system, but rather by the ability to adequately sample the integration space—*i.e.*, the space of possible CPWM paths.

The following describes an importance-sampled, bipolar path integral Monte Carlo (BPIMC) algorithm that can be used to calculate the transmission and reflection probabilities for 1D scattering problems. Given the severe constraints on the set of allowed BPIMC paths discussed above, we find it convenient to characterize a given BPIMC path by a time-ordered sequence of directions h and positions x; the path length M varies from path to path. In 1D the directions h can be either +1 or -1 corresponding to the + and − LMs, respectively. The positions are the N grid points defined previously, and the initial position is always taken to be the left boundary of the interaction region, x_L. The final position, after a sufficient number of time steps M, will be either the left or right boundary, such that paths ending at $x_{R/L}$ contribute to the total transmission/reflection amplitudes, respectively. Each path is associated with a complex amplitude A, and a real weighting factor P; note that both A and P evolve over the course of the path. The initial path amplitude A is chosen to be unity, and the initial weighting factor $P = 1/n$ where n is the number of paths to be considered.

The path amplitude and weighting factor at the final time are developed as follows. At each time step we define a pair of local branching amplitudes A_+ and A_- at position x_i, which depend upon the path direction h at the previous time step:

$$A_+ = \begin{cases} F_i & \text{for } h = 1 \\ C_i & \text{for } h = -1 \end{cases} \quad \text{and} \quad A_- = \begin{cases} C_i & \text{for } h = 1 \\ F_i & \text{for } h = -1 \end{cases}, \qquad (25)$$

where $h = 1$ refers to a path arriving at x_i from the left (on the $+$ LM) and $h = -1$ refers to a path arriving at x_i from the right (on the $-$ LM). A pair of normalized branching probabilities P_+ and P_- is associated with the local amplitudes. The path is updated by comparing $P_\pm$ with a pseudo-random number $0 < \zeta < 1$ such that if $\zeta > P_-$ then the path follows the left moving A_- branch or if $\zeta < P_-$ then the path follows the right moving A_+ branch. The dependence of $P_\pm$ on $A_\pm$ determines how the CPWM paths are to be sampled. For example, $P_\pm = 1/2$ corresponds to completely random paths, and hence a uniform sampling scheme. This approach never fails in principle, but is obviously effective only when the total number of paths to be sampled is fairly small, and not suitable when the number of time steps and also the number of possible paths is large.

A better way of handling this situation is to somehow relate the local "hopping" probabilities to the amplitudes themselves, thus introducing a kind of importance sampling into the algorithm. We have attempted several methods of doing this and the most effective strategy so far has been to define the local probabilities in terms of the magnitudes of $A_\pm$, as

$$P_+ = \frac{|A_+|}{|A_+| + |A_-|} \quad \text{and} \quad P_- = \frac{|A_-|}{|A_+| + |A_-|} \qquad (26)$$

This approach can be regarded as far less efficient than the amplitude-squared-based hopping probabilities implicit in the BTSH, in that hopping probabilities are comparatively high, and therefore the number of paths that must be sampled is much larger. On the other hand, it is fairly robust with respect to summations of amplitudes exhibiting phase cancellations, and unlike synthetic TSH methods, is in principle exact.

Once the $P_\pm$ have been calculated and the local branch selected, the path amplitude and weighting factor are updated as

$$A_{\text{new}} = A\, A_{\pm} \text{ and } P_{\text{new}} = P\, P_{\pm} \qquad (27)$$

After M time steps, when the path has reached x_L or x_R, it makes a contribution of

$$A_{\text{path}} = e^{iEM\Delta t/\hbar} A/P \qquad (28)$$

to the overall transmission $\psi_{+,N}$ or reflection $\psi_{-,1}$ amplitudes; the total transmission and reflection amplitudes are given by a sum over many such paths that arrive at x_N or x_1, respectively, at different times. Note that the exponental prefactor in Eq. (28) is a phase factor that accounts for the time-delay between different paths. The total transmission and reflection probabilities are then given by $\rho_{+,N} = |\psi_{+,N}|^2$ and $\rho_{-,1} = |\psi_{-,1}|^2$, respectively.

We have applied the BPIMC algorithm to the Eckart A system described previously, and the results are summarized in Figure 5. As with the BTSH calculations, the BPIMC is performed over a wide energy range, and for different combinations of the number of grid points N and the number of paths n. For each combination of E, n, and N, the calculations are performed 100 times to characterize the statistical accuracy and convergence of the algorithm. In Figures 5(a)-(b) we plot the accuracy and convergence of the calculated transmission probabilities, respectively, as a function of the ratio E/V_0. The accuracy results are shown for different N values with $n=10^5$. Similar to the BTSH, we find that the overall accuracy of the BPIMC is generally independent of the number of paths. At high energies $E/V_0 > 0.6$, the BPIMC method is performing quite adequately, and is statistically converging to the PWP results. The convergence at high energy is independent of the number of grid points, and a $1/\sqrt{n}$ scaling is found. However, as the energy is lowered, the method begins to encounter difficulties correctly representing the transmission/reflection probabilities, and ultimately fails, even though the PWP algorithm does not. The variation in the transmission probability between trials also becomes very large, and is another symptom of the method's failure in the low-energy regime.

The reason for the BPIMC method's failure at low energies can be easily explained, if not remedied. From Eq. (26), it is clear that at all positions x and energies E, the hopping probabilities—i.e., P_- for $h = 1$, and P_+ for $h = -1$—in the BPIMC approach are *equal*. Thus, hopping exhibits no directional preference. At high E, where the median number of hops per trajectory is less than one (i.e., most sampled trajectories do not hop at all), one thus finds that most trajectories wind up at x_R, thus leading to P_T values in excess of 50%, as is correct. At low E, however, the median number of hops per trajectory is substantially greater than one; the lack of directional hopping preference therefore implies a nearly (50-50) distribution of trajectories that end up at x_R and x_L. Thus, it becomes statistically very difficult to obtain P_R values in excess of 50%—even at low energies, where reflection actually dominates transmission. Note that BTSH

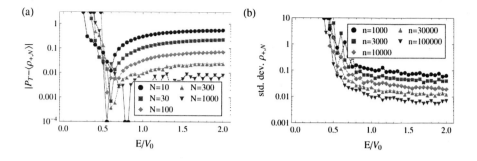

FIG. 5: (color online) Accuracy and convergence benchmarks for the BPIMC algorithm (Sec. IV) applied to the Eckart A potential system. (a) The absolute errors of the average transmission probability $\langle \rho_{+,N} \rangle$ ($n=10^5$ paths), relative to analytical theory, are plotted as a function of E/V_0, for different numbers of grid points N. (b) Standard deviation of the transmission probability ($N=100$) for different numbers of paths n. The method performs well for $E/V_0 > 0.5$; the accuracy is on par with the PWP algorithm and the convergence scales as $1/\sqrt{n}$. At lower energies, the transmission probabilities do not converge, indicating that the method becomes unstable.

avoids this problem, because the hopping probabilities are *not* equal. Indeed, at any given point x, the fewest switches algorithm of Sec. III B allows hopping in only a *single* direction—*i.e.*, one of the two hopping probabilities is effectively zero.

V. SUMMARY

In this paper we have introduced two new algorithms for calculating transmission and reflection probabilities in scattering problems. The BTSH and BPIMC methods are based upon the bipolar decomposition of the stationary scattering state, and utilize stochastic numerical algorithms for which the fundamental entities are trajectories/paths that are completely independent from each other. To test the new methods, we have presented accuracy and convergence benchmark results for a simple symmetric Eckart barrier in 1D.

The BTSH algorithm presented in Sec. III bears a close resemblance to the surface hopping schemes often used in mixed quantum/classical simulations for describing nonadiabatic electronic coupling and interstate transitions. However, the BTSH method can also handle *intra*-state transitions, *i.e.*, partial transmission and reflection in the nuclear dynamics, associated with reflection interference. Though we have not presented results for multisurface systems, similar studies using the CPWM have already been published elsewhere [6], and we do not anticipate any difficulty in modifying the BTSH to include nonadiabatic effects. The main drawback of the present formulation of the BTSH algorithm is that it requires the stationary states to be known in advance in order to compute the bipolar hopping rates, Equation (16). We have attempted several strategies to determine the rates without *a priori* knowledge; however, thus far these have not been successful. A more practical idea might be to develop an approximate way of calculating the bipolar hopping rates. One way to approach this is to use a partially converged PWP calculation as the input for the BTSH method. Preliminary calculations along these lines have been encouraging, although we found it necessary to modify the PWP algorithm slightly to improve the accuracy of these results. Such issues will be left to future work.

The BPIMC method presented in Sec. IV is based upon a matrix–vector representation of the PWP algorithm. In the PWP matrix scheme, the propagation scheme used to solve Eq. (12) is recast as a time-evolution matrix acting on a vector constructed from the bipolar components. The time-evolution matrix is extremely sparse, and we anticipate that sparse linear algebra codes would therefore be very competitive for calculating stationary scattering states of systems with several degrees of freedom. One difficulty in multidimensional scattering problems will be how to deal with additional terms associated with the kinetic energy of bound degrees of freedom that appear in the bipolar equations of motion (see Ref. [8]). Such terms would increase the density of nonzero elements in the time-evolution operator and hence decrease the efficiency of the calculations; nevertheless, we shall keep this prospect as an option for future studies.

The BPIMC approach is developed by realizing that the PWP matrix scheme may be likened to a sum over paths connecting nearest neighbors of a discrete grid covering the scattering region. Instead of summing over all of the possible paths, which would become increasingly prohibitive in high-D problems, the BPIMC algorithm uses importance sampling to greatly restrict the set of explicit paths that need be considered. For the Eckart A model problem we have shown that the BPIMC is successful at medium-to-high energies (as compared with the barrier height), but fails at low energies, *i.e.*, less than or equal to half the energy barrier. Though not ideal, obviously, the performance is in any case much better than for classical trajectory and traditional surface hopping methods, which cannot handle below-barrier dynamics well, if at all. As discussed in Sec. IV B, the failure at low energies can be attributed to hopping probabilities are the same in both directions—unlike the BTSH approach, which admits non-zero hopping probability in one direction only (at a given point in space).

To compare and contrast the BTSH and BPIMC methods further, it can perhaps be said that the former is density-based, whereas the latter is amplitude-based. Apart from the directional preference discussed above, the BTSH hopping probabilities depend on three quantities—$V(x)$, $\psi_+(x)$, and $\psi_-(x)$—whereas those of BPIMC depend only on $V(x)$. The latter are clearly simpler, and moreover—with no explicit dependence on $\psi_\pm(x)$—readily admit a synthetic implementation, unlike BTSH. Both methods, in their current state of development, thus offer comparative strengths and weaknesses. However, insofar as overcoming the latter are concerned, BPIMC appears to be the better candidate at present. At any rate, it is accurate and stable over a fairly wide energy range, and should scale well with increasing dimensionality. Future work on the BPIMC will have to contend with the difficulties at low energies, as well as working out additional issues specific to multidimensional problems.

Acknowledgements. This work was supported by a grant from The Welch Foundation (D-1523), and by a Small Grant for Exploratory Research from the National Science Foundation (CHE-0741321).

[1] B. Poirier, J. Chem. Phys. **121**, 4501 (2004).

[2] C. Trahan and B. Poirier, J. Chem. Phys. **124**, 034115 (2006).

[3] C. Trahan and B. Poirier, J. Chem. Phys. **124**, 034116 (2006).

[4] B. Poirier and T. Djama, in preparation (2008).

[5] B. Poirier, J. Theor. Comput. Chem. **6**, 99 (2007).

[6] B. Poirier and G. Parlant, J. Phys. Chem. A **111**, 10400 (2007).

[7] B. Poirier, J. Chem. Phys. **128**, 164115 (2008).

[8] B. Poirier, J. Chem. Phys. **129**, 084103 (2008).

[9] R. E. Wyatt, *Quantum Dynamics with Trajectories: Introduction to Quantum Hydrodynamics* (Springer, New York, 2005).

[10] D. Bohm, Phys. Rev. **85**, 166 (1952).

[11] D. Bohm, Phys. Rev. **85**, 180 (1952).

[12] P. R. Holland, *The Quantum Theory of Motion* (Cambridge University Press, Cambridge, 1993).

[13] M. V. Berry and K. V. Mount, Rep. Prog. Phys. **35**, 315 (1972).

[14] W. H. Miller, Adv. Chem. Phys. **25**, 69 (1974).

[15] W. H. Miller, J. Phys. Chem. A **105**, 2942 (2001).

[16] J. Heading, *An Introduction to Phase-integral Methods* (Methuen, London, 1962).

[17] N. Fröman and P. O. Fröman, *JWKB Approximation* (North-Holland, Amsterdam, 1965).

[18] M. Gutzwiller, *Chaos in Classical and Quantum Mechanics* (Springer, New York, 1990).

[19] R. G. Littlejohn, J. Stat. Phys. **68**, 7 (1992).

[20] J. B. Keller and S. I. Rubinow, Ann. Phys. (Leipzig) **9**, 24 (1960).

[21] V. I. Arnold, *Mathematical Methods of Classical Mechanics* (Springer, New York, 1978).

[22] E. J. Heller, J. Chem. Phys. **62**, 1544 (1974).

[23] M. P. Allen and T. J. Tildesley, *Computer simulation of liquids* (Clarendon, Oxford, 1987).

[24] J. C. Tully, J. Chem. Phys. **93**, 1061 (1990).

[25] J. C. Tully, *Dynmaics of Molecular Collisions* (Plenum Press, New York, 1975), vol. Part B, p. 217.

[26] F. Webster, P. J. Rossky, and R. A. Friesner, Comp. Phys. Comm. **63**, 494 (1991).

[27] J. C. Tully, Faraday Discuss. **110**, 407 (1998).

[28] J. C. Tully, *Modern Methods for Multidimensional Dynamics Computations in Chemistry* (World Scientific, Singapore, 1998), chap. Nonadiabatic Dynamics, p. 34.

[29] Z. Ahmed, Phys. Rev. A **47**, 4761 (1993).

[30] E. E. Nikitin, *Theory of Elementary Atomic and Molecular Processes in Gases* (Clarendon, Oxford, 1974).

[31] J. C. Tully and R. K. Preston, J. Chem. Phys. **55**, 562 (1971).

[32] G. Parlant and E. A. Gislason, J. Chem. Phys. **91**, 4416 (1989).

[33] Y. Wu and M. F. Herman, J. Chem. Phys. **125**, 154116 (2006).

[34] M. D. Hack and D. G. Truhlar, J. Phys. Chem. A **104**, 7917 (2000).

[35] Y. Xiao and B. Poirier, J. Theor. Comput. Chem. **6**, 309 (2007).

[36] R. Feynman and A. R. Hibbs, *Quantum Mechanics and Integrals* (McGraw-Hill, New York, 1965).

[37] J. M. Thijssen, *Computational Physics* (Cambridge University Press, 1999).

[38] G. A. Voth, *Advances in Chemical Physics* (Wiley, New York, 1996), chap. Path-integral centroid methods in quantum statistical mechanics and dynamics, pp. 135–218.

D. Shalashilin and M. P. de Miranda (eds.)
Multidimensional Quantum Mechanics with Trajectories
© 2009, CCP6, Daresbury

The bipolar derivative propagation method for calculating stationary states for high-dimensional reactive scattering systems

J. B. Maddox and B. Poirier*
Department of Chemistry and Biochemistry,
Texas Tech University, Box 41041,
Lubbock, Texas, 79409-1061, USA

In this article we present a new computational methodology for calculating stationary states of multi-dimensional (multi-D) reactive scattering problems. Our strategy combines the ideas of the derivative propagation method (DPM) [1, 2] with those of the counter-propagating wave methodology (CPWM) [3–5] for calculating stationary scattering states. In what follows, we briefly outline the essential ideas of the DPM and CPWM, and describe a novel refinement of the basic DPM approach that is tailored for use with the CPWM and, most importantly, that is scalable for high-D problems. We present benchmark calculations for the scattering states of a model problem consisting of an Eckart barrier coupled to a f-D harmonic oscillator, where f is as large as 100 modes.

DPMs are typically employed in the context of quantum trajectory methods (QTMs) [6] for dynamical problems, where the time-dependent wavefunction ψ is represented by a slight variant of Bohm's unipolar ansatz, $i.e.$, a single complex-polar term, $\psi = \exp{(C + iS/\hbar)}$. The C-amplitude and phase S are both real, single-valued functions of space and time [7, 8]. In QTMs, one must solve a pair of coupled, nonlocal, hydrodynamic-like equations of motion for C and S along an ensemble of interdependent quantum trajectories. The DPM approximation allows one to decouple these equations for different trajectories. This involves solving a set of hierarchal time-evolution equations for the spatial derivatives of C and S, which are treated as additional variables (DPM quantities), along independently propagated quantum trajectories. The DPM strategy has been applied to: 1-D wave propagation [1], multi-D dynamics [2], the computation of spectroscopic time-correlation functions [9], adaptive QTMs [10, 11], and more recently in the context of complex-valued QTMs [12–15]. In contrast with QTMs, CPWMs are characterized by a two-term, so-called "bipolar," ansatz for the

---

*Electronic address: bill.poirier@ttu.edu

quantum wavefunction, $\phi = \phi_+ + \phi_-$, where the $\phi_\pm$ components correspond to traveling waves moving in opposite directions that are defined over two distinct sets of trajectories having momenta of opposite sign [3]. Consult Sec. I and II of the article on page 145 of these Proceedings for more details.

The new methodology developed here, BDPM, combines elements of both CPWM and DPM. As described below, this will involve a rather useful refinement of how DPM quantities are defined. The motivation for this is to circumvent the computational difficulties associated with the proliferation of derivative terms and also to drastically lower the minimum order in the hierarchal equations that is needed to obtain accurate results. For a fixed BDPM order, the method exhibits *constant* scaling with increasing system dimensionality, vis-à-vis the number of DPM quantities that must be propagated.

In this work, we consider a multi-D reactive scattering system with a Hamiltonian given by

$$\hat{H} = -\frac{\hbar^2}{2m}\vec{\nabla}^2 + V(x, \mathbf{y}), \tag{1}$$

where m is the reduced mass of the problem, $\vec{\nabla}^2$ is the Laplacian over all (orthogonal) coordinates, x represents a single linear reaction coordinate, and $\mathbf{y}$ denotes all other "perpendicular modes," *i.e.*, nonreactive coordinates. Furthermore, we assume that the potential is symmetric along x, and that the x-dependence vanishes asymptotically

$$V_0(\mathbf{y}) \equiv \lim_{x \to \pm\infty} V(x, \mathbf{y}). \tag{2}$$

We note that these assumptions are made merely as a matter of convenience, and that we anticipate the method described below will be much more generally applicable.

In the asymptotically symmetric case, the Hamiltonian describing the isolated reactants (or products, by symmetry) is given by

$$\hat{H}_0 = -\frac{\hbar^2}{2m}\vec{\nabla}_{\mathbf{y}}^2 + V_0(\mathbf{y}), \tag{3}$$

where $\vec{\nabla}_{\mathbf{y}}^2$ is the Laplacian over the perpendicular modes only. We associate $x \to -\infty$ with the reactants, so that increasing x corresponds to the forward reaction direction; hence, we adopt left-incident boundary conditions.

For a given stationary state $\phi(x, \mathbf{y})$ with fixed energy E, there will generally be several open scattering channels corresponding to the asymptotic eigenstates $\phi_n^0(\mathbf{y})$ with $E_n < E$, where $\hat{H}_0\phi_n^0(\mathbf{y}) = E_n\phi_n^0(\mathbf{y})$ is satisfied. For simplicity, however, we assume only one open channel, *i.e.*, the asymptotic ground state $n=0$, so that the appropriate boundary conditions for the bipolar components are given by [5]

$$\phi_+(x \to -\infty, \mathbf{y}) = \phi_0^0(\mathbf{y})e^{ip_0x/\hbar} \tag{4}$$

$$\phi_-(x \to +\infty, \mathbf{y}) = 0, \tag{5}$$

where $p_0 = \sqrt{2m(E - E_0)}$ is the momentum associated with incident kinetic energy of the scattering state. It has been shown in Ref. [5] that an exact bipolar decomposition can be obtained from the steady-state solution of the following coupled total differential equations

$$\frac{d\phi_\pm}{dt} = \frac{i}{\hbar}(E - E_0)\phi_\pm + \frac{i}{\hbar}E_0\phi_\mp - \frac{i}{\hbar}V\phi + \frac{i\hbar}{2m}\vec{\nabla}_\mathbf{y}^2\phi. \tag{6}$$

One key feature of Eq. (6) is the presence of the total time derivative

$$\frac{d\phi_\pm}{dt} = \frac{\partial\phi_\pm}{\partial t} \pm \frac{p_0}{m}\frac{\partial\phi_\pm}{\partial x}, \tag{7}$$

which implies that the time-dependent solutions $\phi_\pm$ are defined in a moving reference frame with equal and opposite constant velocities $\pm p_0/m$ along the reaction coordinate (see Refs. [5, 16] for generalizations of the CPWM where the bipolar trajectories do not have constant velocities, and the potential energy need not be asymptotically symmetric).

The primary task of the CPWM is to calculate the solutions of Eq. (6) in the long-time limit. For a 1-D scattering problem, where V is a function of x only, E_0 and the last term of Eq. (6) both vanish, and the original 1-D constant-velocity CPWM equations are recovered [4]. Since V converges symmetrically as $x \to \pm\infty$, the coupling between $\phi_\pm$ also vanishes asymptotically, and one can use very efficient numerical algorithms [16] to find the desired steady-state solutions. In the multi-D case, however, our previous 1-D numerical schemes will not work because of the non-vanishing asymptotic coupling between $\phi_\pm$ via the $E_0\phi_\mp$ and $\vec{\nabla}_\mathbf{y}^2\phi$ terms. In order to proceed, we must somehow decouple $\phi_\pm$ asymptotically along x.

One way to approach this problem is to use DPM ideas, and treat $\vec{\nabla}_\mathbf{y}^2\phi_\pm$ as a new variable, distinct from $\phi_\pm$, with its own equation of motion; such an expression can easily be derived from Eqs. (6) and (7). This would alleviate the asymptotic coupling problem with $\vec{\nabla}_\mathbf{y}^2\phi$ in Eq. (6), however, the new equations would also be asymptotically coupled, but now, through higher-order derivatives. One could then add these derivatives to the list of DPM quantities, derive more equations, which would lead to even more new terms and equations to contend with, and so on. In low-D problems this has proven to be a useful scheme for decoupling the evolution equations of the Bohmian field functions along interdependent quantum trajectories, so that, the trajectories can then be propagated independently. In high-D problems, however, the DPM as it currently stands, is

168

not very effective because of the huge proliferation of terms and equations that need to be solved, *i.e.*, one for every partial derivative of the C and S fields. Also, low-order DPM is usually not sufficient to obtain suitable accuracy in the dynamics, which adds to the fact that a very large number of equations must typically be solved.

Our philosophy is to look beyond the simple use of partial derivatives and instead define smarter DPM quantities that both avoid exponential proliferation of terms, and provide much higher accuracy for the same DPM order. The two $\vec{\nabla}_\mathbf{y}^2 \phi_\pm$ Laplacian quantities above, for instance, are second order, whereas a conventional DPM treatment would require $f^2 + f$ such terms. An even better second order choice, however, is given by Eq. (10) below, which naturally leads to the first order DPM quantities of Eq. (9) given in terms of the interaction potential, $V_\Delta \equiv (V - V_0)$. We thus have,

$$\phi_\pm^{(0)} \equiv \phi_\pm \tag{8}$$

$$\phi_\pm^{(1)} \equiv \left(\vec{\nabla}_\mathbf{y} V_\Delta\right) \cdot \left(\vec{\nabla}_\mathbf{y} \phi_\pm\right) \tag{9}$$

$$\phi_\pm^{(2)} \equiv (E_0 - \hat{H}_0)\phi_\pm \tag{10}$$

$$\vdots$$

as our new (bipolar) DPM quantities, and we also define $\phi^{(n)} = \phi_+^{(n)} + \phi_-^{(n)}$ at each BDPM order. Up to second-order, *i.e.*, dropping higher-order terms, we obtain the following coupled equations of motion

$$\frac{d\phi_\pm^{(0)}}{dt} = \frac{i}{\hbar}(E - 2E_0)\phi_\pm^{(0)} - \frac{i}{\hbar}V_\Delta \phi^{(0)} + \frac{i}{\hbar}\phi^{(2)} \tag{11}$$

$$\frac{d\phi_\pm^{(1)}}{dt} = \frac{i}{\hbar}(E - 2E_0)\phi_\pm^{(1)} - \frac{i}{\hbar}V_\Delta \phi^{(1)} - \frac{i}{\hbar}\left|\vec{\nabla}_\mathbf{y} V_\Delta\right|^2 \phi^{(0)} \tag{12}$$

$$\frac{d\phi_\pm^{(2)}}{dt} = \frac{i}{\hbar}(E - 2E_0)\phi_\pm^{(2)} - \frac{i}{\hbar}V_\Delta \phi^{(2)} - \frac{i\hbar}{2m}\left(\vec{\nabla}_\mathbf{y}^2 V_\Delta \phi^{(0)} + 2\phi^{(1)}\right) \tag{13}$$

$$\vdots$$

A critical feature of Eqs. (11)-(13) is that for second-order, we have a fixed number of terms and equations, regardless of the system dimensionality, f. Another important property is that the dynamics in one asymptote are exact—unlike a conventional DPM formulation at any finite order. Even in the interaction region, the present second-order BDPM approach is likely to be far more accurate than a corresponding second-order DPM approach. Also, the equations contain no explicit spatial derivatives of $\phi_\pm^{(n)}$, as desired; hence, we have effectively decoupled the equations of motion with respect to the perpendicular coordinates, so that they may be solved independently (or better yet, in parallel) for different values of $\mathbf{y}$.

The goal now is to find the long-time steady state solutions of Eqs. (11)-(13), where $\phi^{(0)}$ is the desired stationary scattering state. There are some subtleties here, meaning that, directly solving these equations using typical CPWM algorithms is somewhat problematic due to the fact that the steady-state solutions $\phi_{\pm}^{(2)}$ do not properly converge to zero in the product and reactant asymptotes, respectively, for second-order BDPM. Rather, they converge to plane-waves, which in turn gives rise to incorrect asymptotic ramping of the $\phi_{\pm}^{(0)}$ solutions; this behavior is no doubt related to the truncation of the BDPM hierarchy; however, we have developed a soft truncation strategy that eliminates these difficulties. The procedure is somewhat involved, so we will save the complete details for a future article; suffice it to say, using this approach, one can obtain converged steady-state solutions $\phi_{\pm}^{(0)}$ that approximate the true stationary state bipolar decomposition to second-order in the BDPM scheme. Given these solutions, the partially state resolved transmission and reflection probabilities P_T and P_R, respectively, for the multi-D system are estimated by the following integrals

$$P_{T/R} = \lim_{x \to \pm \infty} \int_{-\infty}^{+\infty} |\phi_{\pm}^{(0)}(x, \mathbf{y})|^2 d\mathbf{y}, \qquad (14)$$

which are calculated in practice at the edges of a finite interaction region that is large enough so that Eqs. (4) and (5) are valid within a desired level of numerical precision.

We have performed such BDPM calculations for a model "bottle-neck" potential comprised of an Eckart barrier coupled with an isotropic f-D harmonic oscillator

$$V(x, \mathbf{y}) = V_0 \operatorname{sech}^2(\alpha x) + \frac{1}{2} k(x) |\mathbf{y}|^2, \qquad (15)$$

where V_0=0.0018 a.u. (400 cm^{-1}) and α=3 bohr^{-1}. The harmonic force constant, $k(x) = k_0 \left[1 + b \operatorname{sech}^2(\alpha x) \right]$, is modulated along x, relative to its asymptotic value k_0, through the coupling parameter b, where $k_0 = m \omega_0^2$, m=2000 a.u., and $\omega_0 = V_0/\hbar$. The asymptotic ground state wavefunction of the harmonic system is given by

$$\phi_0^0(\mathbf{y}) = \left(\frac{m \omega_0}{\pi \hbar} \right)^{f/4} e^{-m \omega_0 |\mathbf{y}|^2 / 2\hbar}, \qquad (16)$$

where both the amplitude and energy $E_0 = f \hbar \omega_0 / 2$ explicitly depend on the dimensionality.

In Figure 1 we show the converged steady-state densities $\rho_{\pm} = |\phi_{\pm}^{(0)}|^2$ for the stationary scattering states, with energy $E = E_0 + V_0$, of the uncoupled ($b = 0$) and coupled ($b = -0.5$) bottle-neck potential ($f = 1$). Note that for the coupled

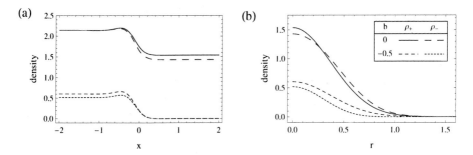

FIG. 1: Steady-state solutions $\rho_\pm = |\phi_\pm^{(0)}|^2$ for the coupled and uncoupled bottle-neck potential (a) as a function of x at $r=0$, and (b) as a function of $r = |\mathbf{y}|$ at $x = \pm2$. The legend in (b) applies to both panels.

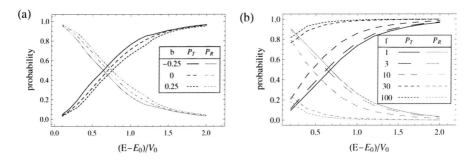

FIG. 2: Partially state resolved transmission/reflection probabilities for the bottle-neck potential (a) with one harmonic mode, where the coupling strength b varies, and (b) with fixed coupling $b=-0.1$, where the number of modes f varies.

case $b < 0$, so that the force constant is weakened by 50% at the transition state ($x=0$). Also, the incident kinetic energy is equal to the barrier height. The densities $\rho_\pm$ are plotted as a function of x along the perpendicular slice $|\mathbf{y}| = 0$ in Figure 1(a). In Figure 1(b), $\rho_\pm$ are plotted as a function of $r = |\mathbf{y}|$ at the edges of the finite interaction region $x = \pm2$ bohr, respectively. The density of the transmitted wave in the product region for the coupled system is both lowered and broadened compared with the uncoupled system; conversely, the reflected wave in the reactant region is both lowered and narrowed.

The probabilities P_T and P_R are plotted in Fig. 2(a) as a function of $(E - E_0)/V_0$ over a broad range of values and for different couplings (both negative and positive with $f = 1$). Clearly, as the bottle-neck is relaxed (negative decreasing b), P_T decreases and P_R increases relative to the uncoupled problem for all energies. Similarly, if the bottle-neck is tightened (positive increasing b), we see that P_T decreases and P_R increases, as expected. The situation in

171

Fig. 2(b) is more interesting; here the coupling is held fixed ($b = -0.1$), but the dimensionality f of the harmonic system is varied. Note that we do *not* attenuate the coupling as f increases [17]. We see that the probabilities P_T and P_R are dramatically shifted to increasing transmission as f increases.

This last result is particularly important; it demonstrates that a second-order BDPM approach works just as well when f is small or large, and with no increase in computational cost (per $\mathbf{y}$ value). Another benefit is that the BDPM calculations are very stable, even when the collective coupling (through many modes) is very large. Although we have used isotropic symmetry to simplify our calculations, this was not necessary. For example, if we had a large set of dissimilar harmonic, anharmonic, or even coupled modes, we could have applied the BDPM approach by first sampling the asymptotic ground state probability distribution function, and then propagating each member of that ensemble independently as we have done here for a fixed grid of radial $r = |\mathbf{y}|$ values. The resultant $P_{T/R}$ would thus be calculated using standard Monte Carlo integration techniques.

Like other DPM algorithms, the BDPM uses derivative quantities to decouple the evolution equations of the wavefunction along quantum trajectories. However, the key difference is that BDPM goes beyond simple partial derivatives; thereby, avoiding a proliferation of terms while simultaneously remaining accurate at low-order. In a follow-up article, the nuances of the method will be made much more clear, as well as extensions to more complicated problems involving curvilinear reaction paths, generalized (not constant) bipolar trajectories, and non-isotropic, asymptotically asymmetric reactant/product Hamiltonians.

Acknowledgments. This work was supported by a grant from The Welch Foundation (D-1523), and by a Small Grant for Exploratory Research from the National Science Foundation (CHE-0741321).

---

[1] C. J. Trahan, K. H. Hughes, and R. E. Wyatt, J. Chem. Phys. **118**, 9911 (2003).

[2] C. J. Trahan, R. E. Wyatt, and B. Poirier, J. Chem. Phys. **122**, 164104 (2005).

[3] B. Poirier, J. Chem. Phys. **121**, 4501 (2004).

[4] C. Trahan and B. Poirier, J. Chem. Phys. **124**, 034116 (2006).

[5] B. Poirier, J. Chem. Phys. **129**, 084103 (2008).

[6] R. E. Wyatt, *Quantum Dynamics with Trajectories: Introduction to Quantum Hydrodynamics* (Springer, New York, 2005).

[7] D. Bohm, Phys. Rev. **85**, 166 (1952).

[8] D. Bohm, Phys. Rev. **85**, 180 (1952).

[9] E. R. Bittner, J. Chem. Phys. **119**, 1358 (2003).

[10] L. R. Pettey and R. E. Wyatt, Chem. Phys. Lett. **424**, 443 (2006).

[11] L. R. Pettey and R. E. Wyatt, Int. J. Quant. Chem. **107**, 1566 (2007).

[12] R. E. Wyatt and B. A. Rowland, J. Chem. Phys. **127**, 044103 (2007).

[13] B. A. Rowland and R. E. Wyatt, J. Phys. Chem. A **111**, 10234 (2007).

[14] Y. Goldfarb, I. Degani, and D. J. Tannor, J. Chem. Phys. **125**, 231103 (2006).

[15] Y. Goldfarb, J. Schiff, and D. J. Tannor, J. Phys. Chem. A **111**, 10416 (2007).

[16] B. Poirier, J. Theor. Comput. Chem. **6**, 99 (2007).

[17] D. Babyuk and R. E. Wyatt, J. Chem. Phys. **124**, 214109 (2006).

D. Shalashilin and M. P. de Miranda (eds.)
Multidimensional Quantum Mechanics with Trajectories
© 2009, CCP6, Daresbury

Theory and applications of the Ring Polymer Molecular Dynamics model

S. Habershon*
*Physical and Theoretical Chemistry Laboratory,
University of Oxford, South Parks Road,
Oxford, OX1 3QZ, United Kingdom*

I. INTRODUCTION

Quantum effects, principally zero-point energy conservation and tunnelling, play an important role in many condensed-phase phenomena. This is evident from isotope substitution experiments, particularly those involving hydrogen exchange. A dramatic illustration is provided by enzyme-catalyzed proton transfer reactions, where deuterium substitution can slow reaction rates by more than an order of magnitude as a result of decreased tunnelling probability [1]. Such experimental indications of the importance of quantum-mechanical effects in condensed-phases have in turn led to the development of a number of theoretical approaches to quantum dynamics [2–7], all of which are by necessity approximate as a result of the exponentially-increasing difficulty of solving the Schrödinger equation as the system size increases. The focus of this article is to describe one such approximate quantum dynamics simulation approach which has been recently developed and successfully tested in our research group.

In a series of papers [8–20], we have described how Feynman's path integral approach, which has been used for many years to calculate *exact* static equilibrium properties of quantum systems, may be generalized to allow calculation of *approximate* quantum correlation functions. The resulting model, named Ring Polymer Molecular Dynamics (RPMD), has been applied to study quantum dynamics in a wide range of condensed-phase systems, with examples including diffusion in [10] and neutron scattering from [11] liquid para-hydrogen at low temperatures, diffusion and orientational relaxation in liquid water [13], hydrogen transport in liquid water and hexagonal ice [18] and proton transfer rates in

---

*Electronic address: scott.habershon@chem.ox.ac.uk

model systems [17]. In all cases, RPMD has been found to capture the dominant effects of quantum mechanical fluctuations in equilibrium dynamic properties.

II. THEORY

The exact static (time-independent) equilibrium properties of a quantum-mechanical system can be computed by exploiting the isomorphism between the classical partition function of a fictitious ring-polymer and the path-integral representation of the quantum-mechanical partition function [21]. Thus, the canonical partition function

$$Z = \text{Tr} \left[e^{-\beta \hat{H}} \right] \tag{1}$$

may be calculated as

$$Z = \lim_{n \to \infty} Z_n \tag{2}$$

where, for a one-dimensional system,

$$Z_n = \frac{1}{(2\pi\hbar)^n} \int \int d\mathbf{p} \, dx \, e^{-\beta_n H_n(\mathbf{p},\mathbf{x})}. \tag{3}$$

Here, $\beta_n = \beta/n = 1/nk_BT$ and $H_n(\mathbf{p},\mathbf{x})$ is the classical Hamiltonian of an n-bead harmonic ring-polymer with an external potential $V(x)$ acting on each bead:

$$H_n(\mathbf{p},\mathbf{x}) = \sum_{j=1}^{n} \left[\frac{p_j^2}{2m} + \frac{1}{2}m\omega_n^2 \left(x_j - x_{j-1} \right)^2 + V(x_j) \right]. \tag{4}$$

where $\omega_n = 1/(\beta_n\hbar)$ and the cyclic condition $x_0 = x_n$ applies. Note that for $n = 1$, the classical partition function and Hamiltonian are recovered in Eqs. 3 and 4. Within the classical isomorphism, the thermal expectation value of a position-dependent operator $A(\hat{x})$ can be calculated as $\langle A \rangle = \lim_{n \to \infty} \langle A \rangle_n$, where

$$\langle A \rangle_n = \frac{1}{(2\pi\hbar)^n Z_n} \int \int d\mathbf{p} \, dx \, e^{-\beta_n H_n(\mathbf{p},\mathbf{x})} A_n(\mathbf{x}), \tag{5}$$

and

$$A_n(\mathbf{x}) = \frac{1}{n} \sum_{j=1}^{n} A(x_j). \tag{6}$$

175

By following the classical dynamics generated by the ring-polymer Hamiltonian (Eq. 4), we can also calculate a ring-polymer time correlation function for two position-dependent operators, $\hat{A}$ and $\hat{B}$:

$$\langle A(0)B(t)\rangle_n = \frac{1}{(2\pi\hbar)^n Z_n} \int\int d\mathbf{p}\, d\mathbf{x}\, e^{-\beta_n H_n(\mathbf{p},\mathbf{x})} A_n(\mathbf{x_0})B_n(\mathbf{x_t}). \tag{7}$$

Because the classical dynamics generated by the ring-polymer Hamiltonian have no obvious connection to the real-time quantum evolution operators $e^{\pm i\hat{H}t/\hbar}$, the relationship of the ring-polymer correlation function to the exact quantum time correlation function it is not immediately clear. However, as highlighted below, several time symmetry properties as well as the behaviour in specific limits indicates that Eq. 7 is in fact a reasonable approximation to the exact canonical (or Kubo-transformed) time correlation function, given by:

$$\tilde{C}_{AB}(t) = \frac{1}{\beta Z}\int_0^\beta d\lambda\, \text{Tr}\left[e^{-(\beta-\lambda)\hat{H}}\hat{A}e^{-\lambda\hat{H}}e^{+i\hat{H}t/\hbar}\hat{B}e^{-i\hat{H}t/\hbar}\right]. \tag{8}$$

This observation forms the basis of the RPMD model, which may be summarized as [8]

$$\tilde{C}_{AB}(t) \approx \frac{1}{(2\pi\hbar)^n Z_n} \int\int d\mathbf{p}\, d\mathbf{x}\, e^{-\beta_n H_n(\mathbf{p},\mathbf{x})} A_n(\mathbf{x_0})B_n(\mathbf{x_t}). \tag{9}$$

Justification of the RPMD approximation embodied in Eq. 9 comes in two forms. First, the exact canonical correlation function (Eq. 8) and the ring-polymer correlation function (Eq. 7) share three symmetry properties. In particular, it is straightforward to show [8] that the exact canonical correlation function obeys the following:

$$\tilde{C}_{AB}(t) = \tilde{C}_{BA}(-t), \tag{10}$$

$$\tilde{C}_{AB}(t) = \tilde{C}_{AB}(t)^*, \tag{11}$$

$$\tilde{C}_{AB}(t) = \tilde{C}_{AB}(-t)^*. \tag{12}$$

Taken together, these symmetry properties indicate that $\tilde{C}_{AB}(t)$ is a real and even function of time. All three symmetry properties also hold for the ring-polymer correlation function (Eq. 7); the first property follows as a natural consequence of using classical dynamics and the fact that the phase-space volume is conserved (Liouville's theorem), the second property arises from the fact that $\langle A(0)B(t)\rangle$ is a real classical object, albeit in an extended phase-space, and the final time-reversal symmetry of Eq. 12 arises in the ring-polymer correlation function as a result of the reversibility of classical mechanics.

Further justification of the RPMD model is provided by considering three important limits [8]. First, the $t = 0$ limit of the ring-polymer correlation function in Eq. 7 is clearly a static equilibrium property which may be calculated exactly within the classical isomorphism. In fact, the $t \to 0$ limit of Eq. 7 corresponds exactly to the zero-time limit of the canonical correlation function of Eq. 8 for any operators $\hat{A}$ and $\hat{B}$ [15]. Furthermore, the RPMD model also reproduces the correct high-temperature (i.e. classical) limit. This is evident from the fact that the ring-polymer radius of gyration,

$$r_g = \left\langle \frac{1}{n} \sum_{j=1}^{n} |x_j - \bar{x}|^2 \right\rangle^{1/2} \simeq \left(\frac{\beta \hbar^2}{12m} \right)^{1/2}, \qquad (13)$$

where $\bar{x}$ is the ring-polymer centroid, approaches zero as $\beta \to 0$. As a result, the ring-polymers collapse to single classical particles at high temperature, the partition function of Eq. 3 takes its classical value and the ring-polymer correlation function (Eq. 9) reverts to its classical analogue. Finally, it is straightforward to show that the ring-polymer correlation function is exact for a harmonic potential when one or other of the correlated operators is a linear function of coordinates and/or momenta [8].

In summary, the RPMD model proposes that the ring-polymer correlation function (Eq. 7), calculated by following the classical dynamics generated by the ring-polymer Hamiltonian (Eq. 4), may be used as an approximation to the exact quantum-mechanical canonical correlation function (Eq. 8). A major advantage of the RPMD model is that the simulations are essentially classical, albeit in an extended ring-polymer phase-space. As a result, many of the techniques developed for classical molecular dynamics simulations, such as multiple time-step methods, may be equally applied in RPMD simulations. Furthermore, evaluation of the forces on the ring-polymer beads may be efficiently distributed across several computer processors. Finally, recent work has demonstrated that, by exploiting the varying time and length-scales of interactions in condensed-phase molecular systems, the computational effort of an RPMD simulation can be made nearly the same as a classical simulation for large system sizes [19, 22].

III. APPLICATION TO ONE-DIMENSIONAL PROBLEMS

Fig. 1 illustrates the performance of the RPMD model for two simple one-dimensional test cases [8]. As expected, the RPMD correlation functions are all exact at $t = 0$; the classical results are clearly incorrect in this limit. Fig. 1(a) demonstrates that the RPMD correlation function is a good approximation of the exact result for times up to the thermal time, $\beta \hbar$, demonstrating that RPMD correctly models quantum statistical effects. Beyond this time, the RPMD correlation function is damped relative to the exact result. This is not unexpected; the RPMD model does not contain the phase information necessary to describe the long-time coherent oscillations of the exact correlation function. However,

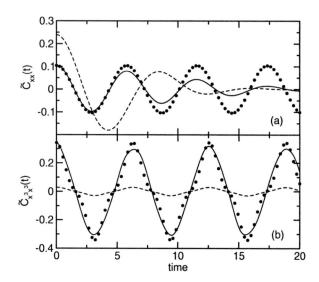

FIG. 1: Classical (dashed lines), RPMD (solid lines) and exact (filled circles) canonical correlation functions for one-dimensional model systems. (a) Position autocorrelation function for the anharmonic potential $V(x) = x^4/4$, (b) Autocorrelation function of $A(x) = x^3$ for the harmonic potential $V(x) = x^2/2$. All simulations were performed at an inverse temperature $\beta = 8$.

RPMD is not designed to capture such long-time oscillations; in condensed-phase systems where RPMD is most applicable, such coherences are quickly damped, suggesting that the short-time accuracy of RPMD may be good enough to capture the dominant quantum effects in these systems. Fig. 1(b) demonstrates that, for a more general non-linear operator, the RPMD correlation function is still a good approximation to the exact result, whereas the classical correlation function fails to properly describe the amplitude of the quantum oscillations. Overall, the results of Fig. 1 serve to illustrate what RPMD can be expected to calculate (approximate short-time behaviour of linear and non-linear operators) and what it cannot (long-time quantum coherence effects).

IV. HYDROGEN ISOTOPE TRANSPORT IN LIQUID WATER

A further example of the capabilities of RPMD is provided by recent simulations of hydrogen, deuterium and muonium diffusion in liquid water and hexagonal ice [18]. Since these particles differ only in their masses (muonium having just one-ninth the mass of hydrogen), such simulations allow a consis-

178

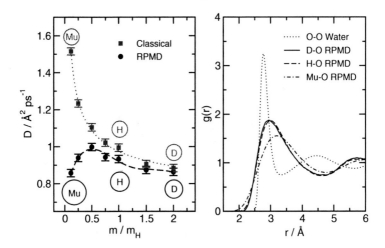

FIG. 2: RPMD simulations of hydrogen isotope diffusion in liquid water at 298 K. The left-hand panel illustrates the variation in diffusion coefficient with particle mass; several imaginary hydrogen isotopes with various intermediate masses have also been simulated. The most important difference between the classical and RPMD simulations is the increased effective radii of the quantum particles as a result of thermal quantum fluctuations. This is illustrated by the radii of the circles for quantum Mu, H and D atoms; the effective radii of the classical particles are identical, corresponding to the van der Waals radii. The right-hand panel illustrates solute-oxygen radial distribution functions determined in quantum simulations.

tent assessment of the role of quantum effects, as well as a more quantitative comparison to experimental isotope effects. Here, we restrict our attention to diffusion in liquid water.

The diffusion coefficient of a solute atom in liquid water can be calculated from the Green-Kubo relation,

$$D = \frac{1}{3} \int_0^\infty \tilde{C}_{\mathbf{v} \cdot \mathbf{v}}(t) dt, \tag{14}$$

where $\tilde{C}_{\mathbf{v} \cdot \mathbf{v}}(t)$ is the solute velocity autocorrelation function. The classical and RPMD diffusion coefficients of hydrogen, muonium and deuterium in a box containing 215 water molecules were calculated at 298 K; standard empirical potentials were used to describe all interatomic interactions.

The main results of these simulations are summarized in Fig. 2. In classical simulations, the mass-dependence of the solute diffusion coefficients is given by

$$D(m) = \left(\frac{m_H}{m} \right)^{1/2} D_{hop} + D_{cav}, \tag{15}$$

where $D_{hop} \approx 0.3 \ \text{Å}^2\text{ps}^{-1}$ and $D_{cav} \approx 0.7 \ \text{Å}^2\text{ps}^{-1}$. This is the functional form one would expect for a mechanism involving uncorrelated hopping between liquid cavities with additional cavity diffusion contributions. However, the RPMD simulations reveal a turnover in the diffusion coefficient for lighter particles. This is the result of an effective "swelling" of the particles due to thermal quantum fluctuations; this effect is greatest for Mu by virtue of its smaller mass. As illustrated in Fig. 2 (right-hand panel), the quantum Mu particle does not fit comfortably into the natural cavities in liquid water. This is demonstrated by the fact that the Mu-O distance is greater than typical O-O distances in liquid water. As a result of the larger effective radii of Mu the rate of intercavity hopping is decreased, counteracting the classical mass-dependence and leading to the turnover behaviour observed in Fig. 2. This behaviour is consistent with the experimental observation that the kinetic isotope effect for hydrogen diffusion in ambient liquid water is close to 1.0 for both deuterium and muonium substitution [18].

V. CONCLUSIONS

This article has briefly described the basis of the RPMD model for simulating quantum dynamics in condensed-phase systems and has highlighted what RPMD can and cannot be expected to do. Recent applications employing RPMD have successfully described the role of quantum effects in a variety of complex systems, including proton transfer in a model polar solvent [17] and hydrogen transport through liquid water and ice [18]. Future work is expected to expand this range of applications to include hydrogen transport through metals and proton transport in a realistic model of liquid water.

Acknowledgements. This work was supported by the U.S. Office of Naval Research under Contract No. N000140510460.

[1] L. Masgrau, A. Roujeinikova, L. O. Johanissen, P. Hothi, J. Basran, K. E. Ranaghan, A. J. Mullholland, M. J. Sutcliffe, N. S. Scrutton and D. Leys, Science **312**, 237 (2006).
[2] X. Sun, H. Wang and W. H. Miller, J. Chem. Phys. **109**, 7064 (1998).
[3] A. Nakayama and N. Makri, Chem. Phys. **304**, 147 (2004).
[4] J. Cao and G. A. Voth, J. Chem. Phys. **100**, 5106 (1994).
[5] S. Jang and G. A. Voth, J. Chem. Phys. **111**, 2371 (1999).
[6] E. Rabani, D. R. Reichman, G. Krilov and B. J. Berne, Proc. Nat. Acad. Sci. USA **99**, 1129 (2002).
[7] E. Rabani and D. R. Reichman, J. Chem. Phys. **120**, 1458 (2004).
[8] I. R. Craig and D. E. Manolopoulos, J. Chem. Phys. **121**, 3368 (2004).

[9] I. R. Craig and D. E. Manolopoulos, J. Chem. Phys. **122**, 084106 (2005).

[10] T. F. Miller III and D. E. Manolopoulos, J. Chem. Phys. **122**, 184503 (2005).

[11] I. R. Craig and D. E. Manolopoulos, Chem. Phys. **322**, 236 (2006).

[12] I. R. Craig and D. E. Manolopoulos, J. Chem. Phys. **123**, 034102 (2005).

[13] T. F. Miller III and D. E. Manolopoulos, J. Chem. Phys. **123**, 154504 (2005).

[14] B. J. Braams, T. F. Miller III and D. E. Manolopoulos, Chem. Phys. Lett. **418**, 179 (2006).

[15] B. J. Braams and D. E. Manolopoulos, J. Chem. Phys. **125**, 124105 (2006).

[16] S. Habershon, B. J. Braams and D. E. Manolopoulos, J. Chem. Phys. **127**, 174108 (2007).

[17] R. Collepardo-Guevara, I. R. Craig and and D. E. Manolopoulos, J. Chem. Phys. **128**, 144502 (2008).

[18] T. E. Markland, S. Habershon and D. E. Manolopoulos, J. Chem. Phys. **128**, 194506 (2008).

[19] T. E. Markland and D. E. Manolopoulos, J. Chem. Phys. **129**, 024105 (2008).

[20] S. Habershon, G. S. Fanourgakis and D. E. Manolopoulos, J. Chem. Phys. **129**, 074501 (2008).

[21] R. P. Feynman and A. R. Hibbs, *Quantum Mechanics and Path Integrals* (McGraw-Hill, New York, 1965).

[22] T. E. Markland and D. E. Manolopoulos, Chem. Phys. Lett. **464**, 256 (2008).